Simplifying the
FAR/AIM
An Essential Guide for the Private Pilot

James E. Guilkey
Christopher Snyder

The Ohio State University Flight Education Division

Wadsworth Publishing Company
Belmont, California
A Division of Wadsworth, Inc.

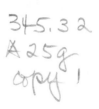

Editor: Julie Butler
Editorial Assistant: Leslie With
Production Editor: Gary Mcdonald
Print Buyer: Barbara Britton
Cover Designer: Steve Markovich

Printed in the United States of America

1 2 3 4 5 6 7 8 9 10—97 96 95 94 93

Library of Congress Cataloging-in-Publication Data

Guilkey, James E.
    Simplifying the FAR/AIM : an essential guide for the private pilot
/ James E. Guilkey, Christopher Snyder.
      p. cm.
    ISBN 0-534-17730-1
    1. Aeronautics—Law and legislation—United States. 2. Air
pilots—Legal status, laws, etc.—United States. 3. Airplanes—
Piloting—Handbooks, manuals, etc.   I. Snyder, Christopher, 1961–
. II. Title. III. Title: Simplifying the Federal Aviation
Regulations and Airman's Information Manual.
KF2400.G85   1993   92-32582
343.73 ' 0975—dc20

Welcome to Simplifying the FAR/AIM, the first in a series of books presenting the Federal Aviation Regulations and Airman's Information Manual in a revolutionary format. During the course of numerous years of piloting and flight instruction, it has become evident that a serious shortcoming exists in the presentation of the FAR/AIM. The combination of bureaucratic language and extensively detailed outlining is a major drawback to the understanding of this topic. By limiting the scope of the FAR/AIM to specific information applicable to the student and private pilots and in turn paraphrasing that information, this publication represents a readable, understandable, and user-friendly reference for the pilot. We have thus hoped to eliminate the obvious lack of understanding and consequent deficiency in knowledge which is prevalent and perpetual throughout flight training.

This publication consists of relevant sections of the FARs, the AIM, and the Practical Test Standards. The FARs are addressed in Part I with pertinent translations in text boxes preceding the actual regulatory text which is in a smaller typeface. This is not to indicate, however, that regulations without text box paraphrasing are unimportant; they have been judged suitably understandable and appear alone in the larger typeface. In Part II, the AIM presents useful information of a nonregulatory nature. Applicable information is again disseminated, paraphrased, and accompanied by functional graphics. Each chapter is followed by FAA-type test questions for review of the information contained therein. Finally, the Practical Test Standards for private pilot certification appear as an appendix, providing precise evaluation principles useful in preparing for the private pilot flight test, a biennial flight review, or as a general study of primary flight maneuvers.

We would like to gratefully acknowledge the assistance of Julie Butler, John Fisher, Jackson Horton, William Jackson III, Nawal Taneja, Tower of Power horns, and the entire team at Wadsworth Publishing Company.

Table of Contents

Preface

PART I - FEDERAL AVIATION REGULATIONS

PART II - AIRMAN'S INFORMATION MANUAL

Section 2. Uncontrolled Airspace

Section 3. Controlled Airspace

Section 4. Special Use Airspace

Section 5. Other Airspace Areas

Chapter 10 Air Traffic Control
Section 1. Services Available To Pilots

Section 2. Radio Communications Phraseology and Techniques

Section 3. Airport Operations

CHAPTER 11. Air Traffic Procedures
Section 1. Preflight

Section 2. Altimeter Setting Procedures

Section

Section 3. Wake Turbulence

Section

Chapter 15   Aeronautical Charts and Related Publications
Section 1. Types of Charts Available

Section

Part 1 - Definitions and Abbreviations

Section 1.1 General definitions.

As used in Subchapters A through K of this chapter, unless the context requires otherwise:

"Administrator" means the Federal Aviation Administrator or any person to whom he has delegated his authority in the matter concerned.

"Aircraft" means a device that is used or intended to be used for flight in the air.

"Aircraft engine" means an engine that is used or is intended to be used for propelling aircraft. It includes turbosuperchargers, appurtenances, and accessories necessary for its functioning, but does not include propellers.

"Airframe" means the fuselage, booms, nacelles, cowlings, fairings, airfoil surfaces (including rotors but excluding propellers and rotating airfoils of engines), and landing gear of an aircraft and their accessories and controls.

"Airplane" means an engine-driven fixed-wing aircraft heavier than air, that is supported in flight by the dynamic reaction of the air against its wings.

"Airport" means an area of land or water that is used or intended to be used for the landing and takeoff of aircraft, and includes its buildings and facilities, if any.

"Airport traffic area" means, unless otherwise specifically designated in Part 93, that airspace within a horizontal radius of 5 statute miles from the geographical center of any airport at which a control tower is operating, extending from the surface up to, but not including, an altitude of 3,000 feet above the elevation of the airport.

"Airship" means an engine-driven lighter-than-air aircraft that can be steered.

"Air traffic" means aircraft operating in the air or on an airport surface, exclusive of loading ramps and parking areas.

"Air traffic clearance" means an authorization by air traffic control, for the purpose of preventing collision between known aircraft, for an aircraft to proceed under specified traffic conditions within controlled airspace.

"Air traffic control" means a service operated by appropriate authority to promote the safe, orderly, and expeditious flow of air traffic.

"Alternate airport" means an airport at which an aircraft may land if a landing at the intended airport becomes inadvisable.

"Altitude engine" means a reciprocating aircraft engine having a rated takeoff power that is producible from sea level to an established higher altitude.

"**Appliance**" means any instrument, mechanism, equipment, part, apparatus, appurtenance, or accessory, including communications equipment, that is used or intended to be used in operating or controlling an aircraft in flight, is installed in or attached to the aircraft, and is not part of an airframe, engine, or propeller.

"**Approved**," unless used with reference to another person, means approved by the Administrator.

"**Area navigation (RNAV)**" means a method of navigation that permits aircraft operations on any desired course within the coverage of station-referenced navigation signals or within the limits of self-contained system capability.

"**Area navigation low route**" means an area navigation route within the airspace extending upward from 1,200 feet above the surface of the earth to, but not including, 18,000 feet MSL.

"**Area navigation high route**" means an area navigation route within the airspace extending upward from, and including, 18,000 feet MSL to flight level 450.

"**Armed forces**" means the Army, Navy, Air Force, Marine Corps, and Coast Guard, including their regular and reserve components and members serving without component status.

"**Balloon**" means a lighter-than-air aircraft that is not engine driven.

"**Brake horsepower**" means the power delivered at the propeller shaft (main drive or main output) of an aircraft engine.

"**Calibrated airspeed**" means indicated airspeed of an aircraft, corrected for position and instrument error. Calibrated airspeed is equal to true airspeed in standard atmosphere at sea level.

"**Category**": (1) As used with respect to the certification, ratings, privileges, and limitations of airmen, means a broad classification of aircraft. Examples include: airplane, rotorcraft, glider, and lighter-than-air; and (2) As used with respect to the certification of aircraft, means a grouping of aircraft based upon intended use or operating limitations. Examples include: transport, normal, utility, acrobatic, limited, restricted, and provisional.

"**Ceiling**" means the height above the earth's surface of the lowest layer of clouds or obscuring phenomena that is reported as "broken," "overcast," or "obscuration," and not classified as "thin" or "partial."

"**Civil aircraft**" means aircraft other than public aircraft.

"**Class**": (1) As used with respect to the certification, ratings, privileges, and limitations of airmen, means a classification of aircraft within a category having similar operating characteristics. Examples include: single engine, multiengine, land, water, gyroplane, helicopter, airship, and free balloon; and (2) As used with respect to the certification of aircraft, means a broad grouping of aircraft having similar characteristics of propulsion, flight, or landing. Examples include: airplane, rotorcraft, glider, balloon, landplane, and seaplane.

"Controlled airspace" means airspace designated as a continental control area, control area, control zone, terminal control area, or transition area, within which some or all aircraft may be subject to air traffic control.

"Critical altitude" means the maximum altitude at which, in standard atmosphere, it is possible to maintain, at a specified rotational speed, a specified power or a specified manifold pressure. Unless otherwise stated, the critical altitude is the maximum altitude at which it is possible to maintain, at the maximum continuous rotational speed, one of the following: (1) The maximum continuous power, in the case of engines for which this power rating is the same at sea level and at the rated altitude. (2) The maximum continuous rated manifold pressure, in the case of engines the maximum continuous power of which is governed by a constant manifold pressure.

"Extended over-water operation" means, with respect to aircraft other than helicopters, an operation over water at a horizontal distance of more than 50 nautical miles from the nearest shoreline.

"Flammable," with respect to a fluid or gas, means susceptible to igniting readily or exploding.

"Flap extended speed" means the highest speed permissible with wing flaps in a prescribed extended position.

"Flight level" means a level of constant atmospheric pressure related to a reference datum of 29.92 inches of mercury. Each is stated in three digits that represent hundreds of feet. For example, flight level 250 represents a barometric altimeter indication of 25,000 feet; flight level 255, an indication of 25,500 feet.

"Flight plan" means specified information, relating to the intended flight of an aircraft, that is filed orally or in writing with air traffic control.

"Flight time" means the time from the moment the aircraft first moves under its own power for the purpose of flight until the moment it comes to rest at the next point of landing ("block-to-block" time).

"Flight visibility" means the average forward horizontal distance, from the cockpit of an aircraft in flight, at which prominent unlighted objects may be seen and identified by day and prominent lighted objects may be seen and identified by night.

"Glider" means a heavier-than-air aircraft, that is supported in flight by the dynamic reaction of the air against its lifting surfaces and whose free flight does not depend principally on an engine.

"Ground visibility" means prevailing horizontal visibility near the earth's surface as reported by the United States National Weather Service or an accredited observer.

"IFR conditions" means weather conditions below the minimum for flight under visual flight rules.

"Indicated airspeed" means the speed of an aircraft as shown on its pitot static airspeed indicator calibrated to reflect standard adiabatic compressible flow at sea level uncorrected for airspeed system errors.

"Instrument" means a device using an internal mechanism to show visually or aurally the attitude, altitude, or operation of an aircraft or aircraft part. It includes electronic devices for automatically controlling an aircraft in flight.

"**Landing gear extended speed**" means the maximum speed at which an aircraft can be safely flown with the landing gear extended.

"**Landing gear operating speed**" means the maximum speed at which the landing gear can be safely extended or retracted.

"**Large aircraft**" means aircraft of more than 12,500 pounds, maximum certificated takeoff weight.

"**Lighter-than-air aircraft**" means aircraft that can rise and remain suspended by using contained gas weighing less than the air that is displaced by the gas.

"**Load factor**" means the ratio of a specified load to the total weight of the aircraft. The specified load is expressed in terms of any of the following: aerodynamic forces, inertia forces, or ground or water reactions.

"**Maintenance**" means inspection, overhaul, repair, preservation, and the replacement of parts, but excludes preventive maintenance.

"**Major alteration**" means an alteration not listed in the aircraft, aircraft engine, or propeller specifications - (1) That might appreciably affect weight, balance, structural strength, performance, powerplant operation, flight characteristics, or other qualities affecting airworthiness; or (2) That is not done according to accepted practices or cannot be done by elementary operations.

"**Major repair**" means a repair - (1) That, if improperly done, might appreciably affect weight, balance, structural strength, performance, powerplant operation, flight characteristics, or other qualities affecting airworthiness; or (2) That is not done according to accepted practices or cannot be done by elementary operations.

"**Manifold pressure**" means absolute pressure as measured at the appropriate point in the induction system and usually expressed in inches of mercury.

"**Medical certificate**" means acceptable evidence of physical fitness on a form prescribed by the Administrator.

"**Minor alteration**" means an alteration other than a major alteration.

"**Minor repair**" means a repair other than a major repair.

"**Navigable airspace**" means airspace at and above the minimum flight altitudes prescribed by or under this chapter, including airspace needed for safe takeoff and landing.

"**Night**" means the time between the end of evening civil twilight and the beginning of morning civil twilight, as published in the American Air Almanac, converted to local time.

"**Operate**," with respect to aircraft, means use, cause to use or authorize to use aircraft, for the purpose (except as provided in 91.13 of this chapter) of air navigation including the piloting of aircraft, with or without the right of legal control (as owner, lessee, or otherwise).

"**Operational control**," with respect to a flight, means the exercise of authority over initiating, conducting, or terminating a flight.

"**Over the top**" means above the layer of clouds or obscuring phenomena forming the ceiling.

"**Parachute**" means a device used or intended to be used to retard the fall of a body or object through the air.

"**Person**" means an individual, firm, partnership, corporation, company, association, joint-stock association, or governmental entity. It includes a trustee, receiver, assignee, or similar representative of any of them.

"**Pilotage**" means navigation by visual reference to landmarks.

"**Pilot-in-command**" means the pilot responsible for the operation and safety of an aircraft during flight time.

"**Pitch setting**" means the propeller blade setting as determined by the blade angle measured in a manner, and at a radius, specified by the instruction manual for the propeller.

"**Positive control**" means control of all air traffic, within designated airspace, by air traffic control.

"**Preventive maintenance**" means simple or minor preservation operations and the replacement of small standard parts not involving complex assembly operations.

"**Prohibited area**" means designated airspace within which the flight of aircraft is prohibited.

"**Propeller**" means a device for propelling an aircraft that has blades on an engine-driven shaft and that, when rotated, produces by its action on the air, a thrust approximately perpendicular to its plane of rotation. It includes control components normally supplied by its manufacturer, but does not include main and auxiliary rotors or rotating airfoils of engines.

"**Public aircraft**" means aircraft used only in the service of a government, or a political subdivision. It does not include any government-owned aircraft engaging in carrying persons or property for commercial purposes.

"**Rated maximum continuous power,**" with respect to reciprocating, turbopropeller, and turboshaft engines, means the approved brake horsepower that is developed statically or in flight, in standard atmosphere at a specified altitude, within the engine operating limitations established under Part 33, and approved for unrestricted periods of use.

"**Rated takeoff power,**" with respect to reciprocating, turbopropeller, and turboshaft engine type certification, means the approved brake horsepower that is developed statically under standard sea level conditions, within the engine operating limitations established under Part 33, and limited in use to periods of not over 5 minutes for takeoff operation.

"**Rating**" means a statement that, as a part of a certificate, sets forth special conditions, privileges, or limitations.

"**Reporting point**" means a geographical location in relation to which the position of an aircraft is reported.

"**Restricted area**" means airspace designated under Part 73 of this chapter within which the flight of aircraft, while not wholly prohibited, is subject to restriction.

"RNAV way point (W/P)" means a predetermined geographical position used for route or instrument approach definition or progress reporting purposes that is defined relative to a VORTAC station position.

"Rotorcraft" means a heavier-than-air aircraft that depends principally for its support in flight on the lift generated by one or more rotors.

"Route segment" means a part of a route. Each end of that part is identified by - (1) A continental or insular geographical location; or (2) A point at which a definite radio fix can be established.

"Sea level engine" means a reciprocating aircraft engine having a rated takeoff power that is producible only at sea level.

"Show," unless the context otherwise requires, means to show to the satisfaction of the Administrator.

"Small aircraft" means aircraft of 12,500 pounds or less, maximum certificated takeoff weight.

"Standard atmosphere" means the atmosphere defined in U.S. Standard Atmosphere, 1962 (geopotential altitude tables).

"Stopway" means an area beyond the takeoff runway, no less wide than the runway and centered upon the extended centerline of the runway, able to support the airplane during an aborted takeoff, without causing structural damage to the airplane, and designated by the airport authorities for use in decelerating the airplane during an aborted takeoff.

"Takeoff power," with respect to reciprocating engines, means the brake horsepower that is developed under standard sea level conditions, and under the maximum conditions of crankshaft rotational speed and engine manifold pressure approved for the normal takeoff, and limited in continuous use to the period of time shown in the approved engine specification.

"True airspeed" means the airspeed of an aircraft relative to undisturbed air.

"Traffic pattern" means the traffic flow that is prescribed for aircraft landing at, taxiing on, or taking off from, an airport.

"Type": (1) As used with respect to the certification, ratings, privileges, and limitations of airmen, means a specific make and basic model of aircraft, including modifications thereto that do not change its handling or flight characteristics. Examples include: C-152, C-172, and PA-28. (2) As used with respect to the certification of aircraft, means those aircraft which are similar in design. Examples include: C-152 and C-152 II.

"United States," in a geographical sense, means (1) the states, the District of Columbia, Puerto Rico, and the possessions, including the territorial waters, and (2) the airspace of those areas.

"VFR over-the-top," with respect to the operation of aircraft, means the operation of an aircraft over-the-top under VFR when it is not being operated on an IFR flight plan.

Section 1.2 Abbreviations and symbols.

In Subchapters A through K of this chapter:

"AGL"   means above ground level.
"ATC"   means air traffic control.
"CAS"   means calibrated airspeed.
"EAS"   means equivalent airspeed.
"FAA"   means Federal Aviation Administration.
"IAS"   means indicated airspeed.
"ICAO"   means International Civil Aviation Organization.
"IFR"   means instrument flight rules.
"MSL"   means mean sea level.
"NDB (ADF)" means nondirectional beacon (automatic direction finder).
"REIL"   means runway end identification lights.
"TACAN" means ultra-high frequency tactical air navigational aid.
"TAS"   means true airspeed.
"TVOR"   means very high frequency terminal omnirange station.

V_A means design maneuvering speed
V_{FE} means maximum flap extended speed.
V_{LE} means maximum landing gear extended speed.
V_{LO} means maximum landing gear operating speed.
V_{NE} means never-exceed speed.
V_{NO} means maximum structural cruising speed.
V_S means the stalling speed or the minimum steady flight speed at which the airplane is controllable.
V_{SO} means the stalling speed or the minimum steady flight speed in the landing configuration.
V_{S1} means the stalling speed or the minimum steady flight speed obtained in a specific configuration.
V_X means speed for best angle of climb.
V_Y means speed for best rate of climb.

"VFR"   means visual flight rules.
"VHF"   means very high frequency.
"VOR"   means very high frequency omnirange station.
"VORTAC" means collocated VOR and TACAN.

Section 1.3 Rules of construction.

(a) In Subchapters A through K of this chapter, unless the context requires otherwise: (1) Words importing the singular include the plural; (2) Words importing the plural include the singular; and (3) Words importing the masculine gender include the feminine.

(b) In Subchapters A through K of this chapter, the word: (1) "Shall" is used in an imperative sense; (2) "May" is used in a permissive sense to state authority or permission to do the act prescribed, and the words "no person

7

may . . . " or "a person may not . . . " mean that no person is required, authorized, or permitted to do the act prescribed; and (3) "Includes" means "includes but is not limited to."

TEST QUESTIONS

1. An Airport Traffic Area is automatically in effect when

A - its associated control tower is in operation.
B - the weather is below VFR minimums.
C - nighttime hours exist.

2. With respect to the certification of *airmen,* which is a category of aircraft?

A - Gyroplane, helicopter, airship, free balloon.
B - Airplane, rotorcraft, glider, lighter-than-air.
C - Single-engine land and sea, multiengine land and sea.

3. With respect to the certification of *airmen,* which is a class of aircraft?

A - Airplane, rotorcraft, glider, lighter-than-air.
B - Single-engine land and sea, multiengine land and sea.
C - Lighter-than-air, airship, hot air balloon, gas balloon.

4. With respect to the certification of *aircraft,* which is a category of aircraft?

A - Normal, utility, acrobatic.
B - Airplane, rotorcraft, glider.
C - Landplane, seaplane.

5. With respect to the certification of *aircraft,* which is a class of aircraft?

A - Airplane, helicopter, glider, hot air balloon.
B - Normal, utility, acrobatic, limited.
C - Transport, restricted, provisional.

6. The definition of nighttime is

A - sunset to sunrise.
B - 1 hour after sunset to 1 hour before sunrise.
C - the time between the end of evening civil twilight and the beginning of morning civil twilight.

7. Which V-speed represents *maximum flap extended* speed?

A - V_{FE}
B - V_{LOF}
C - V_{FC}

8. Which V-speed represents *maximum landing gear extended* speed?

A - V_{LE}
B - V_{LO}
C - V_{FE}

9. V_{NO} is defined as the

A - normal operating range.
B - never-exceed speed.
C - maximum structural cruising speed.

10. V_{SO} is defined as the

A - stalling speed or minimum steady flight speed in the landing configuration.
B - stalling speed or minimum steady flight speed in a specified configuration.
C - stalling speed or minimum takeoff safety speed.

11. Which would provide the greatest gain in altitude in the shortest distance during climb after takeoff?

A - V_Y
B - V_A
C - V_X

12. After takeoff, which airspeed would the pilot use to gain the most altitude in a given period of time?

A - V_Y
B - V_X
C - V_A

ANSWERS

1. A (1.1)   2. B (1.1)   3. B (1.1)   4. A (1.1)   5. A (1.1)
6. C (1.1)   7. A (1.2)   8. A (1.2)   9. C (1.2)   10. A (1.2)
11. C (1.2)   12. A (1.2)

2

Part 61 - Certification: Pilots and Flight Instructors
Subpart A - General

Section
61.1 Applicability.

(a) This part prescribes the requirements for issuing pilot and flight instructor certificates and ratings, the conditions under which those certificates and ratings are necessary, and the privileges and limitations of those certificates and ratings.
(b) Except as provided in 61.71 of this part, an applicant for a certificate or rating must meet the requirements of this part.

61.2 Certification of foreign pilots.

A person who is neither a United States citizen nor a resident alien is issued a certificate under this part (other than under 61.75 or 61.77), outside the United States, only when the Administrator finds that the pilot certificate is needed for the operation of a U.S.-registered civil aircraft or finds that the flight instructor certificate is needed for the training of students who are citizens of the United States.

61.3 Requirement for certificates, ratings, and authorizations.

> When flying an airplane in the United States as a private pilot, you must carry a current medical and appropriate pilot certificates.

(a) Pilot certificate. No person may act as pilot-in-command or in any other capacity as a required pilot flight crewmember of a civil aircraft of United States registry unless he has in his personal possession a current pilot certificate issued to him under this part. However, when the aircraft is operated within a foreign country a current pilot license issued by the country in which the aircraft is operated may be used.
(b) Pilot certificate: foreign aircraft. No person may, within the United States, act as pilot-in-command or in any other capacity as a required pilot flight crewmember of a civil aircraft of foreign registry unless he has in his personal possession a current pilot certificate issued to him under this part, or a pilot license issued to him or validated for him by the country in which the aircraft is registered.
(c) Medical certificate. Except for free balloon pilots piloting balloons and glider pilots piloting gliders, no person may act as pilot-in-command or in any other capacity as a required pilot flight crewmember of an aircraft under a certificate issued to him under this part, unless he has in his personal possession an appropriate current medical certificate issued under Part 67 of this chapter. However, when the aircraft is operated within a foreign country with a current pilot license issued by that country, evidence of current

11

medical qualification for that license, issued by that country, may be used. In the case of a pilot certificate issued on the basis of a foreign pilot license under 61.75, evidence of current medical qualification accepted for the issue of that license is used in place of a medical certificate.

61.5 Certificates and ratings issued under this part.

Your private pilot certificate, when issued, will contain a category and a class rating. The category is "Airplane" and the class is "Single-engine land." Student pilot certificates do not list these ratings.

(a) The following certificates are issued under this part: (1) Pilot certificates: (i) Student pilot. (ii) Recreational pilot. (iii) Private pilot. (iv) Commercial pilot. (v) Airline transport pilot.
(b) The following ratings are placed on pilot certificates (other than student pilot) where applicable: (1) Aircraft category ratings: (i) Airplane. (ii) Rotorcraft. (iii) Glider. (iv) Lighter-than-air.
(2) Airplane class ratings: (i) Single-engine land. (ii) Multiengine land. (iii) Single-engine sea. (iv) Multiengine sea.

61.11 Expired pilot certificates and reissuance.

Unless you received your private pilot certificate before July 1, 1945, it is issued without a specific expiration date. If you received it after this date and it does happen to bear an expiration date, you may not legally fly beyond the listed expiration date but may exchange it for a certificate without an expiration date.

(a) No person who holds an expired pilot certificate or rating may exercise the privileges of that pilot certificate or rating.
(b) Except as provided, the following certificates and ratings have expired and are not reissued:
(2) A private or commercial pilot certificate, or a lighter-than-air or free balloon pilot certificate, issued before July 1, 1945. However, each of those certificates issued after June 30, 1945, and bearing an expiration date, may be reissued without an expiration date.
(c) A private or commercial pilot certificate or a special purpose pilot certificate, issued on the basis of a foreign pilot license, expires on the expiration date stated thereon. A certificate without an expiration date is issued to the holder of the expired certificate only if he meets the requirements of 61.75 of this part for the issue of a pilot certificate based on a foreign pilot license.

61.13 Application and qualification.

An application for a private pilot certificate is made on FAA Form 8710-1. If the airplane in which you take your checkride is not sufficiently equipped to perform an item required on the checkride, a limitation will appear on your certificate. For example, if the examiner wants you to demonstrate night takeoffs and landings, and the airplane is not equipped with position lights (required night-flight equipment), you cannot legally perform the task

12

and your certificate will have the limitation "Night Flying Prohibited" placed on it. Likewise, if you have a medical condition (impaired night vision) which prevents you from performing a required item, the same limitation would be placed on your certificate. If your certificate should be suspended or revoked, you may not fly or apply for a new certificate for 1 year.

(a) An application for a certificate and rating or for an additional rating under this part is made on a form and in a manner prescribed by the Administrator. Each person who is neither a United States citizen nor a resident alien must show evidence that the fee prescribed by Appendix A of Part 187 of this chapter has been paid if that person - (1) Applies for a student pilot certificate to be issued outside the United States; or (2) Applies for a written or practical test to be administered outside the United States for any certificate or rating issued under this part.

(b) An applicant who meets the requirements of this part is entitled to an appropriate pilot certificate with aircraft ratings. Additional aircraft category, class, type and other ratings, for which the applicant is qualified, are added to his certificate. However, the Administrator may refuse to issue certificates to persons who are not citizens of the United States and who do not reside in the United States.

(c) An applicant who cannot comply with all of the flight proficiency requirements prescribed by this part because the aircraft used by him for his flight training or flight test is characteristically incapable of performing a required pilot operation, but who meets all other requirements for the certificate or rating sought, is issued the certificate or rating with appropriate limitations.

(d) An applicant for a pilot certificate who holds a medical certificate under 67.19 of this chapter with special limitations on it, but who meets all other requirements for that pilot certificate, is issued a pilot certificate containing such operating limitations as the Administrator determines are necessary because of the applicant's medical deficiency.

(f) Unless authorized by the Administrator-
(1) A person whose pilot certificate is suspended may not apply for any pilot or flight instructor certificate or rating during the period of suspension.

(g) Unless the order of revocation provides otherwise -
(1) A person whose pilot certificate is revoked may not apply for any pilot or flight instructor certificate or rating for one year after the date of revocation.

61.15 Offenses involving alcohol or drugs.

The following items are grounds for suspending or revoking your pilot certificate or denying your application for a certificate. Additionally, you may not apply for a new certificate for 1 year.

1. Any conviction related to illegal drugs. (61.15)
2. Flying an airplane under the influence of alcohol or drugs. (91.17)
3. Knowingly flying an airplane carrying illegal drugs. (91.19)
4. Two convictions for DUI or DWI within a 3-year period. (61.15)
5. Failure to notify the FAA in writing of a DUI or DWI. (61.15)
6. Refusing to submit to, or furnish results of, an alcohol test. (61.16)

(a) A conviction for the violation of any federal or state statute relating to the growing, processing, manufacture, sale, disposition, possession, transportation, or importation of narcotic drugs, marihuana, or depressant or stimulant drugs or substances is grounds for-
(1) Denial of an application for any certificate or rating issued under this part for a period of

up to 1 year after the date of final conviction; or (2) Suspension or revocation of any certificate or rating issued under this part.

(b) The commission of an act prohibited by 91.17(a) or 91.19(a) of this chapter is grounds for- (1) Denial of an application for a certificate or rating issued under this part for a period of up to 1 year after the date of that act; or (2) Suspension or revocation of any certificate or rating issued under this part.

(c) For the purposes of paragraphs (d) and (e) of this section, a motor vehicle action means - (1) A conviction after November 29, 1990 for the violation of any federal or state statute relating to the operation of a motor vehicle while intoxicated by alcohol or a drug, while impaired by alcohol or a drug, or while under the influence of alcohol or a drug; or (2) The cancellation, suspension, or revocation of a license to operate a motor vehicle by a state after November 29, 1990, for a cause related to the operation of a motor vehicle while intoxicated by alcohol or a drug, while impaired by alcohol or a drug, or while under the influence of alcohol or a drug; or (3) The denial after November 29, 1990, of an application for a license to operate a motor vehicle by a state for a cause related to the operation of a motor vehicle while intoxicated by alcohol or a drug, while impaired by alcohol or a drug, or while under the influence of alcohol or a drug.

(d) Except in the case of a motor vehicle action that results from the same incident or arises out of the same factual circumstances, a motor vehicle action occurring within 3 years of a previous motor vehicle action is grounds for - (1) Denial of an application for any certificate or rating issued under this part for a period of up to 1 year after the date of the last motor vehicle action; or (2) Suspension or revocation of any certificate or rating issued under this part.

(e) Each person holding a certificate issued under this part shall provide a written report of each motor vehicle action to the FAA, Civil Aviation Security Division (AAC-700), P.O. Box 25810, Oklahoma City, OK 73125, not later than 60 days after the motor vehicle action. The report must include - (1) The person's name, address, date of birth, and airman certificate number; (2) The type of violation that resulted in the conviction or the administrative action; (3) The date of the conviction or administrative action; (4) The state that holds the record of conviction or administrative action; and (5) A statement of whether the motor vehicle action related from the same incident or arose out of the same factual circumstances related to a previously reported motor vehicle action.

(f) Failure to comply with paragraph (e) of this section is grounds for- (1) Denial of an application for any certificate or rating issued under this part for a period of up to 1 year after the date of the motor vehicle action; or (2) Suspension or revocation of any certificate or rating issued under this part.

61.16 Refusal to submit to an alcohol test or to furnish test results.

Refer to above comments for 61.15.

A refusal to submit to a test to indicate the percentage by weight of alcohol in the blood, when requested by a law enforcement officer in accordance with 91.17(c) of this chapter, or a refusal to furnish or authorize the release of the test results requested by the Administrator in accordance with 91.17(c) or (d) of this chapter, is grounds for-

(a) Denial of an application for any certificate or rating issued under this part for a period of up to 1 year after the date of that refusal; or

(b) Suspension or revocation of any certificate or rating issued under this part.

61.17 Temporary Certificate.

(a) A temporary pilot certificate or a rating, effective for a period of not

more than 120 days, is issued to a qualified applicant pending a review of his qualifications and the issuance of a permanent certificate or rating by the Administrator. The permanent certificate or rating is issued to an applicant found qualified and a denial thereof is issued to an applicant found not qualified.

(b) A temporary certificate issued under paragraph (a) of this section expires-
(1) At the end of the expiration date stated thereon; or (2) Upon receipt by the applicant of - (i) The certificate or rating sought; or (ii) Notice that the certificate or rating sought is denied.

61.19 Duration of pilot certificates.

A student pilot certificate is valid for 24 calendar months. For example, a certificate issued on January 1, 1992 would expire on January 31, 1994. A private pilot certificate is issued without a specific expiration date. However, possession is *not* 9/10ths of the law. Although you may physically have a pilot certificate, if the FAA suspends or revokes it, it is invalid. In this situation, they will probably ask you to return it, which you must do.

(a) General. The holder of a certificate with an expiration date may not, after that date, exercise the privileges of that certificate.

(b) Student pilot certificate. A student pilot certificate expires at the end of the 24th month after the month in which it was issued.

(c) Other pilot certificates. Any pilot certificate (other than a student pilot certificate) issued under this part is issued without a specific expiration date. However, the holder of a pilot certificate issued on the basis of a foreign pilot license may exercise the privileges of that certificate only while the foreign pilot license on which that certificate is based is effective.

(e) Surrender, suspension, or revocation. Any pilot certificate issued under this part ceases to be effective if it is surrendered, suspended, or revoked.

(f) Return of certificate. The holder of any certificate issued under this part that is suspended or revoked shall, upon the Administrator's request, return it to the Administrator.

61.23 Duration of medical certificates.

For student and private pilot privileges, a first-, second-, or third-class medical certificate is valid for 24 calendar months. For example, a certificate issued on January 1, 1992 would expire on January 31, 1994. The medical standards for qualification are increasingly demanding from third-class to first-class. You must meet the qualifications (which are relatively basic) for at least a third-class medical certificate.

(a) A first-class medical certificate expires at the end of the last day of- (1) The sixth month after the month of the date of examination shown on the certificate, for operations requiring an airline transport pilot certificate; (2) The 12th month after the month of the date of examination shown on the certificate, for operations requiring only a commercial pilot certificate; and (3) The 24th month after the month of the date of examination shown on the certificate, for operations requiring only a private, recreational, or student pilot certificate.

(b) A second-class medical certificate expires at the end of the last day of- (1) The 12th month after the month of the date of examination shown on the certificate, for operations re-

quiring a commercial pilot certificate or an air traffic control tower operator certificate; and
(2) The 24th month after the month of the date of examination shown on the certificate, for operations requiring only a private, recreational, or student pilot certificate.
(c) A third-class medical certificate expires at the end of the 24th month after the month of the date of examination shown on the certificate, for operations requiring a private, recreational, or student pilot certificate.

61.25 Change of name.

An application for the change of a name on a certificate issued under this part must be accompanied by the applicant's current certificate and a copy of the marriage license, court order, or other document verifying the change. The documents are returned to the applicant after inspection.

61.27 Voluntary surrender or exchange of certificate.

The holder of a certificate issued under this part may voluntarily surrender it for cancellation, or for the issue of a certificate of lower grade, or another certificate with specific ratings deleted. If he so requests, he must include the following statement or its equivalent: "This request is made for my own reasons, with full knowledge that my (insert name of certificate or rating, as appropriate) may not be reissued to me unless I again pass the tests prescribed for its issue."

61.29 Replacement of lost or destroyed certificate.

(a) An application for the replacement of a lost or destroyed airman certificate issued under this part is made by letter to the Department of Transportation, Federal Aviation Administration, Airman Certification Branch, Post Office Box 25082, Oklahoma City, OK 73125. The letter must-
(1) State the name of the person to whom the certificate was issued, the permanent mailing address (including zip code), social security number (if any), date and place of birth of the certificate holder, and any available information regarding the grade, number, and date of issue of the certificate, and the ratings on it; and
(2) Be accompanied by a check or money order for $2.00, payable to the Federal Aviation Administration.
(b) An application for the replacement of a lost or destroyed medical certificate is made by letter to the Department of Transportation, Federal Aviation Administration, Aeromedical Certification Branch, Post Office Box 25082, Oklahoma City, OK 73125, accompanied by a check or money order for $2.00.
(c) A person who has lost a certificate issued under this part, or a medical certificate issued under Part 67 of this chapter, or both, may obtain a telegram from the FAA confirming that it was issued. The telegram may be

carried as a certificate for a period not to exceed 60 days pending his receipt of a duplicate certificate under paragraph (a) or (b) of this section, unless he has been notified that the certificate has been suspended or revoked. The request for such a telegram may be made by letter or prepaid telegram, including the date upon which a duplicate certificate was previously requested, if a request had been made, and a money order for the cost of the duplicate certificate. The request for a telegraphic certificate is sent to the office listed in paragraph (a) or (b) of this section, as appropriate. However, a request for both airman and medical certificates at the same time must be sent to the office prescribed in paragraph (a) of this section.

61.31 General limitations.

Except for some specific situations, in order to fly a large (defined in Part 1 as over 12,500 pounds) or turbojet-powered airplane, you must have a type rating on your certificate. You may not carry passengers in an airplane unless you hold category and class ratings for that airplane. Remember the distinction between category (airplane), class (single-engine land), and type (Cessna 152).

For each of the following, you must have received instruction in such an airplane and have a logbook endorsement indicating this:

1. To solo any airplane with a student pilot certificate.
2. To fly a high-performance (sometimes called complex) airplane, unless you have logged PIC time prior to November 1, 1973.
3. To fly a tailwheel airplane, unless you have logged PIC time prior to April 15, 1991.

To fly a high-altitude (pressurized) airplane, you must receive specific ground and flight instruction in such an airplane, unless you have logged PIC time or passed a checkride in such an airplane prior to April 15, 1991.

The rating limitations mentioned above do not apply if you:

1. hold a student pilot certificate.
2. hold a recreational pilot certificate, and are operating as such.
3. are operating under a provisional or experimental type certificate.
4. are taking a practical test (checkride).

(a) Type ratings required. A person may not act as pilot-in-command of any of the following aircraft unless he holds a type rating for that aircraft:
(1) A large aircraft (except lighter-than-air).
(3) A turbojet-powered airplane.
(4) Other aircraft specified by the Administrator through aircraft type certificate procedures.
(b) Authorization in lieu of a type rating.
(1) In lieu of a type rating required under paragraphs (a)(1), (3), and (4) of this section, an aircraft may be operated under an authorization issued by the Administrator, for a flight or series of flights within the United States, if—

(i) The particular operation for which the authorization is requested involves a ferry flight, a practice or training flight, a flight test for a pilot type rating, or a test flight of an aircraft, for a period that does not exceed 60 days; (ii) The applicant shows that compliance with paragraph (a) of this section is impracticable for the particular operation; and (iii) The Administrator finds that an equivalent level of safety may be achieved through operating limitations on the authorization.

(2) Aircraft operated under an authorization issued under this paragraph-

(i) May not be operated for compensation or hire; and (ii) May carry only flight crewmembers necessary for the flight.

(3) An authorization issued under this paragraph may be reissued for an additional 60-day period for the same operation if the applicant shows that he was prevented from carrying out the purpose of the particular operation before his authorization expired. The prohibition of subparagraph (2)(i) of this section does not prohibit compensation for the use of an aircraft by a pilot solely to prepare for or to take a flight test for a type rating.

(c) Category and class rating: carrying another person or operating for compensation or hire. Unless he holds a category and class rating for that aircraft, a person may not act as pilot-in-command of an aircraft that is carrying another person or is operated for compensation or hire. In addition, he may not act as pilot-in-command of that aircraft for compensation or hire.

(d) Category and class rating: other operations. No person may act as pilot-in-command of an aircraft in solo flight in operations not subject to paragraph (c) of this section, unless he meets at least one of the following:

(1) He holds a category and class rating appropriate to that aircraft.

(2) He has received flight instruction in the pilot operations required by this part, appropriate to the category and class of aircraft for first solo, given to him by a certified flight instructor who found him competent to solo that category and class of aircraft and has so endorsed his pilot logbook.

(3) He has soloed and logged pilot-in-command time in that category and class of aircraft before November 1, 1973.

(e) High-performance airplanes. A person holding a private pilot certificate may not act as pilot-in-command of an airplane that has more than 200 horsepower, or that has a retractable landing gear, flaps, and a controllable propeller, unless he has received flight instruction from an authorized flight instructor who has certified in his logbook that he is competent to pilot an airplane that has more than 200 horsepower, or that has a retractable landing gear, flaps, and a controllable propeller, as the case may be. However, this instruction is not required if he has logged flight time as pilot-in-command in high performance airplanes before November 1, 1973.

(f) High-altitude airplanes. (1) Except as provided in paragraph (f)(2) of this section, no person may act as pilot-in-command of a pressurized airplane that has a service ceiling or maximum operating altitude, whichever is lower, above 25,000 feet MSL unless that person has completed the ground and flight training specified in paragraphs (f)(1)(i) and (ii) of this section and has received a logbook or training record endorsement from an authorized instructor certifying satisfactory completion of the training. The training shall consist of: (i) Ground training that includes instruction on high-altitude aerodynamics and meteorology; respiration; effects, symptoms, and causes of hypoxia and any other high-altitude sicknesses; duration of consciousness without supplemental oxygen; effects of prolonged usage of supplemental oxygen; causes and effects of gas expansion and gas bubble formations; preventative measures for eliminating gas expansion, gas bubble formations, and high-altitude sicknesses; physical phenomena and incidents of decompression; and any other physiological aspects of high-altitude flight; and (ii) Flight training in an airplane, or in a simulator that meets the requirements of 121.407 of this chapter, and which is representative of an airplane as described in paragraph (f)(1) of this section. This training shall include normal cruise flight operations while operating above 25,000 feet MSL; the proper emergency procedures for simulated rapid decompression without actually depressurizing the airplane; and emergency descent procedures; (2) The training required in paragraph (f)(1) of this section is not re-

18

quired if a person can document accomplishment of any of the following in an airplane, or in a simulator that meets the requirements of 121.407 of this chapter, and that is representative of an airplane described in paragraph (f)(1) of this section: (i) Served as pilot-in-command prior to April 15, 1991; (ii) Completed a pilot proficiency check for a pilot certificate or rating conducted by the FAA prior to April 15, 1991; (iii) Completed an official pilot-in-command check by the military services of the United States; or (iv) Completed a pilot-in-command proficiency check under parts 121, 125, or 135 conducted by the FAA or by an approved pilot check airman.

(g) Tailwheel airplanes. No person may act as pilot-in-command of a tailwheel airplane unless that person has received flight instruction from an authorized flight instructor who has found the pilot competent to operate a tailwheel airplane and has made a one-time endorsement so stating in the pilot's logbook. The endorsement must certify that the pilot is competent in normal and crosswind takeoffs and landings, wheel landings unless the manufacturer has recommended against such landings, and go-around procedures. This endorsement is not required if a pilot has logged flight time as pilot-in-command of tailwheel airplanes prior to April 15, 1991.

(h) Exception. This section does not require a class rating for gliders, or category and class ratings for aircraft that are not type certificated as airplanes, rotorcraft, or lighter-than-air aircraft. In addition, the rating limitations do not apply to-

(1) The holder of a student pilot certificate;

(2) The holder of a recreational pilot certificate when operating under the provisions of 61.101(f), (g), and (h).

(3) The holder of a pilot certificate when operating under the authority of an experimental or provisional type certificate; or

(4) An applicant when taking a flight test given by the Administrator.

61.33 Tests: General procedure.

Tests prescribed by or under this part are given at times and places, and by persons, designated by the Administrator.

61.35 Written test: Prerequisites and passing grades.

(a) An applicant for a written test must-

(1) Show that he has satisfactorily completed the ground instruction or home study course required by this part for the certificate or rating sought;

(2) Present as personal identification an airman certificate, driver's license, or other official document; and

(3) Present a birth certificate or other official document showing that he meets the age requirement prescribed in this part for the certificate sought not later than 2 years from the date of the application for the test.

(b) The minimum passing grade is specified by the Administrator on each written test sheet or booklet furnished to the applicant.

61.37 Written tests: Cheating or other unauthorized conduct.

(a) Except as authorized by the Administrator, no person may-

(1) Copy, or intentionally remove, a written test under this part;

(2) Give to another, or receive from another, any part or copy of that test;

(3) Give help on that test to, or receive help on that test from, any person

during the period that test is being given;

(4) Take any part of that test in behalf of another person;

(5) Use any material or aid during the period that test is being given; or

(6) Intentionally cause, assist, or participate in any act prohibited by this paragraph.

(b) No person whom the Administrator finds to have committed an act prohibited by paragraph (a) of this section is eligible for any airman certificate or rating, or to take any test therefor, under this chapter for a period of 1 year after the date of that act. In addition, the commission of that act is a basis for suspending or revoking any airman certificate or rating held by that person.

61.39 Prerequisites for flight tests.

(a) To be eligible for a flight test for a certificate or rating issued under this part, the applicant must-

(1) Have passed any required written test since the beginning of the 24th month before the month in which he takes the flight test;

(2) Have the applicable instruction and aeronautical experience prescribed in this part;

(3) Hold a current medical certificate appropriate to the certificate he seeks, or, in the case of a rating to be added to his pilot certificate, at least a third-class medical certificate issued since the beginning of the 24th month before the month in which he takes the flight test;

(4) Meet the age requirement for the issuance of the certificate or rating he seeks; and

(5) Have a written statement from an appropriately certificated flight instructor certifying that he has given the applicant flight instruction in preparation for the flight test within 60 days preceding the date of application, and finds him competent to pass the test and to have satisfactory knowledge of the subject areas in which he is shown to be deficient by his FAA airman written test report. However, an applicant need not have this written statement if he-

(i) Holds a foreign pilot license issued by a contracting State to the Convention on International Civil Aviation that authorizes at least the pilot privileges of the airman certificate sought by him;

(ii) Is applying for a type rating only, or a class rating with an associated type rating.

61.41 Flight instruction received from flight instructors not certificated by FAA.

Flight instruction may be credited toward the requirements for a pilot certificate or rating issued under this part if it is received from-

(a) An armed force of either the United States or a foreign contracting State to the Convention on International Civil Aviation in a program for training military pilots; or

(b) A flight instructor who is authorized to give that flight instruction by the licensing authority of a foreign contracting State to the Convention on International Civil Aviation and the flight instruction is given outside the United States.

61.43 Flight tests: General procedures.

Refer to Appendix I for specific procedures, maneuvers, and evaluation standards.

(a) The ability of an applicant for a private pilot certificate or for an aircraft rating on that certificate to perform the required pilot operations is based on the following:

(1) Executing procedures and maneuvers within the aircraft's performance capabilities and limitations, including use of the aircraft's systems.

(2) Executing emergency procedures and maneuvers appropriate to the aircraft.

(3) Piloting the aircraft with smoothness and accuracy.

(4) Exercising judgment.

(5) Applying his aeronautical knowledge.

(6) Showing that he is the master of the aircraft, with the successful outcome of a procedure or maneuver never seriously in doubt.

(b) If the applicant fails any of the required pilot operations in accordance with the applicable provisions of paragraph (a) of this section, the applicant fails the flight test. The applicant is not eligible for the certificate or rating sought until he passes any pilot operations he has failed.

(c) The examiner or the applicant may discontinue the test at any time when the failure of a required pilot operation makes the applicant ineligible for the certificate or rating sought. If the test is discontinued the applicant is entitled to credit for only those entire pilot operations that he has successfully performed.

61.45 Flight tests: Required aircraft and equipment.

You are responsible for furnishing the airplane for your checkride. This will usually be the airplane that you have done the majority of your training in, so you should be quite comfortable in it. If the airplane does not have a "standard" or "limited" airworthiness certificate, it is not registered in the U.S., or it has an abnormal seating, instrument, or control arrangement, you should check with the examiner prior to the checkride for approval. You are also responsible for providing foggles or an instrument hood.

(a) General. An applicant for a certificate or rating under this part must furnish, for each flight test that he is required to take, an appropriate aircraft of United States registry that has a current standard or limited airworthiness certificate. However, the applicant may, at the discretion of the inspector or examiner conducting the test, furnish an aircraft of U.S. registry that has a current airworthiness certificate other than standard or limited, an aircraft of foreign registry that is properly certificated by the country of registry, or a military aircraft in an operational status if its use is allowed by an appropriate military authority.

(b) Required equipment (other than controls). Aircraft furnished for a flight test must have-

(1) The equipment for each pilot operation required for the flight test;

(2) No prescribed operating limitations that prohibit its use in any pilot operation required on the test;

(3) Pilot seats with adequate visibility for each pilot to operate the aircraft safely, except as provided in paragraph (d) of this section; and

(4) Cockpit and outside visibility adequate to evaluate the performance of the applicant, where an additional jump seat is provided for the examiner.

(c) Required controls. An aircraft furnished under paragraph (a) of this section for any pilot flight test must have engine power controls and flight controls that are easily reached and operable in a normal manner by both pilots, unless after considering all the factors, the examiner determines that the flight test can be conducted safely without them. However, an aircraft having other controls such as nose-wheel steering, brakes, switches, fuel selectors, and engine air flow controls that are not easily reached and operable in a normal manner by both pilots may be used, if more than one pilot is required under its airworthiness certificate, or if the examiner determines that the flight can be conducted safely.

(d) Simulated instrument flight equipment. An applicant for any flight test involving flight maneuvers solely by reference to instruments must furnish equipment satisfactory to the examiner that excludes the visual reference of the applicant outside of the aircraft.

(e) Aircraft with single controls. At the discretion of the examiner, an aircraft furnished under paragraph (a) of this section for a flight test may, in the cases listed herein, have a single set of controls. In such case, the examiner determines the competence of the applicant by observation from the ground or from another aircraft.

(1) A flight test for addition of a class or type rating, not involving demonstration of instrument skills, to a private pilot certificate.

61.47 Flight tests: Status of FAA inspectors and other authorized flight examiners.

An FAA inspector or other authorized flight examiner conducts the flight test of an applicant for a pilot certificate or rating for the purpose of observing the applicant's ability to perform satisfactorily the procedures and maneuvers on the flight test. The inspector or other examiner is not pilot-in-command of the aircraft during the flight test unless he acts in that capacity for the flight, or portion of the flight, by prior arrangement with the applicant or other person who would otherwise act as pilot-in-command of the flight, or portion of the flight. Notwithstanding the type of aircraft used during a flight test, the applicant and the inspector or other examiner are not, with respect to each other (or other occupants authorized by the inspector or other examiner), subject to the requirements or limitations for the carriage of passengers specified in this chapter.

61.49 Retesting after failure.

(a) An applicant for a written or practical test who fails that test may not apply for retesting until 30 days after the date the test was failed. However, in the case of a first failure, the applicant may apply for retesting before the 30 days have expired provided the applicant presents a logbook or training record endorsement from an authorized instructor who has given the applicant remedial instruction and finds the applicant competent to pass the test.

61.51 Pilot logbooks.

> You need to keep track of your instruction and flight time to show that you have met the requirements for a checkride and also in order to be sure that you can legally carry passengers. (See 61.57) While the regulation only specifies a "reliable record," an official pilot logbook provides labeled columns for each required item. Be sure to have your instructor sign the logbook for all dual instruction received as well as ground instruction. Student pilots are required to carry their logbooks on solo cross-country flights. You are required to present your logbook for inspection to any authorized representative of the FAA, NTSB, or state or local law enforcement officer, if requested.

(a) The aeronautical training and experience used to meet the requirements for a certificate or rating, or the recent flight experience requirements of this part must be shown by a reliable record. The logging of other flight time is not required.
(b) Logbook entries. Each pilot shall enter the following information for each flight or lesson logged: (1) General. (i) Date. (ii) Total time of flight. (iii) Place, or points of departure and arrival. (iv) Type and identification of aircraft. (2) Type of pilot experience or training. (i) Pilot-in-command or solo. (ii) Second-in-command. (iii) Flight instruction received from an authorized flight instructor. (iv) Instrument flight instruction from an authorized flight instructor. (v) Pilot ground trainer instruction. (vi) Participating crew (lighter-than-air). (vii) Other pilot time. (3) Conditions of flight. (i) Day or night. (ii) Actual instrument. (iii) Simulated instrument conditions.
(c) Logging of pilot time. - (1) Solo flight time. A pilot may log as solo flight time only that flight time when he is the sole occupant of the aircraft. However, a student pilot may also log as solo flight time that time during which he acts as the pilot-in-command of an airship requiring more than one flight crewmember. (2) Pilot-in-command flight time. (i) A recreational, private, or commercial pilot may log as pilot-in-command time only that flight time during which that pilot is the sole manipulator of the controls of an aircraft for which the pilot is rated, or when the pilot is the sole occupant of the aircraft, or, except for a recreational pilot, when acting as pilot-in-command of an aircraft on which more than one pilot is required under the type certification of the aircraft or the regulations under which the flight is conducted. (5) Instruction time. All time logged as flight instruction, instrument flight instruction, pilot ground trainer instruction, or ground instruction time must be certified by the appropriately rated and certificated instructor from whom it was received.
(d) Presentation of logbook. (1) A pilot must present his logbook (or other record required by this section) for inspection upon reasonable request by the Administrator, an authorized representative of the National Transportation Safety Board, or any state or local enforcement officer. (2) A student pilot must carry his logbook (or other record required by this section) with him on all solo cross-country flights, as evidence of the required instructor clearances and endorsements. (3) A recreational pilot must carry his or her logbook that has the required instructor endorsements on all solo flights - (i) In excess of 50 nautical miles from an airport at which instruction was received; (ii) In airspace in which communication with air traffic control is required; (iii) Between sunset and sunrise; and (iv) In an aircraft for which the pilot is not rated.

23

61.53 Operations during medical deficiency.

No person may act as pilot-in-command, or in any other capacity as a required flight crewmember while he has a known medical deficiency, or increase of a known medical deficiency, that would make him unable to meet the requirements for his current medical certificate.

61.56 Flight review.

> At least every 24 calendar months, you must have a flight review (often called a "BFR" or biennial flight review) consisting of flight maneuvers and ground instruction. If you are a recreational or non-instrument-rated private pilot with less than 400 hours total time, this flight review must be accomplished every 12 calendar months. A flight instructor or examiner can perform the review and must endorse your logbook indicating satisfactory completion. If you have successfully completed a checkride for a certificate or rating within the appropriate 12 or 24 calendar month period or any phase of an FAA-sponsored proficiency award program (such as WINGS), this qualifies as a flight review. Appendix I can be of help in preparing for your flight review.

(a) As used in this section, a flight review consists of a review of- (1) The current general operating and flight rules of Part 91 of this chapter; and (2) Those maneuvers and procedures which, in the discretion of the person giving the review, are necessary for the pilot to demonstrate the safe exercise of the privileges of the pilot certificate.

(b) No person may act as pilot-in-command of an aircraft, within the period specified in paragraph (c) or (d) of this section, as applicable, unless that person has - (1) Accomplished a flight review given in an aircraft for which that pilot is rated by an appropriately rated instructor certificated under this part or other person designated by the Administrator; and (2) A logbook endorsed by the person who gave the review certifying that the pilot has satisfactorily accomplished the flight review.

(c) Except as provided in paragraphs (d) and (e) of this section, each pilot must have complied with the requirements of this section since the beginning of the 24th calendar month before the month in which that pilot acts as pilot-in-command.

(d) Except as provided in paragraph (e) of this section, after August 31, 1993- (1) Each recreational pilot who has logged fewer than 400 hours of flight time as a pilot and each non-instrument-rated private pilot who has logged fewer than 400 hours of flight time as a pilot must have complied with the flight review requirements of this section since the beginning of the 12th calendar month before the month in which that pilot acts as pilot-in-command of an aircraft. The flight review required by this paragraph consists of a minimum of 1 hour of flight instruction and 1 hour of ground instruction. (3) Notwithstanding the requirements of subparagraphs (d)(1) and (d)(2) of this section, each non-instrument-rated private pilot who has logged less than 400 hours of flight time as a pilot and who satisfactorily completes a flight review on or before August 30, 1989, may act as pilot-in-command of an aircraft until the 24th calendar month after the month in which that flight review was satisfactorily completed.

(e) A person who has, within the period specified in paragraphs (c) and (d) of this section, satisfactorily completed a pilot proficiency check conducted by the FAA, an approved pilot check airman, or a U.S. Armed Force, for a pilot certificate, rating, or operating privilege, need not accomplish the flight review required by this section.

(f) A person who has, within the period specified in paragraphs (c) and (d) of this section, satisfactorily completed one or more phases of an FAA-sponsored pilot proficiency award program, need not accomplish the flight review requirements of this section.

(g) The requirements of this section may be accomplished in combination with the requirements of 61.57 and other applicable recency requirements, at the discretion of the instructor.

61.57 Recent flight experience: Pilot-in-command.

> You may not carry passengers in an ASEL unless you have made three takeoffs and landings as sole manipulator of the controls in an ASEL within the last 90 days. If you fly a tailwheel airplane the landings must be to a full stop. To carry passengers at night, the landings must be performed to a full stop at night.

(c) General experience. No person may act as pilot-in-command of an aircraft carrying passengers, nor of an aircraft certificated for more than one required pilot flight crewmember, unless within the preceding 90 days, he has made three takeoffs and three landings as the sole manipulator of the flight controls in an aircraft of the same category and class and, if a type rating is required, of the same type. If the aircraft is a tailwheel airplane, the landings must have been made to a full stop in a tailwheel airplane. For the purpose of meeting the requirements of this paragraph, a person may act as pilot-in-command of a flight under day VFR or day IFR if no persons or property other than as necessary for his compliance thereunder, are carried. This paragraph does not apply to operations requiring an airline transport pilot certificate, or to operations conducted under Part 135 of this chapter.

(d) Night experience. No person may act as pilot-in-command of an aircraft carrying passengers during the period beginning 1 hour after sunset and ending 1 hour before sunrise (as published in the American Air Almanac) unless, within the preceding 90 days, he has made at least three takeoffs and three landings to a full stop during that period in the category and class of aircraft to be used. This paragraph does not apply to operations requiring an airline transport pilot certificate.

61.59 Falsification, reproduction, or alteration of applications, certificates, logbooks, reports, or records.

(a) No person may make or cause to be made - (1) Any fraudulent or intentionally false statement on any application for a certificate, rating, or duplicate thereof, issued under this part; (2) Any fraudulent or intentionally false entry in any logbook, record or report that is required to be kept, made, or used, to show compliance with any requirement for the issuance, or exercise of the privileges, or any certificate or rating under this part; (3) Any reproduction, for fraudulent purpose, of any certificate or rating under this part; or (4) Any alteration of any certificate or rating under this part.

(b) The commission by any person of an act prohibited under paragraph (a) of this section is a basis for suspending or revoking any airman or ground instructor certificate or rating held by that person.

61.60 Change of address.

You must notify the FAA within 30 days of any change in your permanent address. Certified mail with return receipt is recommended to avoid any future confusion.

The holder of a pilot or flight instructor certificate who has made a change in his permanent mailing address may not after 30 days from the date he moved, exercise the privileges of his certificate unless he has notified in writing the Department of Transportation, Federal Aviation Administration, Airman Certification Branch, Box 25082, Oklahoma City, OK 73125, of his new address.

TEST QUESTIONS

1. What document(s) must be in your personal possession while operating as pilot-in-command of an aircraft?

A - Certificates showing accomplishment of a checkout in the aircraft and a current biennial flight review.
B - A pilot certificate with an endorsement showing accomplishment of an annual flight review and a pilot logbook showing recency of experience.
C - An appropriate pilot certificate and an appropriate current medical certificate.

2. Each person who holds a pilot certificate or a medical certificate shall present it for inspection upon the request of the Administrator, the National Transportation Safety Board, or any

A - authorized representative of the Department of Transportation.
B - person in a position of authority.
C - federal, state, or local law enforcement officer.

3. A third-class medical certificate is issued on August 10, this year. To exercise the privileges of a Private Pilot Certificate, the medical certificate will be valid until midnight on

A - August 10, 2 years later.
B - August 31, 2 years later.
C - August 31, 3 years later.

4. The pilot-in-command is required to hold a type rating in which aircraft?

A - Aircraft operated under an authorization issued by the Administrator.
B - Aircraft having a gross weight of more than 12,500 pounds.
C - Aircraft involved in ferry flights, training flights, or test flights.

5. What is the definition of a high-performance airplane?

A - An airplane with 180 horsepower, retractable landing gear, flaps, and a fixed-pitch propeller.
B - An airplane with more than 200 horsepower, retractable landing gear, flaps, and a controllable propeller.
C - An airplane with a normal cruise speed in excess of 200 knots, flaps, and a controllable propeller.

6. Before a person holding a Private Pilot Certificate may act as pilot in command of a high-performance airplane, that person must have

A - passed a flight test in that airplane from an FAA inspector.
B - an endorsement in that person's logbook that she is competent to act as pilot-in-command.
C - received flight instruction from an authorized flight instructor who then endorses that person's logbook.

7. For noninstrument rated private pilots who have logged fewer than 400 hours of flight time to act as pilot-in-command of an aircraft, they must show by logbook endorsement the satisfactory accomplishment of a flight review or completion of a pilot proficiency check within the preceding

A - 6 calendar months.
B - 12 calendar months.
C - 24 calendar months.

8. If recency of experience requirements for night flight are not met and official sunset is 1830, the latest time passengers may be carried is

A - 1829.
B - 1859.
C - 1929.

9. To act as pilot-in-command of an aircraft carrying passengers, the pilot must have made at least three takeoffs and landings within the preceding 90 days in an aircraft of the same

A - make and model.
B - category and class, but not type.
C - category, class, and type.

10. The takeoffs and landings required to meet the recency of experience requirements for carrying passengers in a tailwheel airplane

A - may be touch and go or full stop.
B - must be touch and go.
C - must be to a full stop.

11. The three takeoffs and landings that are required to act as pilot-in-command at night must be done during the time period from

A - sunset to sunrise.
B - 1 hour after sunset to 1 hour before sunrise.
C - the end of evening civil twilight to the beginning of morning civil twilight.

12. If a certificated pilot changes permanent mailing address and fails to notify the FAA Airmen Certification Branch of the new address, the pilot is entitled to exercise the privileges of the pilot certificate for a period of only

A - 30 days after the date of the move.
B - 60 days after the date of the move.
C - 90 days after the date of the move.

ANSWERS

1. C (61.3)	2. C (61.3)	3. B (61.23)	4. B (61.31)
5. B (61.31)	6. C (61.31)	7. B (61.56)	8. C (61.57)
9. C (61.57)	10. C (61.57)	11. B (61.57)	12. A (61.60)

3

Part 61 - Certification: Pilots and Flight Instructors
Subparts B, C, and D

Subpart B - Aircraft Ratings and Special Certificates

Section
61.61 Applicability.

This subpart prescribes the requirements for the issuance of additional aircraft ratings after a pilot or instructor certificate is issued, and the requirements and limitations for special pilot certificates and ratings issued by the Administrator.

61.63 Additional aircraft ratings (other than airline transport pilot).

> Having an additional category (e.g., rotorcraft) or class (e.g., AMEL) added to your ASEL certificate entails essentially the same process as you went through for the original certificate in terms of training, signoffs, and testing. You need not take an additional written test, and some items on the practical test will not need to be performed. See Appendix I.

(a) General. To be eligible for an aircraft rating after his certificate is issued to him, an applicant must meet the requirements of paragraphs (b) through (d) of this section, as appropriate to the rating sought.
(b) Category rating. An applicant for a category rating to be added on his pilot certificate must meet the requirements of this part for the issue of the pilot certificate appropriate to the privileges for which the category rating is sought. However, the holder of a category rating for powered aircraft is not required to take a written test for the addition of a category rating on his pilot certificate.
(c) Class rating. An applicant for an aircraft class rating to be added on his pilot certificate must - (1) Present a logbook record certified by an authorized flight instructor showing that the applicant has received flight instruction in the class of aircraft for which a rating is sought and has been found competent in the pilot operations appropriate to the pilot certificate to which his category rating applies; and (2) Pass a flight test appropriate to his pilot certificate and applicable to the aircraft category and class rating sought.

61.69 Glider towing: Experience and instruction requirements.

No person may act as pilot-in-command of an aircraft towing a glider unless he meets the following requirements:
(a) He holds a current pilot certificate (other than a student or recreational pilot certificate) issued under this part.

(b) He has an endorsement in his pilot logbook from a person authorized to give flight instruction in gliders, certifying that he has received ground and flight instruction in gliders and is familiar with the techniques and procedures essential to the safe towing of gliders, including airspeed limitations, emergency procedures, signals used, and maximum angles of bank.

(c) He has made and entered in his pilot logbook - (1) At least three flights as sole manipulator of the controls of an aircraft towing a glider while accompanied by a pilot who has met the requirements of this section and made and logged at least 10 flights as pilot-in-command of an aircraft towing a glider; or (2) At least three flights as sole manipulator of the controls of an aircraft simulating glider towing flight procedures (while accompanied by a pilot who meets the requirements of this section), and at least three flights as pilot or observer in a glider being towed by an aircraft.

However, any person who, before May 17, 1967, made, and entered in his pilot logbook, 10 or more flights as pilot in command of an aircraft towing a glider in accordance with a certificate of waiver need not comply with paragraphs (c)(1) and (2) of this section.

(d) If he holds only a private pilot certificate he must have had, and entered in his pilot logbook at least - (1) 100 hours of pilot flight time in powered aircraft; or (2) 200 total hours of pilot flight time in powered or other aircraft.

(e) Within the preceding 12 months he has - (1) Made at least three actual or simulated glider tows while accompanied by a qualified pilot who meets the requirements of this section; or (2) Made at least three flights as pilot in command of a glider towed by an aircraft.

61.71 Graduates of certificated pilot schools: Special rules.

Since a Part 141 flight school has had its course curriculum and training syllabus examined and approved by the FAA, satisfactory completion of that course of training and an associated graduation certificate are evidence of a pilot's proficiency. If the flight school is not authorized for practical testing, you must present your graduation certificate when applying for a flight test within 60 days. If the flight school is authorized and you successfully complete the practical test, you have 90 days to apply for a permanent certificate.

(a) A graduate of a flying school that is certificated under Part 141 of this chapter is considered to meet the applicable aeronautical experience requirements of this part if he presents an appropriate graduation certificate within 60 days after the date he is graduated. However, if he applies for a flight test for an instrument rating he must hold a commercial pilot certificate, or hold a private pilot certificate and meet the requirements of 61.65 (e)(1) and 61.123 (except paragraphs (d) and (e) thereof). In addition, if he applies for a flight instructor certificate he must hold a commercial pilot certificate.

(b) An applicant for a certificate or rating under this part is considered to meet the aeronautical knowledge and skill requirements, or both, applicable to that certificate or rating, if the applicant applies within 90 days after graduation from an appropriate course given by a pilot school that is certificated under Part 141 of this chapter and is authorized to test applicants on aeronautical knowledge or skill, or both.

61.73 Military pilots or former military pilots: Special rules.

> If you are or were a military pilot, you are no doubt familiar with the format of presentation that follows and you're on your own.

(a) General. A rated military pilot or former rated military pilot who applies for a private or commercial pilot certificate, or an aircraft or instrument rating, is entitled to that certificate with appropriate ratings or to the addition of a rating on the pilot certificate he holds, if he meets the applicable requirements of this section. This section does not apply to a military pilot or former military pilot who has been removed from flying status for lack of proficiency or because of disciplinary action involving aircraft operations.

(b) Military pilots on active flying status within 12 months. A rated military pilot or former rated military pilot who has been on active flying status within the 12 months before he applies must pass a written test on the parts of this chapter relating to pilot privileges and limitations, air traffic, and general operating rules. He must present documents showing that he meets the requirements of paragraph (d) of this section for at least one aircraft rating, and that he is, or was at any time since the beginning of the 12th month before the month in which he applies - (1) A rated military pilot on active flying status in an armed force of the United States; or (2) A rated military pilot of an armed force of a foreign contracting State to the Convention on International Civil Aviation, assigned to pilot duties (other than flight training) with an armed force of the United States who holds, at the time he applies, a current civil pilot license issued by that foreign State authorizing at least the privileges of the pilot certificate he seeks.

(c) Military pilots not on active flying status within previous 12 months. A rated military pilot or former rated military pilot who has not been on active flying status within the 12 months before he applies must pass the appropriate written and flight tests prescribed in this part for the certificate or rating he seeks. In addition, he must show that he holds an FAA medical certificate appropriate to the pilot certificate he seeks and present documents showing that he was, before the beginning of the 12th month before the month in which he applies, a rated military pilot as prescribed by either subparagraph (1) or (2) of paragraph (b) of this section.

(d) Aircraft ratings: Other than airplane category and type. An applicant for a category, class, or type rating (other than airplane category and type rating) to be added on the pilot certificate he holds, or for which he has applied, is issued that rating if he presents documentary evidence showing one of the following: (1) That he has passed an official United States military checkout as pilot-in-command of aircraft of the category, class, or type for which he seeks a rating since the beginning of the 12th month before the month in which he applies. (2) That he has had at least 10 hours of flight time serving

33

as pilot-in-command of aircraft of the category, class, or type for which he seeks a rating since the beginning of the 12th month before the month in which he applies and previously has had an official United States military checkout as pilot-in-command of that aircraft. (3) That he has met the requirements of subparagraph (1) or (2) of paragraph (b) of this section, has had an official United States military checkout in the category of aircraft for which he seeks a rating, and that he passes an FAA flight test appropriate to that category and the class or type rating he seeks. To be eligible for that flight test, he must have a written statement from an authorized flight instructor, made not more than 60 days before he applies for the flight test, certifying that he is competent to pass the test. A type rating is issued only for aircraft types that the Administrator has certificated for civil operations. Any rating placed on an airline transport pilot certificate is limited to commercial pilot privileges.

(g) Evidentiary documents. The following documents are satisfactory evidence for the purposes indicated: (1) To show that the applicant is a member of the armed forces, an official identification card issued to the applicant by an armed force may be used. (2) To show the applicant's discharge or release from an armed force, or his former membership therein, an original or a copy of a certificate of discharge or release may be used. (3) To show current or previous status as a rated military pilot on flying status with a U.S. armed force, one of the following may be used: (i) An official U.S. armed force order to flight duty as a military pilot. (ii) An official U.S. armed force form or logbook showing military pilot status. (iii) An official order showing that the applicant graduated from a United States military pilot school and is rated as a military pilot. (4) To show flight time in military aircraft as a member of a U.S. armed force, an appropriate U.S. armed force form or summary of it, or a certified United States military logbook may be used. (5) To show pilot-in-command status, an official U.S. armed force record of a military checkout as pilot-in-command, may be used.

61.75 Pilot certificate issued on basis of a foreign pilot license.

The holder of a foreign private pilot certificate may apply for a U.S. certificate provided that he or she meets all of the requirements listed in Part 61, meets all of the ICAO standards, and does not already hold a U.S. certificate. You must meet at least the third-class medical standards as for any private pilot. If you cannot read, speak, and understand English, a limitation based on this will appear on the certificate. As the holder of a U.S. certificate, you are bound by the appropriate U.S. regulations. You are prohibited from performing agricultural aircraft operations.

(a) Purpose. The holder of a current private, commercial, senior commercial, or airline transport pilot license issued by a foreign contracting State to the Convention on International Civil Aviation may apply for a pilot certificate under this section authorizing him to act as a pilot of a civil aircraft of U.S. registry.

34

(b) *Certificate issued.* A pilot certificate is issued to an applicant under this section, specifying the number and state of issuance of the foreign pilot license on which it is based. An applicant who holds a foreign private pilot license is issued a private pilot certificate, and an applicant who holds a foreign commercial, senior commercial, or airline transport license is issued a commercial pilot certificate, if - (1) He meets the requirements of this section; (2) His foreign pilot license does not contain an endorsement that he has not met all of the standards of ICAO for that license; and (3) He does not hold a U.S. pilot certificate of private pilot grade or higher.

(c) *Limitation on licenses used as basis for U.S. certificate.* Only one foreign pilot license may be used as a basis for issuing a pilot certificate under this section.

(d) *Aircraft ratings issued.* Aircraft ratings listed on the applicant's foreign pilot license, in addition to any issued after testing under the provisions of this part, are placed on the applicant's pilot certificate.

(f) *Medical standards and certification.* An applicant must submit evidence that he currently meets the medical standards for the foreign pilot license on which the application for a certificate under this section is based. A current medical certificate issued under Part 67 of this chapter is accepted as evidence that the applicant meets those standards. However, a medical certificate issued under Part 67 of this chapter is not evidence that the applicant meets those standards outside the United States, unless the state that issued the applicant's foreign pilot license also accepts that medical certificate as evidence of meeting the medical standards for his foreign pilot license.

(g) *Limitations placed on pilot certificate.* (1) If the applicant cannot read, speak, and understand the English language, the Administrator places any limitation on the certificate that he considers necessary for safety. (2) A certificate issued under this section is not valid for agricultural aircraft operations, or the operation of an aircraft in which persons or property are carried for compensation or hire. This limitation is also placed on the certificate.

(h) *Operating privileges and limitations.* The holder of a pilot certificate issued under this section may act as a pilot of a civil aircraft of U.S. registry in accordance with the pilot privileges authorized by the foreign pilot license on which that certificate is based, subject to the limitations of this part and any additional limitations placed on his certificate by the Administrator. He is subject to these limitations while he is acting as a pilot of the aircraft within or outside the United States. However, he may not act as pilot-in-command, or in any other capacity as a required flight crewmember, of a civil aircraft of U.S. registry that is carrying persons or property for compensation or hire.

Subpart C - Student and Recreational Pilots

Section
61.81 Applicability.

This subpart prescribes the requirements for the issuance of student pilot certificates and recreational pilot certificates and ratings, the conditions under which those certificates and ratings are necessary, and the general operating rules and limitations for the holders of those certificates and ratings.

61.83 Eligibility requirements: Student pilots.

To be eligible for a student pilot certificate, a person must -
(a) Be at least 16 years of age, or at least 14 years of age for a student pilot certificate limited to the operation of a glider or free balloon;

(b) Be able to read, speak, and understand the English language, or have such operating limitations placed on his pilot certificate as are necessary for the safe operation of aircraft, to be removed when he shows that he can read, speak, and understand the English language; and

(c) Hold at least a current third-class medical certificate issued under Part 67 of this chapter, or in the case of glider or free balloon operations, certify that he has no known medical defect that makes him unable to pilot a glider or free balloon.

61.85 Application.

> When you visit an authorized medical examiner and pass the third-class medical you will be issued a third-class medical certificate and a student pilot certificate. There is actually only one document which you will receive, but it in fact contains both of these certificates.

An application for a student pilot certificate is made on a form and in a manner provided by the Administrator and is submitted to -

(a) A designated aviation medical examiner when applying for an FAA medical certificate in the United States; or

(b) An FAA operations inspector or designated pilot examiner, accompanied by a current FAA medical certificate, or in the case of an application for a glider or free balloon pilot certificate it may be accompanied by a certification by the applicant that he has no known medical defect that makes him unable to pilot a glider or free balloon.

61.87 Solo flight requirements for student pilots.

> Prior to your first solo, your flight instructor will have taught you all of the flight maneuvers and aeronautical knowledge necessary for a safe and successful flight, which are listed below. You will also have passed a written test on these subjects. The instructor must endorse your logbook and student pilot certificate for the particular make and model of aircraft to be flown (e.g., Cessna 152) prior to solo flight. This endorsement remains valid for 90 days.

(a) General. A student pilot may not operate an aircraft in solo flight unless that student meets the requirements of this section. The term "solo flight," as used in this subpart, means that flight time during which a student pilot is the sole occupant of the aircraft, or that flight time during which the student acts as pilot-in-command of an airship requiring more than one flight crewmember.

(b) Aeronautical knowledge. A student pilot must have demonstrated satisfactory knowledge to an authorized instructor, of the appropriate portions of Parts 61 and 91 of the Federal Aviation Regulations that are applicable to student pilots. This demonstration must include the satisfactory completion of a written examination to be administered and graded by the instructor who endorses the student's pilot certificate for solo flight. The written examination must include questions on the applicable regulations and the flight characteristics and operational limitations for the make and model aircraft to be flown.

(c) Pre-solo flight training. Prior to being authorized to conduct a solo flight, a student pilot must have received and logged instruction in at least the applicable maneuvers and procedures listed in paragraphs (d) through (j) of this section for the make and model of aircraft to be flown in solo flight, and must have demonstrated proficiency to an acceptable performance level as judged by the instructor who endorses the student's pilot certificate.

(d) For all aircraft (as appropriate to the aircraft to be flown in solo flight), the student pilot must have received pre-solo flight training in - (1) Flight preparation procedures, including preflight inspections, powerplant operation, and aircraft systems; (2) Taxiing or surface operations, including runups; (3) Takeoffs and landings, including normal and crosswind; (4) Straight and level flight, shallow, medium, and steep banked turns in both directions; (5) Climbs and climbing turns; (6) Airport traffic patterns including entry and departure procedures, and collision and wake turbulence avoidance; (7) Descents with and without turns using high and low drag configurations; (8) Flight at various airspeeds from cruising to minimum controllable airspeed; (9) Emergency procedures and equipment malfunctions; and (10) Ground reference maneuvers.

(e) For airplanes, in addition to the maneuvers and procedures in paragraph (d) of this section, the student pilot must have received pre-solo flight training in - (1) Approaches to the landing area with engine power at idle and with partial power; (2) Slips to a landing; (3) Go-arounds from final approach and from the landing flare in various flight configurations including turns; (4) Forced landing procedures initiated on takeoff, during initial climb, cruise, descent, and in the landing pattern; and (5) Stall entries from various flight attitudes and power combinations with recovery initiated at the first indication of a stall, and recovery from a full stall.

(k) The instruction required by this section must be given by an authorized flight instructor who is certificated - (1) In the category and class of airplanes, for airplanes.

(m) Flight instructor endorsements. No student pilot may operate an aircraft in solo flight unless that student's pilot certificate and logbook have been endorsed for the specific make and model aircraft to be flown by an authorized flight instructor certificated under this part, and the student's logbook has been endorsed within the 90 days prior to the student operating in solo flight, by an authorized flight instructor certificated under this part who has flown with the student. No flight instructor may authorize solo flight without endorsing the student's logbook. The instructor's endorsement must certify that the instructor - (1) Has given the student instruction in the make and model aircraft in which the solo flight is to be made; (2) Finds that the student has met the flight training requirements of this section; and (3) Finds that the student is competent to make a safe solo flight in that aircraft.

(n) Notwithstanding the requirements of paragraphs (a) through (m) of this section, each student pilot, whose student pilot certificate and logbook are endorsed for solo flight by an authorized flight instructor on or before August 30, 1989, may operate an aircraft in solo flight until the 90th day after the date on which the logbook was endorsed for solo flight.

61.89 General limitations.

(a) A student pilot may not act as pilot-in-command of an aircraft- (1) That is carrying a passenger; (2) That is carrying property for compensation or hire; (3) For compensation or hire; (4) In furtherance of a business; (5) On an international flight, except that a student pilot may make solo training flights from Haines, Gustavus, or Juneau, Alaska, to White Horse, Yukon, Canada, and return, over the province of British Columbia; (6) With a flight or surface visibility of less than 3 statute miles during daylight hours or 5 statute miles at night; (7) When the flight cannot be made with visual reference to the surface; or (8) In a manner contrary to any limitations placed in the pilot's logbook by the instructor.

(b) A student pilot may not act as a required pilot flight crewmember on any aircraft for which more than one pilot is required by the type certificate of the aircraft or regulations under which the flight is conducted, except when receiving flight instruction from an authorized flight instructor on board an airship and no person other than a required flight crewmember is carried on the aircraft.

61.93 Cross-country flight requirements (for student and recreational pilots seeking private pilot certification).

In addition to the maneuvers learned and knowledge acquired prior to solo flight, you will receive specific ground and flight training for cross-country flight which is listed below. You will again need to have your student pilot certificate endorsed by the instructor, this time for cross-country flight. Additionally, you will need a logbook endorsement for each cross country flight that you make, and an endorsement indicating instruction in order to practice takeoffs and landings at an airport other than your home base of training.

(a) General. No student pilot may operate an aircraft in solo cross-country flight, nor may that student, except in an emergency, make a solo flight landing at any point other than the airport of takeoff, unless the student has met the requirements of this section. The term cross-country flight, as used in this section, means a flight beyond a radius of 25 nautical miles from the point of departure.

(b) Notwithstanding paragraph (a) of this section, an authorized flight instructor, certificated under this part, may permit the student to practice solo takeoffs and landings at another airport within 25 nautical miles from the airport at which the student receives instruction if the flight instructor - (1) Determines that the student pilot is competent and proficient to make those landings and takeoffs; (2) Has flown with that student prior to authorizing those takeoffs and landings; and (3) Endorses the student pilot's logbook with an authorization to make those landings and takeoffs.

(c) Flight training. A student pilot, in addition to the pre-solo flight training maneuvers and procedures required by 61.87(c), must have received and logged instruction from an authorized flight instructor in the appropriate pilot maneuvers and procedures of this section. Additionally, a student pilot must have demonstrated an acceptable standard of performance, as judged by the authorized flight instructor certificated under this part, who endorses the student's pilot certificate in the appropriate pilot maneuvers and procedures of this section. (1) For all aircraft - (i) The use of aeronautical charts for VFR navigation using pilotage and dead reckoning with the aid of a magnetic compass; (ii) Aircraft cross-country performance, and procurement and analysis of aeronautical weather reports and forecasts, including recognition of critical weather situations and estimating visibility when in flight; (iii) Cross-country emergency conditions including lost procedures, adverse weather conditions, and simulated precautionary off-airport approaches and landing procedures; (iv) Traffic pattern procedures, including normal area arrival and departure, collision avoidance, and wake turbulence precautions; (v) Recognition of operational problems associated with different terrain features in the geographical area in which the cross-country flight is to be flown; and (vi) Proper operation of the instruments and equipment installed in the aircraft to be flown. (2) For airplanes, in addition to paragraph (c)(1) of this section - (i) Short and soft field takeoff, approach, and landing procedures, including crosswind takeoffs and landings; (ii) Takeoffs at best angle and rate of climb; (iii) Control and maneuvering solely by reference to flight instruments including straight and level flight, turns, descents, climbs, and the use of radio aids and radar directives; (iv) The use of radios for VFR navigation and for two-way communication; and (v) For those student pilots seeking night flying privileges, night flying procedures including takeoffs, landings, go-arounds, and VFR navigation.

(d) No student pilot may operate an aircraft in solo cross-country flight, unless - (1) The instructor is an authorized instructor certificated under this part and the student's certificate has been endorsed by the instructor attesting that the student has received the instruction and demonstrated an acceptable level of competency and proficiency in the maneuvers and procedures of this section for the category of aircraft to be flown; and (2) The instructor has endorsed the student's logbook - (i) For each solo cross-country flight, after reviewing the student's preflight planning and preparation, attesting that the student is prepared to make the flight safely under the known circumstances and subject to any conditions listed in the logbook by the instructor; and (ii) For repeated specific cross-country flights that are not greater than 50 nautical miles from the point of departure, after giving the student flight instruction in both directions over the route, including takeoffs and landings at the airports to be used, and has specified the conditions for which the flights can be made.

61.95 Operations in a terminal control area and at airports located within a terminal control area.

(a) A student pilot may not operate an aircraft on a solo flight in the airspace of a terminal control area unless - (1) The student pilot has received both ground and flight instruction from an authorized instructor on that terminal control area and the flight instruction was received in the specific terminal control area for which solo flight is authorized; (2) The logbook of that student pilot has been endorsed within the preceding 90 days for conducting solo flight in that specific terminal control area by the instructor who gave the flight training; and (3) The logbook endorsement specifies that the student pilot has received the required ground and flight instruction and has been found competent to conduct solo flight in that specific terminal control area.

(b) Pursuant to 91.90(b), a student pilot may not operate an aircraft on a solo flight to, from, or at an airport located within a terminal control area unless - (1) That student pilot has received both ground and flight instruction from an authorized instructor to operate at that airport and the flight and ground instruction has been received at the specific airport for which the solo flight is authorized; (2) The logbook of that student pilot has been endorsed within the preceding 90 days for conducting solo flight at that specific airport by the instructor who gave the flight training; and (3) The logbook endorsement specifies that the student pilot has received the required ground and flight instruction and has been found competent to conduct solo flight operations at that specific airport.

61.96 Eligibility requirements: Recreational pilots.

To be eligible for a recreational pilot certificate, a person must-
(a) Be at least 17 years of age;
(b) Be able to read, speak, and understand the English language, or have such operating limitations placed on the pilot certificate as are necessary for the safe operation of aircraft, to be removed when the recreational pilot shows the ability to read, speak, and understand the English language;
(c) Hold at least a current third-class medical certificate issued under Part 67

of this chapter;

(d) Pass a written test on the subject areas on which instruction or home study is required by 61.97;

(e) Pass an oral and flight test on maneuvers and procedures selected by an FAA inspector or designated pilot examiner to determine the applicant's competency in the appropriate flight operations listed in 61.98; and

(f) Comply with the sections of this part that apply to the rating sought.

61.97 Aeronautical knowledge: Recreational pilots.

An applicant for a recreational pilot certificate must have logged ground instruction from an authorized instructor, or must present evidence showing satisfactory completion of a course of instruction or home study in at least the following areas of aeronautical knowledge appropriate to the category and class of aircraft for which a rating is sought:

(a) The Federal Aviation Regulations applicable to recreational pilot privileges, limitations, and flight operations, the accident reporting requirements of the National Transportation Safety Board, and the use of the applicable portions of the Airman's Information Manual and the FAA advisory circulars;

(b) The use of aeronautical charts for VFR navigation using pilotage with the aid of a magnetic compass;

(c) The recognition of critical weather situations from the ground and in flight and the procurement and use of aeronautical weather reports and forecasts;

(d) The safe and efficient operation of aircraft including collision and wake turbulence avoidance;

(e) The effects of density altitude on takeoff and climb performance;

(f) Weight and balance computations;

(g) Principles of aerodynamics, powerplants, and aircraft systems; and

(h) Stall awareness, spin entry, spins, and spin recovery techniques.

61.98 Flight proficiency: Recreational pilots.

The applicant for a recreational pilot certificate must have logged instruction from an authorized flight instructor in at least the pilot operations listed in this section. In addition, the applicant's logbook must contain an endorsement by an authorized flight instructor who has found the applicant competent to perform each of those operations safely as a recreational pilot.

(a) In airplanes. (1) Preflight operations, including weight and balance determination, line inspection, airplane servicing, powerplant operations, and aircraft systems; (2) Airport and traffic pattern operations, collision and wake turbulence avoidance; (3) Flight maneuvering by reference to ground objects; (4) Pilotage with the aid of magnetic compass; (5) Flight at slow airspeeds with realistic distractions and the recognition of and recovery from stalls entered from straight flight and from turns; (6) Emergency operations, including simulated aircraft and equipment malfunctions; (7) Maximum performance takeoffs and landings; and (8) Normal and crosswind takeoffs and landings.

61.99 Airplane rating: Aeronautical experience: Recreational pilots.

(a) An applicant for a recreational pilot certificate with an airplane rating must have had at least a total of 30 hours of flight instruction and solo flight time which must include the following: (1) 15 hours of flight instruction from an authorized flight instructor, including at least - (i) Except as provided for in paragraph (b), 2 hours outside of the vicinity of the airport at which instruction is given, including at least three landings at another airport that is located more than 25 nautical miles from the airport of departure; and (ii) Two hours in airplanes in preparation for the recreational pilot flight test within the 60-day period before the test. (2) 15 hours of solo flight time in airplanes.
(b) Pilots based on small islands. (1) An applicant who is located on an island from which the flight required in 61.99 (a)(1)(i) cannot be accomplished without flying over water more than 10 nautical miles from the nearest shoreline need not comply with 61.99(a)(1)(i). However, if other airports that permit civil operations are available to which a flight may be made without flying over water more than 10 nautical miles from the nearest shoreline, the applicant must show completion of a dual flight between those two airports which must include three landings at the other airport. (2) The pilot certificate issued to a person under paragraph (b)(1) of this section contains an endorsement with the following limitation which may subsequently be amended to include another island if the applicant complies with paragraph (b)(1) of this section with respect to that island: Passenger carrying prohibited in flight more than 10 nautical miles from (appropriate island). (3) The holder of a recreational pilot certificate with an endorsement described in paragraph (b)(2) of this section is entitled to removal of the endorsement if the holder presents satisfactory evidence of compliance with the applicable flight requirements of 61.93(c) to an FAA inspector or designated pilot examiner.

61.101 Recreational pilot privileges and limitations.

(a) A recreational pilot may - (1) Carry not more than one passenger; and (2) Share the operating expenses of the flight with the passenger. (3) Act as pilot-in-command of an aircraft only when - (i) The flight is within 50 nautical miles of an airport at which the pilot has received ground and flight instruction from an authorized instructor certificated under this part; (ii) The flight lands at an airport within 50 nautical miles of the departure airport; and (iii) The pilot carries in that pilot's personal possession a logbook that has been endorsed by the instructor attesting to the instruction required by paragraph (a)(3)(i) of this section.

(b) Except as provided in paragraphs (f) and (g) of this section, a recreational pilot may not act as pilot-in-command of an aircraft - (1) That is certificated - (i) For more than four occupants; (ii) With more than one powerplant; (iii) With a powerplant of more than 180 horsepower; or (iv) With retractable landing gear. (2) That is classified as a glider, airship, or balloon; (3) That is carrying a passenger or property for compensation or hire; (4) For compensation or hire: (5) In furtherance of a business; (6) Between sunset and sunrise; (7) In airspace in which communication with air traffic control is required; (8) At an altitude of more than 10,000 feet MSL or 2,000 feet AGL, whichever is higher; (9) When the flight or surface visibility is less than 3 statute miles; (10) Without visual reference to the surface; (11) On a flight outside the United States; (12) To demonstrate that aircraft in flight to a prospective buyer; (13) That is used in a passenger-carrying airlift and sponsored by a charitable organization; and (14) That is towing any object.

(c) A recreational pilot may not act as a required pilot flight crewmember on any aircraft for which more than one pilot is required by the type certificate or the regulations under which the flight is conducted, except when receiving flight instruction from an authorized flight instructor on board an airship and no person other than a required flight crewmember is carried on the aircraft.

(d) A recreational pilot who has logged fewer than 400 flight hours and who has not logged pilot-in-command time in an aircraft within the preceding 180 days may not act as pilot-in-command of an aircraft until the pilot has received flight instruction from an authorized flight instructor who certifies in the pilot's logbook that the pilot is competent to act as pilot-in-command of the aircraft. This requirement can be met in combination with the requirements of 61.56 and 61.57 at the discretion of the instructor.

(e) The recreational pilot certificate issued under this subpart carries the notation "Holder does not meet ICAO requirements."

(f) For the purpose of obtaining additional certificates or ratings, while under the supervision of an authorized flight instructor, a recreational pilot may fly as sole occupant of an aircraft - (1) For which the pilot does not hold an appropriate category or class rating; (2) Within airspace that requires communication with air traffic control; or (3) Between sunset and sunrise, provided the flight or surface visibility is at least 5 statute miles.

(g) In order to fly solo as provided in paragraph (f) of this section, the recreational pilot must meet the appropriate aeronautical knowledge and flight training requirements of 61.87 for that aircraft. When operating an aircraft under the conditions specified in paragraph (f) of this section, the recreational pilot shall carry the logbook that has been endorsed for each flight by an authorized pilot instructor who - (1) Has given the recreational pilot instruction in the make and model of aircraft in which the solo flight is to be made; (2) Has found that the recreational pilot has met the applicable requirements of 61.87; and (3) Has found that the recreational pilot is competent to make solo flights in accordance with the logbook endorsement.

(h) Notwithstanding paragraph 61.101(a)(3), a recreational pilot may, for the purpose of obtaining an additional certificate or rating, while under the supervision of an authorized flight instructor, act as pilot-in-command of an aircraft on a flight in excess of 50 nautical miles from an airport at which flight instruction is received if the pilot meets the flight training requirements of 61.93 and in that pilot's personal possession is the logbook that has been endorsed by an authorized instructor attesting that: (1) The recreational pilot has received instruction in solo cross-country flight and the training described in 61.93 applicable to the aircraft to be operated, and is competent to make solo cross-country flights in the make and model of aircraft to be flown; and (2) The instructor has reviewed the student's preflight planning and preparation for the specific solo cross-country flight and that the recreational pilot is prepared to make the flight safely under the known circumstances and subject to any conditions listed in the logbook by the instructor.

Subpart D - Private Pilots.

Section
61.102 Applicability.

This subpart prescribes the requirements for the issuance of private pilot certificates and ratings, the conditions under which those certificates and ratings are necessary, and the general operating rules for the holders of those certificates and ratings.

61.103 Eligibility requirements: General.

To be eligible for a private pilot certificate, a person must -

(a) Be at least 17 years of age, except that a private pilot certificate with a free balloon or glider rating only may be issued to a qualified applicant who is at least 16 years of age;

(b) Be able to speak, read, and understand the English language, or have such operating limitations placed on his pilot certificate as are necessary for the safe operation of aircraft, to be removed when he shows that he can read, speak, and understand the English language;

(c) Hold at least a current third-class medical certificate issued under Part 67 of this chapter, or, in the case of a glider or free balloon rating, certify that he has no known medical defect that makes him unable to pilot a glider or free balloon, as appropriate;

(d) Pass a written test on the subject areas on which instruction or home study is required by 61.105;

(e) Pass an oral and flight test on procedures and maneuvers selected by an FAA inspector or examiner to determine the applicant's competency in the flight operations on which instruction is required by the flight proficiency provisions of 61.107; and

(f) Comply with the sections of this part that apply to the rating he seeks.

61.105 Aeronautical knowledge: Private pilots.

An applicant for a private pilot certificate must have logged ground instruction from an authorized instructor, or must present evidence showing that he has satisfactorily completed a course of instruction or home study in at least the following areas of aeronautical knowledge appropriate to the category of aircraft for which a rating is sought.

(a) Airplanes and rotorcraft. (1) The accident reporting requirements of the National Transportation Safety Board and the Federal Aviation Regulations applicable to private pilot privileges, limitations, and flight operations for airplanes or rotorcraft, as appropriate, the use of the Airman's Information Manual, and FAA advisory circulars; (2) VFR navigation using pilotage, dead reckoning, and radio aids; (3) The recognition of critical weather situations from the ground and in flight, the procurement and use of aeronautical weather reports and forecasts; (4) The safe and efficient operation of airplanes or rotorcraft, as appropriate, including high-density airport operations, collision avoidance precautions, and radio communication procedures; (5) Basic aerodynamics and the principles of flight which apply to airplanes or rotorcraft, as appropriate; and (6) Stall awareness, spin entry, spins, and spin recovery techniques for airplanes.

61.107 Flight proficiency: Private pilots.

The applicant for a private pilot certificate must have logged instruction from an authorized flight instructor in at least the following pilot operations. In addition, his logbook must contain an endorsement by an authorized flight instructor who has found him competent to perform each of those operations safely as a private pilot.

(a) In airplanes. (1) Preflight operations, including weight and balance determination, line inspection, and airplane servicing; (2) Airport and traffic pattern operations, including operations at controlled airports, radio communications, and collision avoidance precautions; (3) Flight maneuvering by reference to ground objects; (4) Flight at slow airspeeds with realistic distractions, and the recognition of and recovery from stalls entered from straight flight and from turns; (5) Normal and crosswind takeoffs and landings; (6) Control and maneuvering an airplane solely by reference to instruments, including descents and climbs using radio aids or radar directives; (7) Cross-country flying, using pilotage, dead reckoning, and radio aids, including one 2-hour flight; (8) Maximum performance takeoffs and landings; (9) Night flying, including takeoffs, landings, and VFR navigation; and (10) Emergency operations, including simulated aircraft and equipment malfunctions.

61.109 Airplane rating: Aeronautical experience. (Private pilots)

An applicant for a private pilot certificate with an airplane rating must have had at least a total of 40 hours of flight instruction and solo flight time which must include the following:
(a) 20 hours of flight instruction from an authorized flight instructor, including at least - (1) 3 hours of cross-country; (2) 3 hours at night, including 10 takeoffs and landings for applicants seeking night flying privileges; and (3) 3 hours in airplanes in preparation for the private pilot flight test within 60 days prior to that test.
An applicant who does not meet the night flying requirement in paragraph (a)(2) of this section is issued a private pilot certificate bearing the limitation "Night flying prohibited." This limitation may be removed if the holder of the certificate shows that he has met the requirements of paragraph (a)(2) of this section.
(b) 20 hours of solo flight time, including at least: (1) 10 hours in airplanes. (2) 10 hours of cross-country flights, each flight with a landing at a point more than 50 nautical miles from the original departure point. One flight must be of at least 300 nautical miles with landings at a minimum of three points, one of which is at least 100 nautical miles from the original departure point. (3) Three solo takeoffs and landings to a full stop at an airport with an operating control tower.

61.111 Cross-country flights: Pilots based on small islands.

(a) An applicant who shows that he is located on an island from which the required flights cannot be accomplished without flying over water more than 10 nautical miles from the nearest shoreline need not comply with paragraph (b)(2) of 61.109. However, if other airports that permit civil operations are available to which a flight may be made without flying over water more than 10 nautical miles from the nearest shoreline, he must show that he has completed two round-trip solo flights between those two airports that are farthest apart, including a landing at each airport on both flights.
(b) The pilot certificate issued to a person under paragraph (a) of this section contains an endorsement with the following limitation which may subsequently be amended to include another island if the applicant complies with paragraph (a) of this section with respect to that island: "Passenger carrying prohibited on flights more than 10 nautical miles from (appropriate island)."
(c) If an applicant for a private pilot certificate under paragraph (a) of this section does not have at least 3 hours of solo cross-country flight time, including a round trip flight to an airport at least 50 nautical miles from the place of departure with at least two full stop landings at different points along the route, his pilot certificate is also endorsed as follows: "Holder does not

meet the cross-country flight requirements of ICAO."

(d) The holder of a private pilot certificate with an endorsement described in paragraph (b) or (c) of this section is entitled to a removal of the endorsement if he presents satisfactory evidence to an FAA inspector or designated pilot examiner that he has complied with the applicable solo cross-country flight requirements and has passed a practical test on cross-country flying.

61.118 Private pilot privileges and limitations: Pilot-in-command.

Except as provided in paragraphs (a) through (d) of this section, a private pilot may not act as pilot-in-command of an aircraft that is carrying passengers or property for compensation or hire; nor may he, for compensation or hire, act as pilot-in-command of an aircraft.

(a) A private pilot may, for compensation or hire, act as pilot-in-command of an aircraft in connection with any business or employment if the flight is only incidental to that business or employment and the aircraft does not carry passengers or property for compensation or hire.

(b) A private pilot may share the operating expenses of a flight with his passengers.

(c) A private pilot who is an aircraft salesman and who has at least 200 hours of logged flight time may demonstrate an aircraft in flight to a prospective buyer.

(d) A private pilot may act as pilot-in-command of an aircraft used in a passenger-carrying airlift sponsored by a charitable organization, and for which the passengers make a donation to the organization, if - (1) The sponsor of the airlift notifies the FAA Flight Standards District Office having jurisdiction over the area concerned, at least 7 days before the flight, and furnishes any essential information that the office requests; (2) The flight is conducted from a public airport adequate for the aircraft used, or from another airport that has been approved for the operation by an FAA inspector; (3) He has logged at least 200 hours of flight time; (4) No acrobatic or formation flights are conducted; (5) Each aircraft used is certificated in the standard category and complies with the 100-hour inspection requirement of 91.409 of this chapter, and (6) The flight is made under VFR during the day.

For the purpose of paragraph (d) of this section, a charitable organization means an organization listed in Publication No. 78 of the Department of the Treasury called Cumulative List of Organizations described in section 170(c) of the Internal Revenue Code of 1954, as amended from time to time by published supplemental lists.

61.120 Private pilot privileges and limitations: Second-in-command of aircraft requiring more than one pilot.

Except as provided in paragraphs (a) through (d) of 61.118 a private pilot may not, for compensation or hire, act as second-in-command of an aircraft that is type certificated for more than one required pilot, nor may he act as second-in-command of such an aircraft that is carrying passengers or property for compensation or hire.

TEST QUESTIONS

1. To act as pilot-in-command of an aircraft towing a glider, a person is required to have made within the preceding 12 months

A - at least three flights as observer in a glider being towed by an aircraft.
B - at least three flights in a powered glider.
C - at least three actual or simulated glider tows while accompanied by a qualified pilot.

2. In regard to general privileges and limitations, a private pilot may

A - not be paid in any manner for the operating expenses of a flight.
B - act as pilot in command of an aircraft carrying a passenger for compensation if the flight is in connection with a business or employment.
C - share the operating expenses of a flight with a passenger.

3. What exception, if any, permits a private pilot to act as pilot-in-command of an aircraft carrying passengers who pay for the flight?

A - If the passengers pay all the operating expenses.
B - If a donation is made to a charitable organization for the flight.
C - There is no exception.

4. According to regulations pertaining to general privileges and limitations, a student pilot may

A - be paid for the operating expenses of a flight if at least three takeoffs and three landings were made by the pilot within the preceding 90 days.
B - share the operating expenses of a flight with the passengers.
C - not carry passengers under any circumstances.

5. A student pilot may not operate an aircraft on a solo flight in the airspace of a terminal control area unless the student

A - has made three takeoffs and landings at the primary airport of that TCA within the preceding 90 days.
B - has received ground and flight instruction in that TCA and has an appropriate logbook endorsement.
C - is operating between the beginning of morning civil twilight and the end of evening civil twilight.

ANSWERS

1. C (61.69)   2. C (61.118)   3. B (61.118)   4. C (61.89)   5. B (61.95)

48

4

Part 91 - General Operating and Flight Rules
Subparts A and B

Subpart A - General

Section
91.1 Applicability.

(a) Except as provided in paragraph (b) of this section and 91.703, this part prescribes rules governing the operation of aircraft (other than moored balloons, kites, unmanned rockets, and unmanned free balloons, which are governed by part 101 of this chapter, and ultralight vehicles operated in accordance with part 103 of this chapter) within the United States, including the waters within 3 nautical miles of the U.S. coast.
(b) Each person operating an aircraft in the airspace overlying the waters between 3 and 12 nautical miles from the coast of the United States shall comply with 91.1 through 91.21; 91.101 through 91.143; 91.151 through 91.159; 91.167 through 91.193; 91.203; 91.205; 91.209 through 91.217; 91.221; 91.303 through 91.319; 91.323; 91.605; 91.609; 91.703 through 91.715; and 91.903.

91.3 Responsibility and authority of the pilot-in-command.

(a) The pilot-in-command of an aircraft is directly responsible for, and is the final authority as to, the operation of that aircraft.
(b) In an in-flight emergency requiring immediate action, the pilot-in-command may deviate from any rule of this part to the extent required to meet that emergency.
(c) Each pilot-in-command who deviates from a rule under paragraph (b) of this section shall, upon the request of the Administrator, send a written report of that deviation to the Administrator.

91.7 Civil aircraft airworthiness.

(a) No person may operate a civil aircraft unless it is in an airworthy condition.
(b) The pilot-in-command of a civil aircraft is responsible for determining whether that aircraft is in condition for safe flight. The pilot-in-command shall discontinue the flight when unairworthy mechanical, electrical, or structural conditions occur.

91.9 Civil aircraft flight manual, marking, and placard requirements.

(a) Except as provided in paragraph (d) of this section, no person may operate a civil aircraft without complying with the operating limitations specified in the approved airplane or rotorcraft flight manual, markings and placards, or as otherwise prescribed by the certificating authority of the country of registry.
(b) No person may operate a U.S. registered civil aircraft - (1) For which an airplane or rotorcraft flight manual is required by 21.5 of this chapter unless there is available in the aircraft a current, approved airplane or rotorcraft flight manual or the manual provided for in 121.141(b); and (2) For which an airplane or rotorcraft flight manual is not required by 21.5 of this chapter, unless there is available in the aircraft a current, approved airplane or rotorcraft flight manual, approved manual material, markings, and placards, or any combination thereof.
(c) No person may operate a U.S.-registered civil aircraft unless that aircraft is identified in accordance with Part 45 of this chapter.

91.11 Prohibition against interference with crewmembers.

No person may assault, threaten, intimidate, or interfere with a crewmember in the performance of the crewmember's duties aboard an aircraft being operated.

91.13 Careless or reckless operation.

(a) Aircraft operations for the purpose of air navigation. No person may operate an aircraft in a careless or reckless manner so as to endanger the life or property of another.
(b) Aircraft operations other than for the purpose of air navigation. No person may operate an aircraft, other than for the purpose of air navigation, on any part of the surface of an airport used by aircraft for air commerce (including areas used by those aircraft for receiving or discharging persons or cargo), in a careless or reckless manner so as to endanger the life or property of another.

91.15 Dropping objects.

No pilot-in-command of a civil aircraft may allow any object to be dropped from that aircraft in flight that creates a hazard to persons or property. However, this section does not prohibit the dropping of any object if reasonable precautions are taken to avoid injury or damage to persons or property.

91.17 Alcohol or drugs.

> "Eight hours from bottle to throttle" is the most utilized phrase stemming from this regulation. This does not, however, mean that you are safe to fly simply because you have not *consumed* any alcohol within the last 8 hours. Alcohol can remain in the body for periods well in excess of 8 hours, which could put you over the legal limit or place you "under the influence." Except in an emergency, you may not carry any passenger who appears to be under the influence of drugs or alcohol. When requested to do so, you must take a blood-alcohol test, the results of which can be used against you in a legal proceeding. Also refer to the comments under 61.15.

(a) No person may act or attempt to act as a crewmember of a civil aircraft - (1) Within 8 hours after the consumption of any alcoholic beverage; (2) While under the influence of alcohol; (3) While using any drug that affects the person's faculties in any way contrary to safety; or (4) While having .04 percent by weight or more alcohol in the blood.
(b) Except in an emergency, no pilot of a civil aircraft may allow a person who appears to be intoxicated or who demonstrates by manner or physical indications that the individual is under the influence of drugs (except a medical patient under proper care) to be carried in that aircraft.
(c) A crewmember shall do the following: (1) On request of a law enforcement officer, submit to a test to indicate the percentage by weight of alcohol in the blood, when - (i) The law enforcement officer is authorized under state or local law to conduct the test or to have the test conducted; and (ii) The law enforcement officer is requesting submission to that test to investigate a suspected violation of state or local law governing the same or substantially similar conduct prohibited by paragraph (a)(1), (a)(2), or (a)(4) of this section. (2) Whenever the Administrator has a reasonable basis to believe that a person may have violated paragraph (a)(1), (a)(2), or (a)(4) of this section, that person shall, upon request by the Administrator, furnish the Administrator, or authorize any clinic, hospital, doctor, or other person to release to the Administrator, the results of each test taken within 4 hours after acting or attempting to act as a crewmember that indicates percentage by weight of alcohol in the blood.
(d) Whenever the Administrator has a reasonable basis to believe that a person may have violated paragraph (a)(3) of this section, that person shall, upon request by the Administrator furnish the Administrator, or authorize any clinic, hospital, doctor, or other person to release to the Administrator, the results of each test taken within 4 hours after acting or attempting to act as a crewmember that indicates the presence of any drugs in the body.
(e) Any test information obtained by the Administrator under paragraph (c) or (d) of this section may be evaluated in determining a person's qualifications for any airman certificate or possible violations of this chapter and may be used as evidence in any legal proceeding under section 602, 609, or 901 of the Federal Aviation Act of 1958.

91.19 Carriage of narcotic drugs, marihuana, and depressant or stimulant drugs or substances.

(a) Except as provided in paragraph (b) of this section, no person may operate a civil aircraft within the United States with knowledge that narcotic drugs, marihuana, and depressant or stimulant drugs or substances as defined in federal and state statutes are carried in the aircraft.
(b) Paragraph (a) of this section does not apply to any carriage of narcotic

drugs, marihuana, and depressant or stimulant drugs or substances authorized by or under any federal or state statute or by any federal or state agency.

91.25 Aviation Safety Reporting Program: Prohibition against use of reports for enforcement purposes.

> In an effort to promote a safer flying environment, NASA has instituted a program for reporting abnormal and/or unsafe aircraft operations without fear of criminal prosecution.

The Administrator of the FAA will not use reports submitted to the National Aeronautics and Space Administration under the Aviation Safety Reporting Program (or information derived therefrom) in any enforcement action except information concerning accidents or criminal offenses which are wholly excluded from the program.

Subpart B - Flight Rules

Section
91.101 Applicability.

This subpart prescribes flight rules governing the operation of aircraft within the United States and within 12 nautical miles from the coast of the United States.

91.103 Preflight action.

> Note that this regulation does not specifically call for a preflight inspection of the aircraft. This would, however, fall under the category of "all information concerning that flight." The phrase "not in the vicinity of an airport" can be interpreted as any farther away from the airport than a normal traffic pattern.

Each pilot-in-command shall, before beginning a flight, become familiar with all available information concerning that flight. This information must include -
(a) For a flight under IFR or a flight not in the vicinity of an airport, weather reports and forecasts, fuel requirements, alternatives available if the planned flight cannot be completed, and any known traffic delays of which the pilot-in-command has been advised by ATC;
(b) For any flight, runway lengths at airports of intended use, and the following takeoff and landing distance information: (1) For civil aircraft for which an approved airplane or rotorcraft flight manual containing takeoff and landing distance data is required, the takeoff and landing distance data contained therein; and (2) For civil aircraft other than those specified in paragraph (b)(1) of this section, other reliable information appropriate to the aircraft, relating to aircraft performance under expected values of airport elevation and runway slope, aircraft gross weight, and wind and temperature.

91.105 Flight crewmembers at stations.

(a) During takeoff and landing, and while enroute, each required flight crew-member shall - (1) Be at the crewmember station unless the absence is necessary to perform duties in connection with the operation of the aircraft or in connection with physiological needs; and (2) Keep the safety belt fastened while at the crewmember station.

(b) Each required flight crewmember of a U.S.-registered civil airplane shall, during takeoff and landing, keep the shoulder harness fastened while at the crewmember station. This paragraph does not apply if - (1) The seat at the crewmember's station is not equipped with a shoulder harness; or (2) The crewmember would be unable to perform required duties with the shoulder harness fastened.

91.107 Use of safety belts.

(a) No pilot may take off a U.S.-registered civil aircraft (except an airship or free balloon that incorporates a basket or gondola) unless the pilot-in-command of that aircraft ensures that each person on board is briefed on how to fasten and unfasten that person's safety belt and shoulder harness, if installed. The pilot-in-command shall ensure that all persons on board have been notified to fasten their safety belt and shoulder harness, if installed, before takeoff or landing.

(b) During the takeoff and landing of a U.S.-registered civil aircraft (except an airship or free balloon that incorporates a basket or gondola) each person on board that aircraft must occupy an approved seat or berth with a safety belt and shoulder harness, if installed, properly secured around that person. However, a person who has not reached the second birthday may be held by an adult who is occupying an approved seat or berth, and a person on board for the purpose of engaging in sport parachuting may use the floor of the aircraft as a seat.

(c) This section does not apply to operations conducted under part 121, 125, 127, or 135 of this chapter. Paragraph (b) of this section does not apply to persons subject to 91.105.

91.111 Operating near other aircraft.

(a) No person may operate an aircraft so close to another aircraft as to create a collision hazard.

(b) No person may operate an aircraft in formation flight except by arrangement with the pilot-in-command of each aircraft in the formation.

(c) No person may operate an aircraft, carrying passengers for hire, in formation flight.

91.113 Right-of-way rules: Except water operations.

(a) *Inapplicability.* This section does not apply to the operation of an aircraft on water.

(b) *General.* When weather conditions permit, regardless of whether an operation is conducted under instrument flight rules or visual flight rules, vigilance shall be maintained by each person operating an aircraft so as to see and avoid other aircraft. When a rule of this section gives another aircraft the right-of-way, the pilot shall give way to that aircraft and may not pass over, under, or ahead of it unless well clear.

(c) *In distress.* An aircraft in distress has the right-of-way over all other air traffic.

(d) *Converging.* When aircraft of the same category are converging at approximately the same altitude (except head-on, or nearly so), the aircraft to the other's right has the right-of-way. If the aircraft are of different categories - (1) A balloon has the right-of-way over any other category of aircraft; (2) A glider has the right-of-way over an airship, airplane, or rotorcraft; and (3) An airship has the right-of-way over an airplane or rotorcraft.
However, an aircraft towing or refueling other aircraft has the right-of-way over all other engine-driven aircraft.

(e) *Approaching head-on.* When aircraft are approaching each other head-on, or nearly so, each pilot of each aircraft shall alter course to the right.

(f) *Overtaking.* Each aircraft that is being overtaken has the right-of-way and each pilot of an overtaking aircraft shall alter course to the right to pass well clear.

(g) *Landing.* Aircraft, while on final approach to land or while landing, have the right-of-way over other aircraft in flight or operating on the surface, except that they shall not take advantage of this rule to force an aircraft off the runway surface which has already landed and is attempting to make way for an aircraft on final approach. When two or more aircraft are approaching an airport for the purpose of landing, the aircraft at the lower altitude has the right-of-way, but it shall not take advantage of this rule to cut in front of another which is on final approach to land or to overtake that aircraft.

91.117 Aircraft speed.

(a) Unless otherwise authorized by the Administrator, no person may operate an aircraft below 10,000 feet MSL at an indicated airspeed of more than 250 knots (288 m.p.h.).

(b) Unless otherwise authorized or required by ATC, no person may operate an aircraft within an airport traffic area at an indicated airspeed of more than 200 knots (230 m.p.h.). This paragraph (b) does not apply to any operations within a terminal control area. Such operations shall comply with paragraph

(a) of this section.

(c) No person may operate an aircraft in the airspace underlying a terminal control area, or in a VFR corridor designated through a terminal control area, at an indicated airspeed of more than 200 knots (230 m.p.h.).

(d) If the minimum safe airspeed for any particular operation is greater than the maximum speed prescribed in this section, the aircraft may be operated at that speed.

91.119 Minimum safe altitudes: General.

Except when necessary for takeoff or landing, no person may operate an aircraft below the following altitudes:

(a) *Anywhere.* An altitude allowing, if a power unit fails, an emergency landing without undue hazard to persons or property on the surface.

(b) *Over congested areas.* Over any congested area of a city, town, or settlement, or over any open air assembly of persons, an altitude of 1,000 feet above the highest obstacle within a horizontal radius of 2,000 feet of the aircraft.

(c) *Over other than congested areas.* An altitude of 500 feet above the surface, except over open water or sparsely populated areas. In those cases, the aircraft may not be operated closer than 500 feet to any person, vessel, vehicle, or structure.

91.121 Altimeter settings.

An altimeter is a required piece of equipment for any flight and must be properly set prior to departure. If the correct altimeter setting cannot be established from ATIS or other reliable means, the altimeter should be set so that it indicates field elevation at the departure airport. On a cross-country flight, the altimeter setting should be updated periodically by monitoring an ATIS broadcast within 100 nautical miles of your route of flight, from ATC, or a FSS. Above 18,000 feet MSL, pilots of all aircraft must set altimeters to 29.92, and the indicated altitude, in thousands of feet, is then referred to as a "flight level."

(a) Each person operating an aircraft shall maintain the cruising altitude or flight level of that aircraft, as the case may be, by reference to an altimeter that is set, when operating - (1) Below 18,000 feet MSL, to - (i) The current reported altimeter setting of a station along the route and within 100 nautical miles of the aircraft; (ii) If there is no station within the area prescribed in paragraph (a)(1)(i) of this section, the current reported altimeter setting of an appropriate available station; or (iii) In the case of an aircraft not equipped with a radio, the elevation of the departure airport or an appropriate altimeter setting available before departure; or (2) At or above 18,000 feet MSL, to 29.92 inches of mercury.

(b) The lowest useable flight level is determined by the atmospheric pressure in the area of operation as shown in the following table:

Current altimeter setting	Lowest useable flight level
29.92 (or higher)	180
29.91 through 29.42	185
29.41 through 28.92	190
28.91 through 28.42	195
28.41 through 27.92	200
27.91 through 27.42	205
27.41 through 26.92	210

(c) To convert minimum altitude prescribed under 91.119 and 91.177 to the minimum flight level, the pilot shall take the flight level equivalent of the minimum altitude in feet and add the appropriate number of feet specified below, according to the current reported altimeter setting:

Current altimeter setting	Adjustment factor
29.92 (or higher)	None
29.91 through 29.42	500
29.41 through 28.92	1,000
28.91 through 28.42	1,500
28.41 through 27.92	2,000
27.91 through 27.42	2,500
27.41 through 26.92	3,000

91.123 Compliance with ATC clearances and instructions.

When issued a "clearance" (a specific set of instructions) by ATC, you must follow those instructions, except in an emergency. If you must deviate from your clearance, notify ATC as soon as possible. Never accept a clearance which will cause you to break a regulation and never but *never* accept a clearance that you don't understand. Ask for clarification.

(a) When an ATC clearance has been obtained, no pilot-in-command may deviate from that clearance, except in an emergency, unless an amended clearance is obtained. A pilot-in-command may cancel an IFR flight plan if that pilot is operating in VFR weather conditions outside of positive controlled airspace. If a pilot is uncertain of the meaning of an ATC clearance, the pilot shall immediately request clarification from ATC.
(b) Except in an emergency, no person may operate an aircraft contrary to an ATC instruction in an area in which air traffic control is exercised.
(c) Each pilot-in-command who, in an emergency, deviates from an ATC clearance or instruction shall notify ATC of that deviation as soon as possible.
(d) Each pilot-in-command who (though not deviating from a rule of this subpart) is given priority by ATC in an emergency, shall submit a detailed report of that emergency within 48 hours to the manager of that ATC facility, if requested by ATC.
(e) Unless otherwise authorized by ATC, no person operating an aircraft may operate that aircraft according to any clearance or instruction that has been issued to the pilot of another aircraft for radar air traffic control purposes.

91.125 ATC light signals.

ATC light signals have the meaning shown in the following table:

COLOR AND TYPE OF SIGNAL	MEANING TO AIRCRAFT ON THE SURFACE	MEANING TO AIRCRAFT IN FLIGHT
Steady green	Cleared for takeoff	Cleared to land
Flashing green	Cleared to taxi	Return for landing (to be followed by steady green at proper time).
Steady red	Stop	Give way to other aircraft and continue circling.
Flashing red	Taxi clear of runway in use.	Airport unsafe-do not land.
Flashing white	Return to starting point on airport.	Not applicable.
Alternating red and green.	Exercise extreme caution.	Exercise extreme caution.

91.127 Operation in the vicinity of an airport: General rules.

Unless otherwise indicated by lights, markings, or publications, left-hand traffic is standard at an uncontrolled (no control tower or a nonoperating tower) airport. Refer to Chapter 10, Section 3 for detailed information on uncontrolled airport operations.

(a) Unless otherwise required by Part 93 of this chapter, each person operating an aircraft on or in the vicinity of an airport shall comply with the requirements of this section and, if applicable, of 91.129.

(b) Each person operating an aircraft to or from an airport without an operating control tower shall - (1) In the case of an airplane approaching to land, make all turns of that airplane to the left unless the airport displays approved light signals or visual markings indicating that turns should be made to the right, in which case the pilot shall make all turns to the right; (2) In the case of a helicopter approaching to land, avoid the flow of fixed-wing aircraft; and (3) In the case of an aircraft departing the airport, comply with any traffic patterns established for that airport in Part 93.

(c) Unless otherwise authorized or required by ATC, no person may operate an aircraft within an airport traffic area except for the purpose of landing at, or taking off from, an airport within that area. ATC authorization may be given as individual approval of specific operations or may be contained in written agreements between airport users and the tower concerned.

91.129 Operation at airports with operating control towers.

> Two-way radio communications with the control tower and an appropriate clearance are required before you may operate in an airport traffic area (ATA) when the tower is operated by the FAA. This clearance requirement applies to both ground and flight operations. Nonfederal control towers (identified as NFCT on charts and publications) are operated by municipalities or private entities. The same communications are required unless your radio can only receive. You must then monitor the tower when in the ATA. If the landing runway is equipped with VASI lights, you must remain on or above the glideslope on approach. Also note the definition of a "taxi to" clearance at the end of the text. Refer to Chapter 10, Section 3 for detailed information on controlled airport operations, radio failure, and light gun signals.

(a) General. Unless otherwise authorized or required by ATC, each person operating an aircraft to, from, or on an airport with an operating control tower shall comply with the applicable provisions of this section.

(b) Communications with control towers operated by the United States. No person may, within an airport traffic area, operate an aircraft to, from, or on an airport having a control tower operated by the United States unless two-way radio communications are maintained between that aircraft and the control tower. However, if the aircraft radio fails in flight, the pilot-in-command may operate that aircraft and land if weather conditions are at or above basic VFR weather minimums, visual contact with the tower is maintained, and a clearance to land is received. If the aircraft radio fails while in flight under IFR, the pilot must comply with 91.185.

(c) Communications with other control towers. No person may, within an airport traffic area, operate an aircraft to, from, or on an airport having a control tower that is operated by any person other than the United States unless - (1) If that aircraft's radio equipment so allows, two-way radio communications are maintained between the aircraft and the tower; or (2) If that aircraft's radio equipment allows only reception from the tower, the pilot has the tower's frequency monitored.

(d) Minimum altitudes. When operating to an airport with an operating control tower, each pilot of- (3) An airplane approaching to land on a runway served by a visual approach slope indicator shall maintain an altitude at or above the glide slope until a lower altitude is necessary for a safe landing. However, paragraphs (d)(2) and (3) of this section do not prohibit normal bracketing maneuvers above or below the glide slope that are conducted for the purpose of remaining on the glide slope.

(e) Approaches. When approaching to land at an airport with an operating control tower, each pilot of - (1) An airplane shall circle the airport to the left; and (2) A helicopter shall avoid the flow of fixed-wing aircraft.

(f) Departures. No person may operate an aircraft taking off from an airport with an operating control tower except in compliance with the following: (1) Each pilot shall comply with any departure procedures established for that airport by the FAA.

(h) Clearances required. No person may, at an airport with an operating control tower, operate an aircraft on a runway or taxiway, or take off or land an aircraft, unless an appropriate clearance is received from ATC. A clearance to "taxi to" the takeoff runway assigned to the aircraft is not a clearance to cross that assigned takeoff runway or to taxi on that runway at any point, but is a clearance to cross other runways that intersect the taxi route to that assigned takeoff runway. A clearance to "taxi to" any point other than an assigned takeoff runway is a clearance to cross all runways that intersect the taxi route to that point.

91.130 Airport radar service areas.

Prior to entering or operating in an ARSA, you must establish two-way radio communications with ATC and receive a clearance. The one exception to this rule is if you are departing from an airport which is in the ARSA but is not the "primary airport" which the ARSA is surrounding. This type of airport is known as a "satellite airport." You must then establish communication with ATC as soon as possible after departure. A Mode C equipped transponder is required equipment in an ARSA.

(a) General. For the purposes of this section, the primary airport is the airport designated in Part 71, Subpart L, for which the airport radar service area is designated. A satellite airport is any other airport within the airport radar service area.
(b) Deviations. An operator may deviate from any provision of this section under the provisions of an ATC authorization issued by the ATC facility having jurisdiction of the airport radar service area. ATC may authorize a deviation on a continuing basis or for an individual flight, as appropriate.
(c) Arrivals and overflights. No person may operate an aircraft in an airport radar service area unless two-way radio communication is established with the ATC facility having jurisdiction over the airport radar service area prior to entering that area and is thereafter maintained with ATC facility having jurisdiction over the airport radar service area while within that area.
(d) Departures. No person may operate an aircraft in an airport radar service area except as follows: (1) From the primary airport or satellite airport with an operating control tower, unless two-way radio communication is established and maintained with the control tower in accordance with 91.87 of this part, and thereafter as instructed by ATC while operating in the airport radar service area. (2) From a satellite airport without an operating control tower, unless two-way radio communication is established as soon as practicable after departing and thereafter maintained with the ATC facility having jurisdiction over the airport radar service area.
(e) Traffic patterns. No person may take off or land an aircraft at a satellite airport within an airport radar service area except in compliance with FAA arrival and departure traffic patterns.
(f) Equipment requirements. Unless otherwise authorized by the ATC facility having jurisdiction over the airport radar service area, no person may operate an aircraft within an airport radar service area unless that aircraft is equipped with the applicable equipment specified in 91.215.

91.131 Terminal control areas.

> The following are required for operation in a TCA:
>
> 1. Two-way radio communication and an ATC clearance.
> 2. A Mode C-equipped transponder.
> 3. A private pilot certificate or a student pilot certificate along with a log book endorsement indicating training in that specific TCA. At the busiest airports in the U.S., listed below in section (b)(2), a student pilot may not takeoff or land.

(a) Operating rules. No person may operate an aircraft in a terminal control area designated in Part 71 of this chapter except in compliance with the following rules: (1) No person may operate an aircraft within a terminal control area unless that person has received an appropriate authorization from ATC prior to operation of that aircraft in that area. (3) Any person conducting pilot training operations at an airport within a terminal control area shall comply with any procedures established by ATC for such operations in terminal control areas.
(b) Pilot requirements. (1) No person may takeoff or land a civil aircraft at an airport within a terminal control area or operate a civil aircraft within a terminal control area unless: (i) The pilot-in-command holds at least a private pilot certificate; or, (ii) The aircraft is operated by a student pilot who has met the requirements of 61.95. (2) Notwithstanding the provisions of paragraph (b)(1)(ii) of this section, at the following TCA primary airports, no person may takeoff or land a civil aircraft unless the pilot-in-command holds at least a private pilot certificate: (i) Atlanta Hartsfield Airport, GA. (ii) Boston Logan Airport, MA. (iii) Chicago O'Hare International Airport, IL. (iv) Dallas/Fort Worth International Airport, TX. (v) Los Angeles International Airport, CA. (vi) Miami International Airport, FL. (vii) Newark International Airport, NJ. (viii) New York Kennedy Airport, NY. (ix) New York LaGuardia Airport, NY. (x) San Francisco International Airport, CA. (xi) Washington National Airport, DC. (xii) Andrews Air Force Base, MD.
(c) Communications and navigation equipment requirements for all operations. Unless otherwise authorized by ATC, no person may operate an aircraft within a terminal control area unless that aircraft is equipped with an operable two-way radio capable of communications with ATC on appropriate frequencies for that terminal control area.
(d) Transponder requirement. No person may operate an aircraft in a terminal control area unless the aircraft is equipped with the applicable operating transponder and automatic altitude reporting equipment specified in paragraph (a) of 91.215, except as provided in paragraph (d) of that section.

91.133 Restricted and prohibited areas.

> You may not operate in any airspace designated as "prohibited" (such as over the White House). You must obtain permission to operate in any airspace designated as "restricted."

(a) No person may operate an aircraft within a restricted area (designated in Part 73) contrary to the restrictions imposed, or within a prohibited area, unless that person has the permission of the using or controlling agency, as appropriate.
(b) Each person conducting, within a restricted area, an aircraft operation (approved by the using agency) that creates the same hazards as the operations for which the restricted area was designated may deviate from the rules of this subpart that are not compatible with the

operation of the aircraft.

91.135 Positive control areas and route segments.

> As a VFR private pilot, you are prohibited from operating in any airspace designated as a "positive control area" or a "positive control route segment."

(a) Except as provided in paragraph (b) of this section, no person may operate an aircraft in a positive control area or positive control route segment designated in Part 71 of this chapter unless the aircraft is - (1) Operated under IFR at a specific flight level assigned by ATC; (2) Equipped with instruments and equipment required for IFR operations; (3) Flown by a pilot rated for instrument flight; and (4) Equipped, when in a positive control area, with - (i) The applicable equipment specified in 91.215; and (ii) A radio providing direct pilot/controller communication on the frequency specified by ATC for the area concerned.

91.137 Temporary flight restrictions.

> The FAA can temporarily restrict any airspace if it feels that it is necessary and will issue a NOTAM to indicate this. There are a number of exceptions, but in general you cannot operate in this temporarily restricted airspace.

(a) The Administrator will issue a Notice to Airmen (NOTAM) designating an area within which temporary flight restrictions apply and specifying the hazard or condition requiring their imposition, whenever he determines it is necessary in order to - (1) Protect persons and property on the surface or in the air from a hazard associated with an incident on the surface; (2) Provide a safe environment for the operation of disaster relief aircraft; or (3) Prevent an unsafe congestion of sightseeing and other aircraft above an incident or event which may generate a high degree of public interest.
The Notice to Airmen will specify the hazard or condition that requires the imposition of temporary flight restrictions.
(b) When a NOTAM has been issued under paragraph (a)(1) of this section, no person may operate an aircraft within the designated area unless that aircraft is participating in the hazard relief activities and is being operated under the direction of the official in charge of on-scene emergency response activities.
(c) When a NOTAM has been issued under paragraph (a)(2) of this section, no person may operate an aircraft within the designated area unless at least one of the following conditions is met: (1) The aircraft is participating in hazard relief activities and is being operated under the direction of the official in charge of on-scene emergency response activities. (2) The aircraft is carrying law enforcement officials. (3) The aircraft is operating under the ATC approved IFR flight plan. (4) The operation is conducted directly to or from an airport within the area, or is necessitated by the impracticability of VFR flight above or around the area due to weather or terrain; notification is given to the Flight Service Station (FSS) or ATC facility specified in the NOTAM to receive advisories concerning disaster relief aircraft operations; and the operation does not hamper or endanger relief activities and is not conducted for the purpose of observing the disaster. (5) The aircraft is carrying properly accredited news representatives, and prior to entering the area, a flight plan is filed with the appropriate FAA or ATC facility specified in the Notice to Airmen and the operation is conducted above the altitude used by the disaster relief aircraft, unless otherwise authorized by the official in charge of on-scene emergency response activities.
(d) When a NOTAM has been issued under paragraph (a)(3) of this section, no person may operate an aircraft within the designated area unless at least one of the following conditions is met: (1) The operation is conducted directly to or from an airport within the area, or is

necessitated by the impracticability of VFR flight above or around the area due to weather or terrain, and the operation is not conducted for the purpose of observing the incident or event. (2) The aircraft is operating under an ATC approved IFR flight plan. (3) The aircraft is carrying incident or event personnel, or law enforcement officials. (4) The aircraft is carrying properly accredited news representatives and, prior to entering that area, a flight plan is filed with the appropriate FSS or ATC facility specified in the NOTAM.

(e) Flight plans filed and notifications made with an FSS or ATC facility under this section shall include the following information: (1) Aircraft identification, type, and color. (2) Radio communications frequencies to be used. (3) Proposed times of entry of, and exit from, the designated area. (4) Name of news media or organization and purpose of flight. (5) Any other information requested by ATC.

91.139 Emergency air traffic rules.

The FAA can institute emergency air traffic rules as it sees fit in order to control air traffic in an emergency situation. A NOTAM will be issued documenting these rules.

(a) This section prescribes a process for utilizing Notices to Airmen (NOTAMs) to advise of the issuance and operations under emergency air traffic rules and regulations and designates the official who is authorized to issue NOTAMs on behalf of the Administrator in certain matters under this section.

(b) Whenever the Administrator determines that an emergency condition exists, or will exist, relating to the FAA's ability to operate the air traffic control system and during which normal flight operations under this chapter cannot be conducted consistent with the required levels of safety and efficiency - (1) The Administrator issues an immediately effective air traffic rule or regulation in response to that emergency condition; and (2) The Administrator or the Associate Administrator for Air Traffic may utilize the NOTAM system to provide notification of the issuance of the rule or regulation.

Those NOTAMs communicate information concerning the rules and regulations that govern flight operations, the use of navigation facilities, and designation of that airspace in which the rules and regulations apply.

(c) When a NOTAM has been issued under this section, no person may operate an aircraft, or other device governed by the regulation concerned, within the designated airspace except in accordance with the authorizations, terms, and conditions prescribed in the regulation covered by the NOTAM.

91.141 Flight restrictions in the proximity of the Presidential and other parties.

No person may operate an aircraft over or in the vicinity of any area to be visited or traveled by the President, the Vice President, or other public figures contrary to the restrictions established by the Administrator and published in a Notice to Airmen (NOTAM).

91.143 Flight limitation in the proximity of space flight operations.

No person may operate any aircraft of U.S. registry, or pilot any aircraft under the authority of an airman certificate issued by the Federal Aviation Administration within areas designated in a Notice to Airmen (NOTAM) for space flight operations except when authorized by ATC, or operated under the control of the Department of Defense Manager for Space Transportation System Contingency Support Operations.

[Judging from the name of the governing authority, your request will still be mired in red tape by the time the space operation is completed, so you may as well wait it out!]

91.151 Fuel requirements for flight in VFR conditions.

(a) No person may begin a flight in an airplane under VFR conditions unless (considering wind and forecast weather conditions) there is enough fuel to fly to the first point of intended landing and, assuming normal cruising speed - (1) During the day, to fly after that for at least 30 minutes; or (2) At night, to fly after that for at least 45 minutes.

91.153 VFR flight plan: Information required.

(a) Information required. Unless otherwise authorized by ATC, each person filing a VFR flight plan shall include in it the following information: (1) The aircraft identification number and, if necessary, its radio call sign. (2) The type of the aircraft or, in the case of a formation flight, the type of each aircraft and the number of aircraft in the formation. (3) The full name and address of the pilot-in-command or, in the case of a formation flight, the formation commander. (4) The point and proposed time of departure. (5) The proposed route, cruising altitude (or flight level), and true airspeed at that altitude. (6) The point of first intended landing and the estimated elapsed time until over that point. (7) The amount of fuel on board (in hours). (8) The number of persons in the aircraft, except where that information is otherwise readily available to the FAA.   (9) Any other information the pilot-in-command or ATC believes is necessary for ATC purposes.
(b) Cancellation. When a flight plan has been activated, the pilot-in-command, upon cancelling or completing the flight under the flight plan, shall notify an FAA Flight Service Station or ATC facility.

91.155 Basic VFR weather minimums.

(a) Except as provided in 91.155(b) and 91.157, no person may operate an aircraft under VFR when the flight visibility is less, or at a distance from clouds that is less, than that prescribed for the corresponding altitude in the following table on page 64.
(b) Inapplicability. Notwithstanding the provisions of paragraph (a) of this section, the following operations may be conducted outside of controlled airspace below 1,200 feet above the surface: (2) Airplane. When the visibility is less than 3 miles but not less than 1 mile during night hours, an

airplane may be operated in an airport traffic pattern within one-half mile of the runway.

(c) Except as provided in 91.157, no person may operate an aircraft, under VFR, within a control zone beneath the ceiling when the ceiling is less than 1,000 feet.

(d) Except as provided in 91.157, no person may take off or land an aircraft, or enter the traffic pattern of an airport, under VFR, within a control zone - (1) Unless ground visibility at that airport is at least 3 statute miles, or (2) If ground visibility is not reported at that airport, unless flight visibility during landing or takeoff, or while operating in the traffic pattern, is at least 3 statute miles.

(e) For the purposes of this section, an aircraft operating at the base altitude of a transition area or control area is considered to be within the airspace directly below that area.

AIRSPACE OR OPERATION	FLIGHT VISIBILITY	DISTANCE FROM CLOUDS
Anywhere	5 statute miles	1,000 feet above 1,000 feet below 1 mile horizontal
10,000 feet MSL		
Controlled airspace, or uncontrolled - night	3 statute miles	1,000 feet above 500 feet below 2,000 feet horizontal
Uncontrolled - day	1 statute mile	
1,200 feet AGL		
Controlled airspace, or uncontrolled - night	3 statute miles	1,000 feet above 500 feet below 2,000 feet horizontal
Uncontrolled - day, or in an airport traffic pattern within 1/2 mile of the runway - night	1 statute mile	clear of clouds
Surface		

91.157 Special VFR weather minimums.

> You may request a "special VFR" clearance from ATC to operate in a control zone when conditions are below basic VFR minimums (3 miles visibility and 1,000 feet ceiling). If you are given this clearance, you must maintain 1 mile visibility and remain clear of clouds. As a VFR private pilot, you may not fly under special VFR at night.

(a) Except as provided in 91.113, when a person has received an appropriate ATC clearance, the special weather minimums of this section instead of those contained in 91.155 apply to the operation of an aircraft by that person in a control zone under VFR.
(b) No person may operate an aircraft in a control zone under VFR except clear of clouds.
(c) No person may operate an aircraft (other than a helicopter) in a control zone under VFR unless flight visibility is at least 1 statute mile.
(d) No person may take off or land an aircraft (other than a helicopter) at any airport in a control zone under VFR - (1) Unless ground visibility at that airport is at least 1 statute mile; or (2) If ground visibility is not reported at that airport, unless flight visibility during takeoff or landing is at least 1 statute mile.
(e) No person may operate an aircraft (other than a helicopter) in a control zone under the special weather minimums of this section, between sunset and sunrise (or in Alaska, when the sun is more than 6 degrees below the horizon) unless: (1) That person meets the applicable requirements for instrument flight under part 61 of this chapter; and (2) The aircraft is equipped as required in 91.205(d).

91.159 VFR cruising altitude or flight level.

Except while holding in a holding pattern of 2 minutes or less, or while turning, each person operating an aircraft under VFR in level cruising flight more than 3,000 feet above the surface shall maintain the appropriate altitude or flight level prescribed below, unless otherwise authorized by ATC:
(a) When operating below 18,000 feet MSL and -
(1) On a magnetic course of zero degrees through 179 degrees, any odd thousand foot MSL altitude +500 feet (such as 3,500, 5,500, or 7,500); or
(2) On a magnetic course of 180 degrees through 359 degrees, any even thousand foot MSL altitude +500 feet (such as 4,500, 6,500, or 8,500).

TEST QUESTIONS

1. The final authority as to the operation of an aircraft is the

A - Federal Aviation Administration.
B - pilot-in-command.
C - aircraft manufacturer.

2. A person may not act as a crewmember of a civil aircraft if alcoholic beverages have been consumed by that person within the preceding

A - 8 hours.
B - 12 hours.
C - 24 hours.

3. Preflight action, as required for all flights away from the vicinity of an airport, shall include

A - the designation of an alternate airport.
B - a study of arrival procedures at airports of intended use.
C - an alternate course of action if the flight cannot be completed as planned.

4. Seatbelts are required to be properly secured about which persons in an aircraft and when?

A - Pilots only, during takeoffs and landings.
B - Passengers, during takeoffs and landings only.
C - Each person on board the aircraft during the entire flight.

5. What action should the pilots of a glider and an airplane take if on a head-on collision course?

A - The airplane pilot should give way.
B - The glider pilot should give way to the right.
C - Both pilots should give way to the right.

6. Unless otherwise authorized, the maximum indicated airspeed at which a reciprocating engine-equipped aircraft should be flown within an Airport Traffic Area is

A - 156 knots.
B - 180 knots.
C - 200 knots.

7. Except when necessary for takeoff or landing, what is the minimum safe altitude for a pilot to operate an aircraft anywhere?

A - An altitude allowing, if a power unit fails, an emergency landing without undue hazard to persons or property on the surface.
B - An altitude of 500 feet above the surface and no closer than 500 feet to any person, vessel, vehicle, or structure.
C - An altitude of 500 feet above the highest obstacle within a horizontal radius of 1,000 feet.

8. Prior to takeoff, the altimeter should be set to which altitude or altimeter setting?

A - The current local altimeter setting, if available, or the departure airport elevation.
B - The corrected density altitude of the departure airport.
C - The corrected pressure altitude for the departure airport.

9. While on final approach for landing, an alternating green and red light followed by a flashing red light is received from the control tower. Under these circumstances, the pilot should

A - discontinue the approach, fly the same traffic pattern and approach again, and land.
B - exercise extreme caution and abandon the approach, realizing that the airport is unsafe for landing.
C - abandon the approach, circle the airport to the right, and expect a flashing white light when the airport is safe for landing.

10. Unless otherwise authorized, two-way radio communications with Air Traffic Control are required for landings or takeoffs

A - at all tower-controlled airports regardless of weather conditions.
B - at all tower-controlled airports only when weather conditions are less than VFR.
C - at all tower-controlled airports within control zones only when weather conditions are less than VFR.

11. What minimum radio equipment is required for operation within an Airport Radar Service Area?

A - Two-way radio communications equipment, transponder, and DME.
B - Two-way radio communications equipment and transponder.
C - Two-way radio communications equipment, transponder, and encoding altimeter.

12. What minimum radio equipment is required to operate within a TCA?

A - Two-way radio communications equipment, transponder, and DME.
B - Two-way radio communications equipment and transponder.
C - Two-way radio communications equipment, transponder, and encoding altimeter.

13. What is the specific fuel requirement for flight under VFR at night in an airplane?

A - Enough to complete the flight at normal cruising speed with adverse wind conditions.
B - Enough to fly to the first point of intended landing and to fly after that for 30 minutes at normal cruising speed.
C - Enough to fly to the first point of intended landing and to fly after that for 45 minutes at normal cruising speed.

14. During operations outside controlled airspace at altitudes of more than 1,200 feet AGL, but less than 10,000 feet MSL, the minimum flight visibility for VFR flight at night is

A - 1 mile.
B - 3 miles.
C - 5 miles.

15. What is the minimum weather condition required for airplanes operating under special VFR in a control zone?

A - 1 mile flight visibility.
B - 1 mile flight visibility and 1,000-foot ceiling.
C - 3 miles flight visibility and 1,000-foot ceiling.

16. Which cruising altitude is appropriate for a VFR flight on a magnetic course of 135°?

A - Even thousands.
B - Even thousands plus 500 feet.
C - Odd thousands plus 500 feet.

ANSWERS

1. B (91.3)	2. A (91.17)	3. C (91.103)	4. B (91.107)
5. C (91.113)	6. C (91.117)	7. A (91.119)	8. A (91.121)
9. B (91.125)	10. A (91.129)	11. C (91.130)	12. C (91.131)
13. C (91.151)	14. B (91.155)	15. A (91.157)	16. C (91.159)

Part 91 - General Operating and Flight Rules
Subparts C, D, E, H, and J

Subpart C - Equipment, Instrument, and Certificate Requirements

Section
91.203 Civil aircraft: Certifications required.

An easy way to remember the certificates and documents which are required to be aboard the aircraft is the acronym "ARROW":

> <u>A</u>irworthiness Certificate
> <u>R</u>egistration
> <u>R</u>adio Station License
> <u>O</u>perating Limitations
> <u>W</u>eight and Balance Information

The airworthiness certificate must be visible in the cockpit. An FAA Form 337 must also be carried aboard if a fuel tank has been installed in the cabin.

(a) except as provided in 91.715, no person may operate a civil aircraft unless it has within it the following: (1) An appropriate and current airworthiness certificate. Each U.S. airworthiness certificate used to comply with this subparagraph (except a special flight permit, a copy of the applicable operations specifications issued under 21.197(c) of this chapter, appropriate sections of the air carrier manual required by Parts 121 and 135 of this chapter containing that portion of the operations specifications issued under 21.197(c), or an authorization under 91.611) must have on it the registration number assigned to the aircraft under Part 47 of this chapter. However, the airworthiness certificate need not have on it an assigned special identification number before 10 days after that number is first affixed to the aircraft. A revised airworthiness certificate having on it an assigned special identification number, that has been affixed to the aircraft, may only be obtained upon application to an FAA Flight Standards district office. (2) An effective U.S. registration certificate issued to its owner or, for operation within the United States, the second duplicate copy (pink) of the Aircraft Registration Application as provided for in 47.31(b), or a registration certificate issued under the laws of a foreign country.
(b) No person may operate a civil aircraft unless the airworthiness certificate required by paragraph (a) of this section or a special flight authorization issued under 91.715 is displayed at the cabin or cockpit entrance so that it is legible to passengers or crew.
(c) No person may operate an aircraft with a fuel tank installed within the passenger compartment or a baggage compartment unless the installation was accomplished pursuant to Part 43 of this chapter, and a copy of FAA Form 337 authorizing that installation is on board the aircraft.
(d) No person may operate a civil airplane (domestic or foreign) into or out of an airport in the United States unless it complies with the fuel venting and exhaust emissions requirements

of Part 34 of this chapter.

91.205 Powered civil aircraft with standard category U.S. airworthiness certificates: Instrument and equipment requirements.

The following operable aircraft equipment is required for daytime VFR flight:
1. Airspeed indicator.
2. Altimeter.
3. Magnetic direction indicator (compass).
4. Tachometer.
5. Oil pressure gauge.
6. Temperature gauge if engine is liquid-cooled.
   Oil temperature gauge if engine is air-cooled.
7. Manifold pressure gauge for aircraft with a constant-speed propeller.
8. Fuel gauge for each tank.
9. Landing gear position indicator if gear is retractable.
10. Safety belt for each occupant over 2 years old.
11. Shoulder harnesses for each front seat if the aircraft was manufactured after July 18, 1978. Shoulder harnesses for all seats if manufactured after December 12, 1986.
12. An Emergency Locator Transmitter (ELT). (See 91.207.)

The following operable equipment is required for nighttime VFR flight:

1. All equipment listed above.
2. Approved position lights.
3. Approved anticollision light.
4. An adequate source of electrical energy for all installed electrical and radio equipment (battery and/or alternator).
5. One spare set of fuses or three fuses of each type required. (Most newer aircraft have circuit breakers which would excuse you from this requirement.)

(a) General. Except as provided in paragraphs (c)(3) and (e) of this section, no person may operate a powered civil aircraft with a standard category U.S. airworthiness certificate in any operation described in paragraphs (b) through (f) of this section unless that aircraft contains the instruments and equipment specified in those paragraphs (or FAA-approved equivalents) for that type of operation, and those instruments and items of equipment are in operable condition.
(b) Visual-flight rules (day). For VFR flight during the day, the following instruments and equipment are required: (1) Airspeed indicator. (2) Altimeter. (3) Magnetic direction indicator. (4) Tachometer for each engine. (5) Oil pressure gauge for each engine using pressure system. (6) Temperature gauge for each liquid-cooled engine. (7) Oil temperature gauge for each air-cooled engine. (8) Manifold pressure gauge for each altitude engine. (9) Fuel gauge indicating the quantity of fuel in each tank. (10) Landing gear position indicator, if the aircraft has a retractable landing gear. (11) If the aircraft is operated for hire over water and beyond power-off gliding distance from shore, approved flotation gear readily available to

each occupant and at least one pyrotechnic signaling device. As used in this section, "shore" means that area of the land adjacent to the water which is above the high water mark and excludes land areas which are intermittently under water. (12) Except as to airships, an approved safety belt with an approved metal-to-metal latching device for each occupant 2 years of age or older. (13) For small civil airplanes manufactured after July 18, 1978, an approved shoulder harness for each front seat. The shoulder harness must be designed to protect the occupant from serious head injury when the occupant experiences the ultimate inertia forces specified in 23.561(b)(2) of this chapter. Each shoulder harness installed at a flight crewmember station must permit the crewmember, when seated and with the safety belt and shoulder harness fastened, to perform all functions necessary for flight operations. For purposes of this paragraph - (i) The date of manufacture of an airplane is the date the inspection acceptance records reflect that the airplane is complete and meets the FAA-approved type design data; and (ii) A front seat is a seat located at a flight crewmember station or any seat located alongside such a seat. (14) An emergency locator transmitter, if required by 91.207. (15) For normal, utility, and acrobatic category airplanes with a seating configuration, excluding pilot seats, of 9 or less, manufactured after December 12, 1986, a shoulder harness for - (i) Each front seat that meets the requirements of 23.785 (g) and (h) of this chapter in effect on December 12, 1985; (ii) Each additional seat that meets the requirements of 23.785 (g) of this chapter in effect on December 12, 1985.

(c) Visual flight rules (night). For VFR flight at night, the following instruments and equipment are required: (1) Instruments and equipment specified in paragraph (b) of this section. (2) Approved position lights. (3) An approved aviation red or aviation white anticollision light system on all U.S.-registered civil aircraft. Anticollision light systems initially installed after August 11, 1971, on aircraft for which a type certificate was issued or applied for before August 11, 1971, must at least meet the anticollision light standards of part 23, 25, 27, or 29 of this chapter, as applicable, that were in effect on August 10, 1971, except that the color may be either aviation red or aviation white. In the event of failure of any light of the anticollision light system, operations with the aircraft may be continued to a stop where repairs or replacement can be made. (4) If the aircraft is operated for hire, one electric landing light. (5) An adequate source of electrical energy for all installed electrical and radio equipment. (6) One spare set of fuses, or three spare fuses of each kind required, that are accessible to the pilot in flight.

91.207 Emergency locator transmitters.

Except for the conditions described in paragraphs (d) and (e) below, you must have an Emergency Locator Transmitter (ELT) properly installed in the aircraft. The batteries must be replaced when the transmitter has been in use for more than one cumulative hour or 50% of their useful life has expired. Upon replacement, the new expiration date must be marked on the transmitter and in the aircraft maintenance records.

(a) Except as provided in paragraphs (d) and (e) of this section, no person may operate a U.S.-registered civil airplane unless - (1) There is attached to the airplane an automatic type emergency locator transmitter that is in operable condition and meets the applicable requirements of TSO-C91 for the following operations: (i) Those operations governed by the supplemental air carrier and commercial operator rules of Parts 121 and 125; (ii) Charter flights governed by the domestic and flag air carrier rules of Part 121 of this chapter; and (iii) Operations governed by Part 135 of this chapter; or (2) For operations other than those specified in paragraph (a)(1)(i) of this section, there must be attached to the airplane a personal type or an automatic type emergency locator transmitter that is in operable condition and meets the applicable requirements of TSO-C91.

(b) Each emergency locator transmitter required by paragraph (a) of this section must be attached to the airplane in such a manner that the probability of damage to the transmitter in the event of crash impact is minimized. Fixed and deployable automatic type transmitters must be attached to the airplane as far aft as practicable.

(c) Batteries use in the emergency locator transmitters required by paragraphs (a) and (b) of this section must be replaced (or recharged, if the batteries are rechargeable) - (1) When the transmitter has been in use for more than 1 cumulative hour; or (2) When 50 percent of their useful life (or for rechargeable batteries, 50 percent of their useful life of charge), as established by the transmitter manufacturer under TSO-C91, paragraph (g)(2) of this section, has expired.

The new expiration date for replacing (or recharging) the battery must be legibly marked on the outside of the transmitter and entered in the aircraft maintenance record. Paragraph (c)(2) of this section does not apply to batteries (such as water-activated batteries) that are essentially unaffected during probable storage intervals.

(d) Notwithstanding paragraph (a) of this section, a person may - (1) Ferry a newly acquired airplane from the place where possession of it was taken to a place where the emergency locator transmitter is to be installed; and (2) Ferry an airplane with an inoperative emergency locator transmitter from a place where repairs or replacement cannot be made to a place where they can be made.

No person other than required crewmembers may be carried aboard an airplane being ferried under paragraph (d) of this section.

(e) Paragraph (a) of this section does not apply to - (1) Turbojet-powered aircraft; (2) Aircraft while engaged in scheduled flights by scheduled air carriers; (3) Aircraft while engaged in training operations conducted entirely within a 50-nautical mile radius of the airport from which such local flight operations began; (4) Aircraft while engaged in flight operations incident to design and testing; (5) New aircraft while engaged in flight operations incident to their manufacture, preparation, and delivery; (6) Aircraft while engaged in flight operations incident to the aerial application of chemicals and other substances for agricultural purposes; (7) Aircraft certificated by the Administrator for research and development purposes; (8) Aircraft while used for showing compliance with regulations, crew training, exhibition, air racing, or market surveys; (9) Aircraft equipped to carry not more than one person; and (10) An aircraft during any period for which the transmitter has been temporarily removed for inspection, repair, modification, or replacement, subject to the following: (i) No person may operate the aircraft unless the aircraft records contain an entry which includes the date of initial removal, the make, model, serial number, and reason for removing the transmitter, and a placard located in view of the pilot to show "ELT not installed." (ii) No person may operate the aircraft more than 90 days after the ELT is initially removed from the aircraft.

91.209 Aircraft lights.

No person may, during the period from sunset to sunrise (or, in Alaska during the period a prominent unlighted object cannot be seen from a distance of 3 statute miles or the sun is more than 6 degrees below the horizon) -

(a) Operate an aircraft unless it has lighted position lights;

(b) Park or move an aircraft in, or in dangerous proximity to, a night flight operations area of an airport unless the aircraft - (1) Is clearly illuminated; (2) Has lighted position lights; or (3) Is in an area which is marked by obstruction lights;

(c) Anchor an aircraft unless the aircraft - (1) Has lighted anchor lights; or (2) Is in an area where anchor lights are not required on vessels; or

(d) Operate an aircraft, required by 91.205(c)(3) to be equipped with an anticollision light system, unless it has approved and lighted aviation red or aviation white anticollision lights. However, the anticollision lights need not be lighted when the pilot-in-command determines that, because of operating conditions, it would be in the interest of safety to turn the lights off.

91.211 Supplemental oxygen.

O$_2$ Requirements - Unpressurized Aircraft

Passengers must be provided with oxygen.
15,000 feet MSL Flight crew must use oxygen.
14,000 feet MSL Flight crew must use oxygen for flight time over 30 minutes.

12,500 feet MSL

(a) General. No person may operate a civil aircraft of U.S. registry - (1) At cabin pressure altitudes above 12,500 feet (MSL) up to and including 14,000 feet (MSL) unless the required minimum flight crew is provided with and uses supplemental oxygen for that part of the flight at those altitudes that is of more than 30 minutes duration; (2) At cabin pressure altitudes above 14,000 feet (MSL) unless the required minimum flight crew is provided with and uses supplemental oxygen during the entire flight time at those altitudes; and (3) At cabin pressure altitudes above 15,000 feet (MSL) unless each occupant of the aircraft is provided with supplemental oxygen.

(b) Pressurized cabin aircraft. (1) No person may operate a civil aircraft of U.S. registry with a pressurized cabin - (i) At flight altitudes above flight level 250 unless at least a 10-minute supply of supplemental oxygen, in addition to any oxygen required to satisfy paragraph (a) of this section, is available for each occupant of the aircraft for use in the event that a descent is necessitated by loss of cabin pressurization; and (ii) At flight altitudes above flight level 350 unless one pilot at the controls of the airplane is wearing and using an oxygen mask that is secured and sealed and that either supplies oxygen at all times or automatically supplies oxygen whenever the cabin pressure altitude of the airplane exceeds 14,000 feet (MSL), except that the one pilot need not wear and use an oxygen mask while at or below flight level 410 if there are two pilots at the controls and each pilot has a quick-donning type of oxygen mask that can be placed on the face with one hand from the ready position within 5 seconds, supplying oxygen and properly secured and sealed. (2) Notwithstanding paragraph (b)(1)(ii) of this section, if for any reason at any time it is necessary for one pilot to leave the controls of the aircraft when operating at flight altitudes above flight level 350, the remaining pilot at the controls shall put on and use an oxygen mask until the other pilot has returned to that crewmember's station.

91.213 Inoperative instruments and equipment.

In the event that certain aircraft instruments or equipment are not working properly, specific procedures must be followed in order to fly the airplane. The majority of single engine airplanes are not manufactured with a minimum equipment list, which specifies the essential instruments and equipment

for flight. Given this fact, the following list describes the procedures for a legal flight:

1. The inoperative equipment cannot be required by -
    a. the type certification of the aircraft. *
    b. 91.205 (required equipment) or any other rule of Part 91.
    c. an airworthiness directive.
    d. a Kinds of Operations Equipment List. *
    * Refer to the aircraft Pilot's Operating Handbook.
2. The equipment must be removed or deactivated.
3. A placard must appear in the cockpit indicating "inoperative."
4. Any maintenance must be recorded in the maintenance records.
5. A certificated pilot or mechanic must determine that a safe flight can be accomplished without the equipment.

(a) Except as provided in paragraph (d) of this section, no person may take off an aircraft with inoperative instruments or equipment installed unless the following conditions are met: (1) An approved Minimum Equipment List exists for that aircraft. (2) The aircraft has within it a letter of authorization, issued by the FAA Flight Standards district office having jurisdiction over the area in which the operator is located, authorizing operation of the aircraft under the Minimum Equipment List. The letter of authorization may be obtained by written request of the airworthiness certificate holder. The Minimum Equipment List and the letter of authorization constitute a supplemental type certificate for the aircraft. (3) The approved minimum equipment list must - (i) Be prepared in accordance with the limitations specified in paragraph (b) of this section; and (ii) Provide for the operation of the aircraft with the instruments and equipment in an inoperable condition. (4) The aircraft records available to the pilot must include an entry describing the inoperable instruments and equipment. (5) The aircraft is operated under all applicable conditions and limitations contained in the Minimum Equipment List and the letter authorizing the use of the list.

(b) The following instruments and equipment may not be included in a Minimum Equipment List: (1) Instruments and equipment that are either specifically or otherwise required by the airworthiness requirements under which the aircraft is type certificated and which are essential for safe operations under all operating conditions. (2) Instruments and equipment required by an airworthiness directive to be in operable condition unless the airworthiness directive provides otherwise. (3) Instruments and equipment required for specific operations by this part.

(c) A person authorized to use an approved Minimum Equipment List issued for a specific aircraft under Part 121, 125, or 135 of this chapter shall use that Minimum Equipment List in connection with operations conducted with that aircraft under this part without additional approval requirements.

(d) Except for operations conducted in accordance with paragraph (a) or (c) of this section, a person may take off an aircraft in operations conducted under this part with inoperative instruments and equipment without an approved Minimum Equipment List provided - (1) The flight operation is conducted in a - (i) Rotorcraft, nonturbine-powered airplane, glider, or lighter-than-air aircraft for which a master Minimum Equipment List has not been developed; or (ii) Small rotorcraft, nonturbine-powered small airplane, glider, or lighter-than-air aircraft for which a master Minimum Equipment List has been developed; and (2) The inoperative instruments and equipment are not - (i) Part of the VFR-day type certification instruments and equipment prescribed in the applicable airworthiness regulations under which the aircraft was type certificated; (ii) Indicated as required on the aircraft's equipment list, or on the Kinds of Operations Equipment List for the kind of flight operation being conducted; (iii) Required by 91.205 or any other rule of this part for the specific kind of flight operation being conducted; or (iv) Required to be operational by an airworthiness

directive; and (3) The inoperative instruments and equipment are - (i) Removed from the aircraft, the cockpit control placarded, and the maintenance recorded in accordance with 43.9 of this chapter; or (ii) Deactivated and placarded "Inoperative." If deactivation of the inoperative instrument or equipment involves maintenance, it must be accomplished and recorded in accordance with Part 43 of this chapter; and (4) A determination is made by a pilot, who is certificated and appropriately rated under Part 61 of this chapter, or by a person, who is certificated and appropriately rated to perform maintenance on the aircraft, that the inoperative instrument or equipment does not constitute a hazard to the aircraft. An aircraft with inoperative instruments or equipment as provided in paragraph (d) of this section is considered to be in a properly altered condition acceptable to the Administrator.
(e) Notwithstanding any other provision of this section, an aircraft with inoperable instruments or equipment may be operated under a special flight permit issued in accordance with 21.197 and 21.199 of this chapter.

91.215 ATC transponder and altitude reporting equipment and use.

If you are flying an airplane with a transponder installed (most aircraft) and it has been inspected and calibrated within the preceding 24 calendar months, you are required to turn it on, unless ATC tells you otherwise. This goes for the Mode C function as well. For Part 91 operations, you must have an operable transponder equipped with Mode C in the following airspace:

1. Terminal Control Area (TCA).
2. Within 30 nautical miles of the primary airport in a TCA, between the surface and 10,000 feet MSL.
3. In and below a Positive Control Area (PCA), unless flying at 2,500 feet AGL or below.
4. In and above an Airport Radar Service Area (ARSA) between the surface and 10,000 feet MSL.
5. At or above 10,000 feet MSL.
6. Within a 10 nautical mile radius of the following airports, between the surface and 10,000 feet MSL, excluding the airspace below 1,200 feet AGL outside of the Airport Traffic Area (ATA):
    (a) Logan International Airport, Billings MT.

There are certain exceptions to the rules listed above:

1. If you happen to be flying an airplane which was not certificated with an electrical system, then you may fly within the 30-mile radius associated with a TCA, provided that you are not in the TCA itself or in a PCA. You are also allowed to operate in the airspace above 10,000 feet MSL.
2. Don't assume that if your transponder becomes inoperative while enroute that you will automatically be in violation. Work with ATC; they will work with you. On the other hand, if you _know_ that you have a problem with it prior to departure, telephone ATC at least one hour before you'll be there, advise them of the situation, and make arrangements.

(a) All airspace: U.S.-registered civil aircraft. For operations not conducted under Part 121, 127, or 135 of this chapter, ATC transponder equipment installed within the time periods indicated below must meet the performance and environmental requirements of the following TSOs.

(1) Through July 1, 1992: (i) Any class of TSO-C74b or any class of TSO-C74c as appropriate, or (ii) The appropriate class of TSO-C112 (Mode S).

(2) After July 1, 1992: The appropriate class of TSO-C112 (Mode S). For purposes of paragraph (a)(2) of this section, "installation" does not include - (i) Temporary installation of TSO-74b or TSO-74c substitute equipment, as appropriate, during maintenance of the permanent equipment; (ii) Reinstallation of equipment after temporary removal for maintenance; or (iii) For fleet operations, installation of equipment in a fleet aircraft after removal of the equipment for maintenance from another aircraft in the same operator's fleet.

(b) All airspace. No person may operate an aircraft in the airspace described in paragraphs (b)(1) through (b)(5) of this section, unless that aircraft is equipped with an operable coded radar beacon transponder having either Mode 3/A 4096 code capability, replying to Mode 3/A interrogations with the code specified by ATC, or a Mode S capability, replying to Mode 3/A interrogations with the code specified by ATC and intermode and Mode S interrogations in accordance with the applicable provisions specified in TSO-C112, and that aircraft is equipped with automatic pressure altitude reporting equipment having Mode C capability that automatically replies to Mode C interrogations by transmitting pressure altitude information in 100-foot increments. This requirement applies -

(1) All aircraft. In terminal control areas and positive control areas;

(2) Effective July 1, 1989 - All aircraft. In all airspace within 30 nautical miles of a terminal control area primary airport from the surface upward to 10,000 feet MSL;

(3) Effective July 1, 1989. Notwithstanding paragraph (b)(2) of this section, any aircraft which was not originally certificated with an engine-driven electrical system or which has not subsequently been certified with such a system installed, balloon, or glider may conduct operations in the airspace within 30 nautical miles of a terminal control area primary airport provided such operations are conducted - (i) Outside any terminal control area and positive control area; and (ii) Below the altitude of the terminal control area ceiling or 10,000 feet MSL whichever is lower; and

(4) Effective December 30, 1990 - All aircraft. (i) In the airspace of an airport radar service area, and (ii) In all airspace above the ceiling and within the lateral boundaries of an airport radar service area upward to 10,000 feet MSL; and

(5) All aircraft except any aircraft which was not originally certificated with an engine-driven electrical system or which has not been certified with such a system installed, balloon, or glider. (i) In all airspace of the 48 contiguous states and the District of Columbia: (A) Through June 30, 1989. Above 12,500 feet MSL and below the floor of a positive control area, excluding the airspace at and below 2,500 feet AGL. (B) Effective July 1, 1989. At and above 10,000 feet MSL and below the floor of a positive control area, excluding the airspace at and below 2,500 AGL; and (ii) Effective December 30, 1990. In the airspace from the surface to 10,000 feet MSL within a 10-nautical-mile radius of any airport listed in Appendix D of this part excluding the airspace below 1,200 feet AGL outside of the airport traffic area for that airport.

(c) Transponder-on operation. While in the airspace as specified in paragraph (b) of this section or in all controlled airspace, each person operating an aircraft equipped with an operable ATC transponder maintained in accordance with 91.413 of this part shall operate the transponder, including Mode C equipment if installed, and shall reply on the appropriate code or as assigned by ATC.

(d) ATC authorized deviations. ATC may authorize deviations from paragraph (b) of this section -

(1) Immediately, to allow an aircraft with an inoperative transponder to continue to the airport of ultimate destination, including any intermediate stops, or to proceed to a place where suitable repairs can be made or both;

(2) Immediately, for operations of aircraft with an operating transponder but without operat-

ing automatic pressure altitude reporting equipment having a Mode C capability; and
(3) On a continuing basis, or for individual flights, for operations of aircraft without a transponder, in which case the request for a deviation must be submitted to the ATC facility having jurisdiction over the airspace concerned at least 1 hour before the proposed operation.

Appendix D - Airports/Locations Where the Transponder Requirements of Section 91.215(b)(5)(ii) Apply.

Section 1. The requirements of 91.215(b)(5)(ii) apply to operations in the vicinity of each of the following airports. Logan International Airport, Billings MT.

91.217 Data correspondence between automatically reported pressure altitude data and the pilot's altitude reference.

> You may not operate Mode C if ATC requests that you turn it off, if it is not properly calibrated, or if it was not legitimately manufactured to meet the required standards.

No person may operate any automatic pressure altitude reporting equipment associated with a radar beacon transponder -
(a) When deactivation of that equipment is directed by ATC;
(b) Unless, as installed, that equipment was tested and calibrated to transmit altitude data corresponding within 125 feet (on a 95 percent probability basis) of the indicated or calibrated datum of the altimeter normally used to maintain flight altitude, with that altimeter referenced to 29.92 inches of mercury for altitudes from sea level to the maximum operating altitude of the aircraft; or
(c) Unless the altimeters and digitizers in that equipment meet the standards of TSO-C10b and TSO-C88, respectively.

Subpart D - Special Flight Operations

Section
91.303 Aerobatic flight.

No person may operate an aircraft in aerobatic flight -
(a) Over any congested area of a city, town, or settlement;
(b) Over an open air assembly of persons;
(c) Within a control zone or federal airway;
(d) Below an altitude of 1,500 feet above the surface; or
(e) When flight visibility is less than 3 statute miles.
For the purposes of this section, aerobatic flight means an intentional maneuver involving an abrupt change in an aircraft's attitude, an abnormal attitude, or abnormal acceleration, not necessary for normal flight.

91.305 Flight test areas.

No person may flight test an aircraft except over open water, or sparsely populated areas, having light air traffic.

91.307 Parachutes and parachuting.

(a) No pilot of a civil aircraft may allow a parachute that is available for emergency use to be carried in that aircraft unless it is an approved type and - (1) If a chair type (canopy in back), it has been packed by a certificated and appropriately rated parachute rigger within the preceding 120 days; or (2) If any other type, it has been packed by a certificated and appropriately rated parachute rigger - (i) Within the preceding 120 days, if its canopy, shrouds, and harness are composed exclusively of nylon, rayon, or other similar synthetic fiber or materials that are substantially resistant to damage from mold, mildew, or other fungi and other rotting agents propagated in a moist environment; or (ii) Within the preceding 60 days, if any part of the parachute is composed of silk, pongee, or other natural fiber, or materials not specified in paragraph (a)(2)(i) of this section.

(b) Except in an emergency, no pilot-in-command may allow, and no person may make, a parachute jump from an aircraft within the United States except in accordance with Part 105.

(c) Unless each occupant of the aircraft is wearing an approved parachute, no pilot of a civil aircraft carrying any person (other than a crewmember) may execute any intentional maneuver that exceeds - (1) A bank of 60 degrees relative to the horizon; or (2) A nose-up or nose-down attitude of 30 degrees relative to the horizon.

(d) Paragraph (c) of this section does not apply to - (1) Flight tests for pilot certification or rating; or (2) Spins and other flight maneuvers required by the regulations for any certificate or rating when given by - (i) A certificated flight instructor; or (ii) An airline transport pilot instructing in accordance with 61.169 of this chapter.

(e) For the purposes of this section, "approved parachute" means - (1) A parachute manufactured under a type certificate or a technical standard order (C-23 series); or (2) A personnel-carrying military parachute identified by an NAF, AAF, or AN drawing number, an AAF order number, or any other military designation or specification number.

92.309 Towing: Gliders.

(a) No person may operate a civil aircraft towing a glider unless - (1) The pilot-in-command of the towing aircraft is qualified under 61.69 of this chapter; (2) The towing aircraft is equipped with a tow-hitch of a kind, and installed in a manner, that is approved by the Administrator; (3) The towline used has a breaking strength not less than 80 percent of the maximum certificated operating weight of the glider and not more than twice this operating weight. However, the towline used may have a breaking strength more than twice the maximum certificated operating weight of the glider if - (i) A safety link is installed at the point of attachment of the towline to the glider with a breaking strength not less than 80 percent of the maximum certificated operating weight of the glider and not greater than twice this operating weight; (ii) A safety link is installed at the point of attachment of the towline to the towing aircraft with a breaking strength greater than, but not more than 25 percent greater, than that of the safety link at the towed glider end of the towline and not greater than twice the maximum certificated operating weight of the glider; (4) Before conducting any towing operation within a control zone, or before making each towing flight within a control zone if required by ATC, the pilot-in-command notifies the control tower if one is in operation in that control zone. If such a control tower is not in operation, the pilot in command must notify the FAA Flight Service Station serving the control zone before conducting any towing operation in that control zone; and (5) The pilots of the towing aircraft and the glider have agreed upon a general course of action, including takeoff and release signals, airspeeds, and emergency procedures for each pilot.

(b) No pilot of a civil aircraft may intentionally release a towline, after release of a glider, in a manner that endangers the life or property of another.

91.311 Towing: Other than under 91.309.

No pilot of a civil aircraft may tow anything with that aircraft (other than under 91.309) except in accordance with the terms of a certificate of waiver issued by the Administrator.

91.313 Restricted category civil aircraft: Operating limitations.

(a) No person may operate a restricted category civil aircraft - (1) For other than the special purpose for which it is certificated; or (2) In an operation other than one necessary to accomplish the work activity directly associated with that special purpose.

(b) For the purpose of paragraph (a) of this section, operating a restricted category civil aircraft to provide flight crewmember training in a special purpose operation for which the aircraft is certificated is considered to be an operation for that special purpose.

(c) No person may operate a restricted category civil aircraft carrying persons or property for compensation or hire. For the purposes of this paragraph, a special purpose operation involving the carriage of persons or material necessary to accomplish that operation, such as crop dusting, seeding, spraying, and banner towing (including the carrying of required persons or material to the location of that operation), and operation for the purpose of providing flight crewmember training in a special purpose operation, are not considered to be the carriage of persons or property for compensation or hire.

(d) No person may be carried on a restricted category civil aircraft unless that person - (1) Is a flight crewmember; (2) Is a flight crewmember trainee; (3) Performs an essential function in connection with a special purpose operation for which the aircraft is certificated; or (4) Is necessary to accomplish the work activity directly associated with that special purpose.

(e) Except when operating in accordance with the terms and conditions of a certificate of waiver or special operating limitations issued by the Administrator, no person may operate a restricted category civil aircraft within the United States - (1) Over a densely populated area; (2) In a congested airway; or (3) Near a busy airport where passenger transport operations are conducted.

(g) No person may operate a small restricted-category civil airplane manufactured after July 18, 1978, unless an approved shoulder harness is installed for each front seat. The shoulder harness must be designed to protect each occupant from serious head injury when the occupant experiences the ultimate inertia forces specified in 23.561(b)(2) of this chapter. The shoulder harness installation at each flight crewmember station must permit the crewmember, when seated and with the safety belt and shoulder harness fastened, to perform all functions necessary for flight operations. For purposes of this paragraph - (i) The date of manufacture of an airplane is the date the inspection acceptance records reflect that the airplane is complete and meets the FAA-approved type design data; and (ii) A front seat is a seat at a flight crewmember station or any seat located alongside such a seat.

91.317 Provisionally certificated civil aircraft: Operating limitations.

(a) No person may operate a provisionally certificated civil aircraft unless that person is eligible for a provisional airworthiness certificate under 21.213 of this chapter.

(b) No person may operate a provisionally certificated civil aircraft outside the United States unless that person has specific authority to do so from the Administrator and each foreign country involved.

(c) Unless otherwise authorized by the Director, Flight Standards Service, no person may operate a provisionally certificated civil aircraft in air transportation.

(d) Unless otherwise authorized by the Administrator, no person may operate a provisionally certificated civil aircraft except - (1) In direct conjunction with the type or supplemental type certification of that aircraft; (2) For training flight crews, including simulated air carrier operations; (3) Demonstration flight by the manufacturer for prospective purchasers; (4) Market surveys by the manufacturer; (5) Flight checking of instruments, accessories, and equipment that do not affect the basic airworthiness of the aircraft; or (6) Service testing of the aircraft.

(e) Each person operating a provisionally certificated civil aircraft shall operate within the prescribed limitations displayed in the aircraft or set forth in the provisional aircraft flight manual or other appropriate document. However, when operating in direct conjunction with the type or supplemental type certification of the aircraft, that person shall operate under the experimental aircraft limitations of 21.191 of this chapter and when flight testing, shall operate under the requirements of 91.305 of this part.

(f) Each person operating a provisionally certificated civil aircraft shall establish approved procedures for - (1) The use and guidance of flight and ground personnel in operating under this section; and (2) Operating in and out of airports where takeoffs or approaches over populated areas are necessary. No person may operate that aircraft except in compliance with the approved procedures.

(g) Each person operating a provisionally certificated civil aircraft shall ensure that each flight crewmember is properly certificated and has adequate knowledge of, and familiarity with, the aircraft and procedures to be used by that crewmember.

(h) Each person operating a provisionally certificated civil aircraft shall maintain it as required by applicable regulations and as may be specially prescribed by the Administrator.

(i) Whenever the manufacturer, or the Administrator, determines that a change in design, construction, or operation is necessary to ensure safe operation, no person may operate a provisionally certificated civil aircraft until that change has been made and approved. Section 21.99 of this chapter applies to operations under this section.

(j) Each person operating a provisionally certificated civil aircraft - (1) May carry in that aircraft only persons who have a proper interest in the operations allowed by this section or who are specifically authorized by both the manufacturer and the Administrator; and (2) Shall advise each person carried that the aircraft is provisionally certificated.

(k) The Administrator may prescribe additional limitations or procedures that the Administrator considers necessary, including limitations on the number of persons who may be carried in the aircraft.

91.319 Aircraft having experimental certificates: Operating limitations.

(a) No person may operate an aircraft that has an experimental certificate - (1) For other than the purpose for which the certificate was issued; or (2) Carrying persons or property for compensation or hire.

(b) No person may operate an aircraft that has an experimental certificate outside of an area assigned by the Administrator until it is shown that - (1) The aircraft is controllable throughout its normal range of speeds and throughout all the maneuvers to be executed; and (2) The aircraft has no hazardous operating characteristics or design features.

(c) Unless otherwise authorized by the Administrator in special operating limitations, no person may operate an aircraft that has an experimental certificate over a densely populated area or in a congested airway. The Administrator may issue special operating limitations for particular aircraft to permit takeoffs and landings to be conducted over a densely populated area or in a congested airway, in accordance with terms and conditions specified in the authorization in the interest of safety in air commerce.

(d) Each person operating an aircraft that has an experimental certificate shall- (1) Advise each person carried of the experimental nature of the aircraft; (2) Operate under VFR, day only, unless otherwise specifically authorized by the Administrator; and (3) Notify the control tower of the experimental nature of the aircraft when operating the aircraft into or out of airports with operating control towers.

(e) The Administrator may prescribe additional limitations that the Administrator considers necessary, including limitations on the persons that may be carried in the aircraft.

Subpart E - Maintenance, Preventive Maintenance, and Alterations

Section
91.401 Applicability.

(a) This subpart prescribes rules governing the maintenance, preventive maintenance, and alterations of U.S.-registered civil aircraft operating within or outside of the United States.

(b) Sections 91.405, 91.409, 91.411, 91.417, and 91.419 of this subpart do not apply to an aircraft maintained in accordance with a continuous airworthiness maintenance program as provided in Part 121, 127, 129, or 135.411(a)(2) of this chapter.

(c) Sections 91.405 and 91.409 of this part do not apply to an airplane inspected in accordance with Part 125 of this chapter.

91.403 General.

> While it is the responsibility of the PIC to determine that the aircraft is safe for flight, the owner or operator is responsible for ensuring that the required maintenance is performed.

(a) The owner or operator of an aircraft is primarily responsible for maintaining that aircraft in an airworthy condition, including compliance with Part 39 of this chapter.

(b) No person may perform maintenance, preventive maintenance, or alterations on an aircraft other than as prescribed in this subpart and other applicable regulations, including Part 43 of this chapter.

(c) No person may operate an aircraft for which a manufacturer's maintenance manual or instructions for continued airworthiness has been issued that contains an airworthiness limitations section unless the mandatory replacement times, inspection intervals, and related procedures specified in that section or alternative inspection intervals and related procedures set forth in an operations specification approved by the Administrator under Part 121, 127, or 135 of this chapter or in accordance with an inspection program approved under 91.409(e) have been complied with.

91.405 Maintenance required.

Each owner or operator of an aircraft -

(a) Shall have that aircraft inspected as prescribed in subpart E of this part and shall between required inspections, except as provided in paragraph (c) of this section, have discrepancies repaired as prescribed in part 43 of this chapter;

(b) Shall ensure that maintenance personnel make appropriate entries in the aircraft maintenance records indicating the aircraft has been approved for return to service;

(c) Shall have any inoperative instrument or item of equipment, permitted to be inoperative by 91.213(d)(2) of this part, repaired, replaced, removed, or inspected at the next required inspection; and

(d) When listed discrepancies include inoperative instruments or equipment, shall ensure that a placard has been installed as required by 43.11 of this chapter.

91.407 Operation after maintenance, preventive maintenance, rebuilding, or alteration.

(a) No person may operate any aircraft that has undergone maintenance, preventive maintenance, rebuilding, or alteration unless - (1) It has been approved for return to service by a person authorized under 43.7 of this chapter; and (2) The maintenance record entry required by 43.9 or 43.11, as applicable, of this chapter has been made.

(b) No person may carry any person (other than crewmembers) in an aircraft that has been maintained, rebuilt, or altered in a manner that may have appreciably changed its flight characteristics or substantially affected its operation in flight until an appropriately rated pilot with at least a private pilot certificate flies the aircraft, makes an operational check of the maintenance performed or alteration made, and logs the flight in the aircraft records.

(c) The aircraft does not have to be flown as required by paragraph (b) of this section if, prior to flight, ground tests, inspection, or both show conclusively that the maintenance, preventive maintenance, rebuilding or alteration has not appreciably changed the flight characteristics or substantially affected the flight operation of the aircraft.

91.409 Inspections.

> For private pilot operations, an airplane must have an annual inspection (which is documented in the maintenance records) by a certified airplane mechanic every 12 calendar months. For example, if an annual inspection was performed on January 1, 1992, the next inspection would be due not later than January 31, 1993 to legally fly the airplane beyond that date.

(a) Except as provided in paragraph (c) of this section, no person may operate an aircraft unless, within the preceding 12 calendar months, it has had - (1) An annual inspection in accordance with Part 43 of this chapter and has been approved for return to service by a person authorized by 43.7 of this chapter; or (2) An inspection for the issuance of an airworthiness certificate in accordance with Part 21 of this chapter.

No inspection performed under paragraph (b) of this section may be substituted for any inspection required by this paragraph unless it is performed by a person authorized to perform annual inspections and is entered as an "annual" inspection in the required maintenance records.

(b) Except as provided in paragraph (c) of this section, no person may operate an aircraft carrying any person (other than a crewmember) for hire, and no person may give flight instruction for hire in an aircraft which that person provides, unless within the preceding 100 hours of time in service the aircraft has received an annual or 100-hour inspection and been approved for return to service in accordance with Part 43 of this chapter or has received an inspection for the issuance of an airworthiness certificate in accordance with Part 21 of this chapter. The 100-hour limitation may be exceeded by not more than 10 hours while en route to reach a place where the inspection can be done. The excess time used to reach a place where the inspection can be done must be included in computing the next 100 hours of time in service.

(c) Paragraphs (a) and (b) of this section do not apply to - (1) An aircraft that carries a special flight permit, a current experimental certificate, or a provisional airworthiness certificate; (2) An aircraft inspected in accordance with an approved aircraft inspection program under Part 125, 127, or 135 of this chapter and so identified by the registration number in the operations specifications of the certificate holder having the approved inspection program; (3) An aircraft subject to the requirements of paragraph (d) or (e) of this section.

(d) Progressive inspection. Each registered owner or operator of an aircraft desiring to use a progressive inspection program must submit a written request to the FAA Flight Standards district office having jurisdiction over the area in which the applicant is located, and shall provide - (1) A certificated mechanic holding an inspection authorization, a certificated airframe repair station, or the manufacturer of the aircraft to supervise or conduct the progressive inspection; (2) A current inspection procedures manual available and readily understandable to pilot and maintenance personnel containing, in detail - (i) An explanation of the progressive inspection, including the continuity of inspection responsibility, the making of reports, and the keeping of records and technical reference material; (ii) An inspection schedule, specifying the intervals in hours or days when routine and detailed inspections will be performed and including instructions for exceeding an inspection interval by not more than 10 hours while en route and for changing an inspection interval because of service experience; (iii) Sample routine and detailed inspection forms and instructions for their use; and (iv) Sample reports and records and instructions for their use; (3) Enough housing and equipment for necessary disassembly and proper inspection of the aircraft; and (4) Appropriate current technical information for the aircraft.

The frequency and detail of the progressive inspection shall provide for the complete inspection of the aircraft within each 12 calendar months and be consistent with the manufacturer's recommendations, field service experience, and the kind of operation in which the airplane is engaged. The progressive inspection schedule must ensure that the aircraft, at all times, will be airworthy and will conform to all applicable FAA aircraft specifications, type certificate data sheets, airworthiness directives, and other approved data. If the progressive inspection is discontinued, the owner or operator shall immediately notify the local FAA Flight Standards district office, in writing, of the discontinuance. After the discontinuance, the first annual inspection under 91.409(a)(1) is due within 12 calendar months after the last complete inspection of the aircraft under the progressive inspection. The 100-hour inspection under 91.409(b) is due within 100 hours after that complete inspection. A complete inspection of the aircraft, for the purpose of determining when the annual or 100-hour inspections are due, requires a detailed inspection of the aircraft and all its components in accordance with the progressive inspection. A routine inspection of the aircraft and a detailed inspection of several components is not considered to be a complete inspection.

91.413 ATC transponder tests and inspections.

> A transponder must be tested by a certificated radio repair station every 24 calendar months.

(a) No person may use an ATC transponder that is specified in 91.215(a), 121.345(c), 127.123(b), or 135.143(c) of this chapter unless within the preceding 24 calendar months, the ATC transponder has been tested and inspected and found to comply with Appendix F of Part 43 of this chapter; and
(b) Following any installation or maintenance on an ATC transponder where data correspondence error could be introduced, the integrated system has been tested, inspected, and found to comply with paragraph (c), Appendix E, of Part 43 of this chapter.
(c) The tests and inspections specified in this section must be conducted by - (1) A certificated repair station properly equipped to perform those functions and holding - (i) A radio rating, Class III; (ii) A limited radio rating appropriate to make and model transponder to be tested; (iii) A limited rating appropriate to the test to be performed; (iv) A limited rating for a manufacturer issued for the transponder in accordance with 145.101(b)(4) of this chapter; or (2) A holder of a continuous airworthiness maintenance program as provided in Part 121, 127, or 135.411(a)(2) of this chapter; or (3) The manufacturer of the aircraft on which the transponder to be tested is installed, if the transponder was installed by that manufacturer.

91.417 Maintenance records.

> If you are the owner of an airplane, you are required to keep proper maintenance records and make them available for inspection to the FAA or NTSB upon request. These records must contain specific information as listed below; communication and coordination with your mechanic are essential.

(a) Except for work performed in accordance with 91.411 and 91.413, each registered owner or operator shall keep the following records for the periods specified in paragraph (b) of this section: (1) Records of the maintenance, preventive maintenance, and alteration and records of the 100-hour, annual, progressive, and other required or approved inspections, as appropriate, for each aircraft (including the airframe) and each engine, propeller, rotor, and appliance of an aircraft. The records must include - (i) A description (or reference to data acceptable to the Administrator) of the work performed; and (ii) The date of completion of the work performed; and (iii) The signature, and certificate number of the person approving the aircraft for return to service. (2) Records containing the following information: (i) The total time in service of the airframe, each engine, each propeller, and each rotor. (ii) The current status of life-limited parts of each airframe, engine, propeller, rotor, and appliance. (iii) The time since last overhaul of all items installed on the aircraft which are required to be overhauled on a specified time basis. (iv) The current inspection status of the aircraft, including the time since the last inspection required by the inspection program under which the aircraft and its appliances are maintained. (v) The current status of applicable airworthiness directives (AD) including, for each, the method of compliance, the AD number, and revision date. If the AD involves recurring action, the time and date when the next action is required. (vi) Copies of the forms prescribed by 43.9(a) of this chapter for each major alteration to the airframe and currently installed engines, rotors, propellers, and appliances.
(b) The owner or operator shall retain the following records for the periods prescribed: (1) The records specified in paragraph (a)(1) of this section shall be retained until the work is

repeated or superceded by other work or for 1 year after the work is performed. (2) The records specified in paragraph (a)(2) of this section shall be retained and transferred with the aircraft at the time the aircraft is sold. (3) A list of defects furnished to a registered owner or operator under 43.11 of this chapter shall be retained until the defects are repaired and the aircraft is approved for return to service.

(c) The owner or operator shall make all maintenance records required to be kept by this section available for inspection by the Administrator or any authorized representative of the National Transportation Safety Board (NTSB). In addition, the owner or operator shall present Form 337 described in paragraph (d) of this section for inspection upon request of any law enforcement officer.

(d) When a fuel tank is installed within the passenger compartment or a baggage compartment pursuant to Part 43 of this chapter, a copy of FAA Form 337 shall be kept on board the modified aircraft by the owner or operator.

91.419 Transfer of maintenance records.

Any owner or operator who sells a U.S.-registered aircraft shall transfer to the purchaser, at the time of sale, the following records of that aircraft, in plain language form or in coded form at the election of the purchaser, if the coded form provides for the preservation and retrieval of information in a manner acceptable to the Administrator:

(a) The records specified in 91.417(a)(2).

(b) The records specified in 91.417(a)(1) which are not included in the records covered by paragraph (a) of this section, except that the purchaser may permit the seller to keep physical custody of such records. However, custody of records by the seller does not relieve the purchaser of the responsibility under 91.417(c) to make the records available for inspection by the Administrator or any authorized representative of the National Transportation Safety Board (NTSB).

91.421 Rebuilt engine maintenance records.

(a) The owner or operator may use a new maintenance record, without previous operating history, for an aircraft engine rebuilt by the manufacturer or by an agency approved by the manufacturer.

(b) Each manufacturer or agency that grants zero time to an engine rebuilt by it shall enter in the new record - (1) A signed statement of the date the engine was rebuilt; (2) Each change made as required by airworthiness directives; and (3) Each change made in compliance with manufacturer's service bulletins, if the entry is specifically requested in that bulletin.

(c) For the purposes of this section, a rebuilt engine is a used engine that has been completely disassembled, inspected, repaired as necessary, reassembled, tested, and approved in the same manner and to the same tolerances and limits as a new engine with either new or used parts. However, all parts used in it must conform to the production drawing tolerance and limits for new parts or be of approved oversized or undersized dimensions for a new engine.

Subpart H - Foreign Aircraft Operations and Operations of U.S.-Registered Civil Aircraft Outside of the United States

Section
91.701 Applicability.

This subpart applies to the operations of civil aircraft of U.S. registry outside of the United States and the operations of foreign civil aircraft within the United States.

91.703 Operations of civil aircraft of U.S. registry outside of the United States.

If you are planning on flying your airplane over open ocean, you must abide by a special set of rules which can be purchased by mail from the address listed at the end of this regulation. When operating your aircraft in a foreign country, you are expected to abide by the air traffic and operating regulations of that country.

(a) Each person operating a civil aircraft of U.S. registry outside of the United States shall -
(1) When over the high seas, comply with annex 2 (Rules of the Air) to the convention on International Civil Aviation and with 91.117(c), 91.130, and 91.131; (2) When within a foreign country, comply with the regulations relating to the flight and maneuver of aircraft there in force; (3) Except for 91.307(b), 91.309, 91.323, and 91.711, comply with this part so far as it is not inconsistent with applicable regulations of the foreign country where the aircraft is operated or annex 2 of the Convention on International Civil Aviation; and (4) When over the North Atlantic within airspace designated as Minimum Navigation Performance Specifications airspace, comply with 91.705.
(b) Annex 2 to the Convention on International Civil Aviation, Eighth Edition - July 1986, with amendments through amendment 28 effective November 1987, to which reference is made in this part, is incorporated into this part and made a part hereof as provided in 5 U.S.C. 552 and pursuant to 1 CFR part 51, annex 2 (including a complete historic file of changes thereto) is available for public inspection at the Rules Docket, AGC-10 Federal Aviation Administration, 800 Independence Avenue SW., Washington, DC 20591. In addition, Annex 2 may be purchased from the International Civil Aviation Organization (Attention: Distribution Officer), P.O. Box 400, Succursale, Place De L'Aviation Internationale, 1000 Sherbrooke Street West, Montreal, Quebec, Canada H3A 2R2.

91.707 Flights between Mexico or Canada and the United States.

Unless otherwise authorized by ATC, no person may operate a civil aircraft between Mexico or Canada and the United States without filing an IFR or VFR flight plan, as appropriate.

Subpart J - Waivers

Section
91.903 Policy and procedures.

(a) The Administrator may issue a certificate of waiver authorizing the operation of aircraft in deviation from any rule listed in this subpart if the Administrator finds that the proposed operation can be safely conducted under the terms of that certificate of waiver.
(b) An application for a certificate of waiver under this part is made on a form and in a manner prescribed by the Administrator and may be submitted to any FAA office.
(c) A certificate of waiver is effective as specified in that certificate of waiver.

91.905 List of rules subject to waivers.

91.107 Use of safety belts.
91.111 Operating near other aircraft.
91.113 Right-of-way rules: Except water operations.
91.117 Aircraft speed.
91.119 Minimum safe altitudes: General.
91.121 Altimeter settings.
91.123 Compliance with ATC clearances and instructions.
91.125 ATC light signals.
91.127 Operating on or in the vicinity of an airport: General rules.
91.129 Operating at airports with operating control towers.
91.131 Terminal control areas.
91.133 Restricted and prohibited areas.
91.135 Positive control areas and route segments.
91.137 Temporary flight restrictions.
91.141 Flight restrictions in the proximity of the Presidential and other parties.
91.143 Flight limitation in the proximity of space flight operations.
91.153 VFR flight plan: Information required.
91.155 Basic VFR weather minimums.
91.157 Special VFR weather minimums.
91.159 VFR cruising altitude or flight level.
91.209 Aircraft lights.
91.303 Aerobatic flight.
91.305 Flight test areas.
91.311 Towing: Other than under 91.309.
91.313(e) Restricted category civil aircraft: Operating limitations.
91.707 Flights between Mexico or Canada and the United States.

TEST QUESTIONS

1. In addition to a valid Airworthiness Certificate, what documents or records must be aboard an aircraft during flight?

A - Aircraft engine and airframe logbooks and owner's manual.
B - Radio operator's permit and repair and alteration forms.
C - Operating limitations and Registration Certificate.

2. When are nonrechargeable batteries of an emergency locator transmitter (ELT) required to be replaced?

A - Every 24 months.
B - When 50 percent of their useful life expires.
C - At the time of each 100-hour or annual inspection.

3. Except in Alaska, during what time period should lighted position lights be displayed on an aircraft?

A - End of evening civil twilight to the beginning of morning civil twilight.
B - 1 hour after sunset to 1 hour before sunrise.
C - Sunset to sunrise.

4. Unless each occupant is provided with supplemental oxygen, no person may operate a civil aircraft of U.S. registry above a maximum cabin pressure altitude of

A - 12,500 feet MSL.
B - 14,000 feet MSL.
C - 15,000 feet MSL.

5. With certain exceptions, all aircraft within 30 miles of a TCA primary airport from the surface upward to 10,000 feet MSL must be equipped with

A - an operable VOR or TACAN receiver and a transponder.
B - instruments and equipment required for IFR operations.
C - an operable transponder having Mode 3/A 4096 code capability and Mode C altitude encoding capability.

6. No person may operate an aircraft in acrobatic flight when

A - flight visibility is less than 5 miles.
B - over any congested area of a city, town, or settlement.
C - less than 2,500 feet AGL.

7. With certain exceptions, when must each occupant of an aircraft wear an approved parachute?

A - When a door is removed from the aircraft to facilitate parachute jumpers.
B - When intentionally pitching the nose of the aircraft up or down at least 30°.
C - When intentionally banking in excess of 30°.

8. The minimum allowable strength of a towline used for an aerotow of a glider having a certificated gross weight of 700 pounds is

A - 560 pounds.
B - 700 pounds.
C - 1,000 pounds.

9. Unless otherwise specifically authorized, no person may operate an aircraft that has an experimental certificate

A - within a control zone.
B - along a congested airway.
C - within an Airport Traffic Area.

10. The responsibility for ensuring that maintenance personnel make the appropriate entries in the aircraft maintenance records indicating the aircraft has been approved for return to service lies with the

A - owner or operator.
B - pilot-in-command.
C - mechanic who performed the work.

11. If an alteration or repair substantially affects an aircraft's operation in flight, that aircraft must be test flown by an appropriately rated pilot and approved for return to service prior to being operated

A - by any student or private pilot.
B - with passengers aboard.
C - for compensation or hire.

12. A 100-hour inspection was due at 3302.5 hours on the tachometer. The 100-hour inspection was actually done at 3309.5 hours. When is the next 100-hour inspection due?

A - 3312.5 hours.
B - 3402.5 hours.
C - 3409.5 hours.

13. No person may use an ATC transponder unless it has been tested and inspected within at least the preceding

A - 6 calendar months.
B - 12 calendar months.
C - 24 calendar months.

14. Preventive maintenance has been performed on an aircraft. What paperwork is required?

A - A full, detailed description of the work done must be entered in the airframe logbooks.
B - The date the work was completed, and the name of the person who did the work must be entered in the airframe and engine logbook.
C - The signature, certificate number, and kind of certificate held by the person approving the work and a description of the work must be entered in the aircraft maintenance records.

ANSWERS

1. C (91.203)	2. B (91.207)	3. C (91.209)	4. C (91.211)
5. C (91.215)	6. B (91.303)	7. B (91.307)	8. A (91.309)
9. B (91.319)	10. A (91.417)	11. B (91.407)	12. B (91.409)
13. C (91.413)	14. C (91.417)		

6

NTSB Part 830 - Notification and Reporting of Aircraft Accidents or Incidents and Overdue Aircraft, and Preservation of Aircraft Wreckage, Mail, Cargo, or Records. Subparts A through E

Subpart A - General

Section
830.1 Applicability.

This part contains rules pertaining to:
(a) Notification and reporting of aircraft accidents and incidents and certain other occurrences in the operation of aircraft when they involve civil aircraft of the United States wherever they occur, or foreign civil aircraft when such events occur in the United States, its territories or possessions.
(b) Reporting aircraft accidents and listed incidents in the operation of aircraft when they involve certain public aircraft.
(c) Preservation of aircraft wreckage, mail, cargo, and records involving all civil aircraft in the United States, its territories or possessions.

830.2 Definitions.

As the reporting requirements are different for an "accident" and an "incident," it is important to note the differences in the following definitions of these words. "Substantial damage" is also an important parameter to be familiar with.

As used in this part the following words or phrases are defined as follows:
"Aircraft accident" means an occurrence associated with the operation of an aircraft which takes place between the time any person boards the aircraft with the intention of flight and all such persons have disembarked, and in which any person suffers death or serious injury, or in which the aircraft receives substantial damage.
"Civil aircraft" means any aircraft other than public aircraft.
"Fatal injury" means any injury which results in death within 30 days of the accident.
"Incident" means an occurrence other than an accident, associated with the operation of an aircraft, which affects or could affect the safety of operations.
"Operator" means any person who causes or authorizes the operation of an aircraft, such as the owner, lessee, or bailee of an aircraft.
"Public aircraft" means an aircraft used exclusively in the service of any government or of any political subdivision thereof, including the government

of any state, territory, or possession of the United States, or the District of Columbia, but not including any government-owned aircraft engaged in carrying persons or property for commercial purposes. For purposes of this section, "used exclusively in the service of" means, for other than the federal government, an aircraft which is owned and operated by a governmental entity for other than commercial purposes or which is exclusively leased by such governmental entity for not less than 90 continuous days.

"Serious injury" means any injury which: (1) Requires hospitalization for more than 48 hours, commencing within 7 days from the date on which the injury was received; (2) results in a fracture of any bone (except simple fractures of fingers, toes, or nose); (3) causes severe hemorrhages, nerve, muscle, or tendon damage; (4) involves any internal organ; or (5) involves second- or third-degree burns, or any burns affecting more than 5 percent of the body surface.

"Substantial damage" means damage or failure which adversely affects the structural strength, performance, or flight characteristics of the aircraft, and which would normally require major repair or replacement of the affected component. Engine failure or damage limited to an engine if only one engine fails or is damaged, bent fairings or cowling, dented skin, small punctured holes in the skin or fabric, ground damage to rotor or propeller blades, and damage to landing gear, wheels, tires, flaps, engine accessories, brakes, or wingtips are not considered "substantial damage" for the purpose of this part.

Subpart B - Initial Notification of Aircraft Accidents, Incidents, and Overdue Aircraft

Section
830.5 Immediate notification.

The operator of an aircraft shall immediately, and by the most expeditious means available, notify the nearest National Transportation Safety Board (NTSB) field office[1] when:
(a) An aircraft accident or any of the following listed incidents occur: (1) Flight control system malfunction or failure; (2) Inability of any required flight crewmember to perform normal flight duties as a result of injury or illness; (3) Failure of structural components of a turbine engine excluding compressor and turbine blades and vanes; (4) In-flight fire; or (5) Aircraft collide in flight. (6) Damage to property, other than the aircraft, estimated to exceed $25,000 for repair (including materials and labor) or fair market value in the event of total loss, whichever is less.
(b) an aircraft is overdue and is believed to have been involved in an accident.

[1] The National Transportation Safety Board field offices are listed under U.S. Government in the telephone directories in the following cities: Anchorage, AK; Atlanta, GA; Chicago, IL; Denver, CO; Fort Worth, TX; Kansas City, MO; Los Angeles, CA; Miami, FL; New York, NY; Seattle, WA.

830.6 Information to be given in notification.

The notification required in 830.5 shall contain the following information, if available:
(a) Type, nationality, and registration marks of the aircraft;
(b) Name of owner and operator of the aircraft;
(c) Name of the pilot-in-command;
(d) Date and time of the accident;
(e) Last point of departure and point of intended landing of the aircraft;
(f) Position of the aircraft with reference to some easily defined geographical point;
(g) Number of persons aboard, number killed, and number seriously injured;
(h) Nature of the accident, the weather and the extent of damage to the aircraft, so far as is known; and
(i) A description of any explosives, radioactive materials, or other dangerous articles carried.

Subpart C - Preservation of Aircraft Wreckage, Mail, Cargo, and Records

Section
830.10 Preservation of aircraft wreckage, mail, cargo, and records.

(a) The operator of an aircraft involved in an accident or incident for which notification must be given is responsible for preserving to the extent possible any aircraft wreckage, cargo, and mail aboard the aircraft, and all records, including all recording mediums of flight, maintenance, and voice recorders, pertaining to the operation and maintenance of the aircraft and to the airmen until the NTSB takes custody thereof or a release is granted pursuant to 831.12(b) of this chapter.
(b) Prior to the time the NTSB or its authorized representative takes custody of the aircraft wreckage, mail, or cargo, such wreckage, mail, or cargo may not be disturbed or moved except to the extent necessary: (1) To remove persons injured or trapped; (2) To protect the wreckage from further damage; (3) To protect the public from injury.
(c) Where it is necessary to move aircraft wreckage, mail, or cargo, sketches, descriptive notes, and photographs shall be made, if possible, of the original positions and condition of the wreckage and any significant impact marks.
(d) The operator of an aircraft involved in an accident or incident shall retain all records, reports, internal documents, and memoranda dealing with the accident or incident, until authorized by the NTSB to the contrary.

95

Subpart D - Reporting of Aircraft Accidents, Incidents, and Overdue Aircraft

Section
830.15 Reports and statements to be filed.

(a) Reports. The operator of an aircraft shall file a report on NTSB Form 6120.1 (OMB No. 3147-005) or NTSB Form 7120.2 (OMB No. 3147-0001)[2] within 10 days after an accident, or after 7 days if an overdue aircraft is still missing. A report on an incident for which notification is required by 830.5(a) shall be filed only as requested by an authorized representative of the Board.

(b) Crewmember statement. Each crewmember, if physically able at the time the report is submitted, shall attach a statement setting forth the facts, conditions, and circumstances relating to the accident or incident as they appear to him. If the crewmember is incapacitated, he shall submit the statement as soon as he is physically able.

(c) Where to file the reports. The operator of an aircraft shall file any report with the field office of the NTSB nearest the accident or incident.

Subpart E - Reporting of Public Aircraft Accidents and Incidents

Section
830.20 Reports to be filed.

The operator of a public aircraft other than an aircraft of the armed forces or intelligence agencies shall file a report on NTSB Form 6120.1 (OMB No. 3147-0001) within 10 days after an accident or incident listed in 830.5(a). The operator shall file the report with the field office of the NTSB nearest the accident or incident.

---

[2] Forms are obtainable from the NTSB field offices (see footnote 1, page 94), The National Transportation Safety Board, Washington, DC 20594, and the Federal Aviation Administration, Flight Standards District Office.

TEST QUESTIONS

1. If an aircraft is involved in an accident which results in substantial damage to the aircraft, the nearest NTSB field office should be notified

A - immediately.
B - within 48 hours.
C - within 7 days.

2. Which incident requires an immediate notification to the nearest NTSB field office?

A - A forced landing due to engine failure.
B - Landing gear damage, due to hard landing.
C - Flight control system malfunction or failure.

3. Which incident requires an immediate notification to be made to the nearest NTSB field office?

A - An overdue aircraft that is believed to be involved in an accident.
B - An in-flight radio communications failure.
C - An in-flight generator or alternator failure.

4. May aircraft wreckage be moved prior to the time the NTSB takes custody?

A - Yes, but only if moved by a federal, state, or local law enforcement officer.
B - Yes but only to protect the wreckage from further damage.
C - No, it may not be moved under any circumstances.

5. The operator of an aircraft that has been involved in an accident is required to file an accident report within how many days?

A - 5.
B - 7.
C - 10.

ANSWERS
1. A (830.5) 2. C (830.5) 3. A (830.5) 4. B (830.10) 5. C (830.15)

7

PART II - AIRMAN'S INFORMATION MANUAL

NAVIGATION AIDS

SECTION 1. AIR NAVIGATION RADIO AIDS

1-1 General

In the broad sense of the term, radio navigation includes any method by which a pilot follows a predetermined flight path over the earth's surface by utilizing the properties of radio waves. The navigation can be conducted by any one or any combination of the following three basic systems:

    1. Self-contained airborne systems entirely independent of ground facilities. The Doppler radar navigation system currently used for long over-water and transpolar flights is an example.

    2. Ground facilities that continuously monitor and determine the exact aircraft position, on the basis of which the pilot is given navigational guidance by radio communications. Ground-controlled radar navigation is becoming increasingly important to instrument flight operations. Long range radar operated by Air Route Traffic Control Centers (ARTCC) can provide continuous navigational guidance to aircraft operating along most of the routes between major metropolitan terminals.

    3. A combination of ground and airborne equipment, by means of which the ground facilities transmit signals to airborne instruments. The pilot determines and controls ground track on the basis of instrument indications. Various types of air navigation aids are in use today, each serving a special purpose. These aids have varied owners and operators, namely: the Federal Aviation Administration (FAA), the military services, private organizations, individual states, and foreign governments. The FAA has the statutory authority to establish, operate, and maintain air navigation facilities and to prescribe standards for the operation of any of these aids which are used for instrument flight in federally controlled airspace. These aids are tabulated in the Airport/Facility Directory.

1-2 VHF Omni-Directional Range (VOR)

  a. The VOR, or omnirange, is the primary navigation facility for civil aviation in the National Airspace System. As a VHF facility, it eliminates atmospheric static interference and other limitations associated with the older low-frequency facilities that the VOR has replaced. The VOR generates directional information and transmits it by ground equipment to the aircraft, providing 360-degree magnetic courses TO or FROM the VOR station. These courses are called radials and are oriented FROM the station. They can be visualized as spokes on a wheel with the station representing the wheel hub.

b. VOR operation is based upon the principle that the phase difference between two AC voltages may be used to determine azimuth location. The principle may be more readily visualized by imagining two light signals, both at the same geographic position. The first light is a flashing (reference) signal, visible from any point around the compass. The second light is a narrow beam (variable signal) that rotates continuously at a specific rate. Thus, if you are at any point around the circle, you will see the rotating beam only at the instant that it sweeps past your position. Assume the reference light flashes only when the rotating (variable) beam passes through magnetic north (360 degrees), indicating that the two signals are "in phase." So any time the VOR receiver located in the aircraft detects both signals simultaneously, it indicates the position as the 360 degree radial. If the rotating beam completes one revolution per minute, the VOR receiver can determine your bearing from any point around the compass rose by noting the time interval between reception of flashing and rotating signals. For example, if the rotating beam is received 20 seconds after the flashing signal, it has made 20/60 of a revolution. Thus, you are located one-third of the way around the compass rose, which equates to the 120-degree radial. In terms of the azimuth, the reference and variable signals are 120 degrees "out of phase."

c. The components of a VOR receiver can be described as follows:

　　　1. Frequency selector - The frequency selector may be a knob or knobs or "crank," manually rotated to select any of the appropriate frequencies.

　　　2. Course selector - By turning the course selector, known as the OBS (omni bearing selector), a desired course may be selected. This may appear in a window or under an index.

　　　3. Course deviation needle (CDI) - The deviation indicator is composed of a dial and a needle hinged to move laterally across the dial. The needle centers when the aircraft is on the selected radial or its reciprocal. Full needle deflection from the center position to either side of the dial indicates that the aircraft is 10 degrees or more off course, assuming normal needle sensitivity.

　　　4. TO/FROM indicator - The TO/FROM indicator is also known as the sense indicator or ambiguity indicator. The TO/FROM indicator shows whether

the selected course will take the aircraft to or from the station. It does not indicate whether the aircraft is heading to or from the station.

5. Flags - Flags are normally used to indicate signal strength. The device used to indicate an unreliable signal is the OFF flag, which appears during periods of weak signal strength. The OFF flag retracts from view when there is sufficient signal strength. In some instances, insufficient signal strength may be indicated by a blank TO/FROM window.

d. VORs operate within the 108.0 to 117.95 MHz frequency band and have a power output necessary to provide coverage within their assigned operational service volume. They are subject to line-of-sight restrictions, and the range varies proportionally to the altitude of the receiving equipment. The normal service ranges for the various classes of VORs are provided below:

STANDARD SERVICE VOLUME CLASS DESIGNATOR	ALTITUDE AND RANGE BOUNDARIES
T (Terminal)	From 1,000 feet above ground level (AGL) up to and including 12,000 feet (AGL) at radial distances out to 25 NM.
L (Low Altitude)	From 1,000 feet above ground level (AGL) up to and including 18,000 feet (AGL) at radial distances out to 40 NM.
H (High Altitude)	From 1,000 feet above ground level up to and including 14,500 feet (AGL) at radial distances out to 40 NM. From 14,500 feet (AGL) up to and including 60,000 feet (AGL) at radial distances out to 100 NM. From 18,000 feet (AGL) up to and including 45,000 feet (AGL) at radial distances out to 130 NM.

e. Most VORs are equipped for voice transmission on the VOR frequency. VORs without voice capability are indicated by the letter W (without voice) included in the class designator.

f. The only positive method of identifying a VOR is by its Morse Code identification or by the recorded automatic voice identification which is always indicated by the use of the word VOR following the range's name. Reliance on determining the identification of an omnirange should never be placed on listening to voice transmissions by the Flight Service Station (FSS) or approach control facility involved. Many Flight Service Stations remotely operate several omniranges with different names. In some cases, none of the VORs have the name of the "parent" Flight Service Station. During periods of maintenance, the facility may radiate a T-E-S-T code (- . ... -) or the code may be removed.

g. Voice identification has been added to numerous VORs. The transmission consists of a voice announcement, "JOEYVILLE VOR," alternating with the usual Morse Code identification.

h. The effectiveness of the VOR depends upon proper use and adjustment of both ground and airborne equipment.

    1. Accuracy: The accuracy of course alignment of the VOR is excellent, being generally plus or minus 1 degree.

    2. Roughness: On some VORs, minor course roughness may be observed, evidenced by course needle or brief flag alarm activity; some receivers are more susceptible to these irregularities than others. Slow movement of the deviation needle on the aircraft instrument is called course bends; fast deviations of the needle are called course scalloping. At a few stations, usually in mountainous terrain, the pilot may occasionally observe a brief course needle oscillation, similar to the indication of approaching station. Pilots flying over unfamiliar routes are cautioned to be on the alert for these vagaries, and in particular, to use the TO/FROM indicator to determine positive station passage.

    (a) Certain propeller RPM settings or helicopter rotor speeds can cause the VOR Course Deviation Indicator to fluctuate as much as plus or minus 6 degrees. Slight changes to the RPM setting will normally smooth out this roughness. Pilots are urged to check for this modulation phenomenon prior to reporting a VOR station or aircraft equipment for unsatisfactory operation.

1-3 VOR Receiver Check.

a. The FAA VOR test facility (VOT) transmits a test signal which provides users a convenient means to determine the operational status and accuracy of a VOR receiver while on the ground where a VOT is located. The airborne use of the VOT is permitted ; however, its use is strictly limited to those areas/altitudes specifically authorized in the Airport/Facility Directory or appropriate supplement.

b. To use the VOT service, tune in the VOT frequency on your VOR receiver. With the Course Deviation Indicator (CDI) centered, the omni-bearing selector (OBS) should read 0 degrees with the TO/FROM indication showing FROM or the omni-bearing selector should read 180 degrees with the TO/FROM indication showing TO. Should the VOR receiver operate an RMI (Radio Magnetic Indicator), it will indicate 180 degrees on any OBS setting. Two means of identification are used. One is a series of dots and the other is a continuous tone. Information concerning an individual test signal can be obtained from the local FSS.

c. Periodic VOR receiver calibration is most important. If a receiver's Automatic Gain Control or modulation circuit deteriorates, it is possible for it to display acceptable accuracy and sensitivity close into the VOR or VOT and display out-of-tolerance readings when located at greater distances where weaker signal areas exist. The likelihood of this deterioration varies between receivers, and is generally considered a function of time. The best assurance of having an accurate receiver is periodic calibration. Yearly intervals are recommended at which time an authorized repair facility should recalibrate the receiver to the manufacturer's specifications.

1-4   Distance Measuring Equipment (DME).

a. Used in conjunction with the nationwide VOR system, distance measuring equipment (DME) has made it possible for you to know the exact geographical position of your aircraft immediately by observation of your VOR and DME indicating equipment. Without DME, you can determine your position by triangulation methods using a single VOR receiver, dual VOR receivers, or a combination of VOR receiver(s) and low frequency equipment. With DME and VOR equipment in combination, direct reading instruments tell you the distance and bearing TO or FROM the station.

b. In the operation of DME, paired pulses at a specific spacing are sent out from the aircraft (this is the interrogation) and are received at the ground station. The ground station (transponder) then transmits paired pulses back to the aircraft at the same pulse spacing but on a different frequency. The time required for the round trip of this signal exchange is measured in the airborne DME unit and is translated into distance (nautical miles) from the aircraft to the ground station.

c. Operating on the line-of-sight principle, DME furnishes distance information with a very high degree of accuracy. Reliable signals may be received at distances up to 199 NM at line-of-sight altitude with an accuracy of better than 1/2 mile or

3 percent of the distance, whichever is greater. Distance information received from DME equipment is slant-range distance and not actual horizontal distance. The difference between a measured distance on the surface and the DME slant-range distance is known as slant-range error and is smallest at low altitude and long range. This error is greatest when the aircraft is directly over the facility, at which time the DME receiver will display altitude in nautical miles above the facility.

d. DME operates on frequencies in the UHF spectrum between 962 MHz and 1213 MHz. Aircraft equipped with TACAN equipment will receive distance information from a VORTAC automatically, while aircraft with VOR must have a separate DME airborne unit.

e. VOR/DME, VORTAC, ILS/DME, and LOC/DME navigation facilities established by the FAA provide course and distance information from collocated components under a frequency pairing plan. Aircraft receiving equipment which provides for automatic DME selection assures reception of azimuth and distance information from a common source when designated VOR/DME, VORTAC, ILS/DME, and LOC/DME are selected.

f. Due to the limited number of available frequencies, assignment of paired frequencies is required for certain military noncollocated VOR and TACAN facilities which serve the same area but which may be separated by distances up to a few miles. The military is presently undergoing a program to collocate VOR and TACAN facilities or to assign nonpaired frequencies to those that cannot be collocated.

g. VOR/DME, VORTAC, ILS/DME, and LOC/DME facilities are identified by synchronized identifications which are transmitted on a time share basis. The VOR or localizer portion of the facility is identified by a coded tone modulated at 1020 Hz or a combination of code and voice. The TACAN or DME is identified by a coded tone modulated at 1350 Hz. The DME or TACAN coded identification is transmitted one time for each three or four times that the VOR or localizer coded identification is transmitted. When either the VOR or DME is inoperative, it is important to recognize which identifier is retained for the operative facility. A single coded identification with a repetition interval of approximately 30 seconds indicates that the DME is operative.

h. Aircraft equipment which provides for automatic DME selection assures reception of azimuth and distance information from a common source when designated VOR/DME, VORTAC, and ILS/DME navigation facilities are selected. Pilots are cautioned to disregard any distance displays from automatically selected DME equipment when VOR or ILS facilities, which do not have the DME feature installed, are being used for position determination.

1-5 Tactical Air Navigation (TACAN).

a. For reasons peculiar to military or naval operations (unusual siting conditions, the pitching and rolling of a navy vessel, etc.) the civil VOR/DME system of air navigation was considered unsuitable for military or naval use. A new navigation system, TACAN, was therefore developed by the military and naval forces to more readily lend itself to military and naval requirements. As a result, the FAA has been in the process of integrating TACAN facilities with the civil VOR/DME program. Although the theoretical, or technical principles of operations of TACAN equipment are quite different from those of VOR/DME facilities, the end result, as far as the navigating pilot are concerned, is the same. These integrated facilities are called VORTACs.

b. TACAN ground equipment consists of either a fixed or mobile transmitting unit. The airborne unit in conjunction with the ground unit reduces the transmitted signal to a visual presentation of both azimuth and distance information. TACAN is a pulse system and operates in the UHF band of frequencies. Its use requires TACAN airborne equipment and does not operate through conventional VOR equipment.

1-6 VHF Omni-Directional Range/Tactical Air Navigation (VORTAC).

a. A VORTAC is a facility consisting of two components, VOR and TACAN, which provides three individual services: VOR azimuth, TACAN azimuth, and TACAN distance (DME) at one site. Although consisting of more than one component, incorporating more than one operating frequency, and using more than one antenna system, a VORTAC is considered to be a unified navigation aid. Both components of a VORTAC are envisioned as operating simultaneously and providing the three services at all times.

b. Transmitted signals of VOR and TACAN are each identified by three-letter code transmission and are interlocked so that pilots using VOR azimuth with TACAN distance can be assured that both signals being received are definitely from the same ground station. The frequency channels of the VOR and the TACAN at each VORTAC facility are "paired" in accordance with a national plan to simplify airborne operation.

1-7 Nondirectional Radio Beacon (NDB).

a. The low-frequency nondirectional radio beacon, or homing facility, was one of the earliest electronic navigation aids adopted by the FAA. A low- or medium-frequency radio beacon transmits nondirectional signals whereby the pilot of an aircraft properly equipped can determine his bearing and "home" on the station. These facilities normally operate in the frequency band of 190 to 535 kHz and transmit a continuous carrier with either 400 or 1020 Hz modulation. All radio beacons except the compass locators transmit a continuous three-letter identification in code except during voice transmissions.

b. When a radio beacon is used in conjunction with Instrument Landing System markers, it is called a Compass Locator.

c. Voice transmissions are made on radio beacons unless the letter W (without voice) is included in the class designator (HW).

d. Radio beacons are subject to disturbances that may result in erroneous bearing information. Such disturbances result from such factors as lightning, precipitation static, etc. At night, radio beacons are vulnerable to interference from distant stations. Nearly all the disturbances which affect the ADF bearing also affect the facility's identification. Noisy identification usually occurs when the ADF needle is erratic. Voice, music, or erroneous identification may be heard when a steady false bearing is displayed. Since ADF receivers do not have a flag to warn the pilot when erroneous bearing information is being displayed, the pilot should continuously monitor the NDB's identification.

e. Though they may vary with age, the typical ADF receiver and indicator include the following components:

1. Indicator (Bearing pointer) - Shows the relative bearing to the station.

2. Frequency band selector - This permits the use of any ground transmitter, within the appropriate frequency range. Commercial broadcasting stations as well as the nondirectional homing beacons can be used.

3. Function switch - When the function switch is set to ADF, the bearing pointer of the indicator shows relative bearing to the station. When the switch is set to ANT, audio is received from the station tuned and the bearing pointer is automatically stowed at the 90 degree position. The BFO (Beat Frequency Oscillator) switch position is used to obtain better reception of unmodulated frequencies. The switch actuates a signal in the receiver which is added to the incoming signals, producing a continuous tone.

4. Tuning knob - Used to tune in the appropriate frequency.

5. ON/OFF switch - Used to turn the unit on and may also control the volume.

f. There are four types of nondirectional homing facilities in use:

1. HH facilities have a power output of 2,000 or more watts and a reception

range of 75 nautical miles. They are generally used with overwater routes.

    2. H facilities have a power output of 50 to 1999 watts and a reception range of 50 nautical miles.

    3. MH facilities have a power output of less than 50 watts and a reception range of 25 nautical miles.

    4. ILS compass locator facilities have a power output of less than 25 watts and a reception range of 15 nautical miles.

1-8 NAVAID Identifier Removal During Maintenance.

During periods of routine or emergency maintenance, coded identification (or code and voice, where applicable) is removed from certain FAA NAVAIDs. Removal of identification serves as a warning to pilots that the facility is officially off the air for tune-up or repair and may be unreliable even though intermittent or constant signals are received.

NOTE: During periods of maintenance VHF ranges may radiate a T-E-S-T code (-. ... -).

1-9 VHF Direction Finder.

a. The VHF Direction Finder (VHF/DF) is one of the common systems that helps pilots without their being aware of its operation. It is a ground-based radio receiver used by the operator of the ground station. FAA facilities that provide VHF/DF service are identified in the Airport/Facility Directory.

b. The equipment consists of a directional antenna system and a VHF radio receiver.

c. The VHF/DF receiver display indicates the magnetic direction of the aircraft from the ground station each time the aircraft transmits. Normal procedure requires the pilot to key the microphone for approximately 10 seconds, thus allowing the station to determine the aircraft fix.

d. DF equipment is of particular value in locating lost aircraft and in helping to identify aircraft on radar.

SECTION 2. RADAR SERVICES AND PROCEDURES

2-1 Radar.

a. The FAA first began installing radar equipment at airports in the late 1940s.

107

Further development of radar systems and their expanded use in the Air Traffic Control system have greatly modified and simplified both VFR as well as IFR flying procedures.

b. Capabilities

1. Radar is a method whereby radio waves are transmitted into the air and are then received when they have been reflected by an object in the path of the beam. Range is determined by measuring the time it takes (at the speed of light) for the radio wave to go out to the object and then return to the receiving antenna. The direction of a detected object from a radar site is determined by the position of the rotating antenna when the reflected portion of the radio wave is received.

2. More reliable maintenance and improved equipment have reduced radar system failures to a negligible factor. Most facilities actually have some components duplicated, one operating and another which immediately takes over when a malfunction occurs to the primary component.

c. Limitations.

1. It is very important for the aviation community to recognize the fact that there are limitations to radar service and that ATC controllers may not always be able to issue traffic advisories concerning aircraft which are not under ATC control and cannot be seen on radar. (See Figure 7-1.)

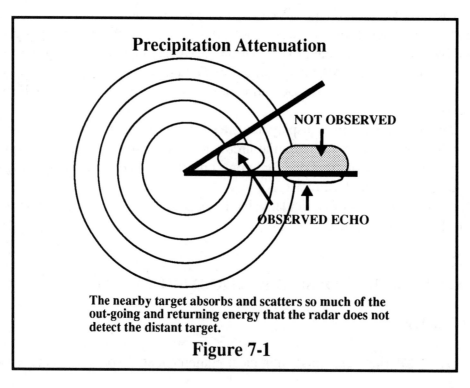

Precipitation Attenuation

NOT OBSERVED

OBSERVED ECHO

The nearby target absorbs and scatters so much of the out-going and returning energy that the radar does not detect the distant target.

Figure 7-1

(a) The characteristics of radio waves are such that they normally travel in a continuous straight line unless they are:

(1) "Bent" by abnormal atmospheric phenomena such as temperature inversions.

(2) Reflected or attenuated by dense objects such as heavy clouds, precipitation, ground obstacles, mountains, etc.; or

(3) Screened by high terrain features.

(b) The bending of radar pulses, often called anomalous propagation or ducting, may cause many extraneous blips to appear on the radar operator's display if the beam has been bent towards the ground or may decrease the detection range if the wave is bent upward. It is difficult to solve the effects of anomalous propagation, but by using beacon radar and electronically eliminating stationary and slow moving targets by a method called moving target indicator (MTI) usually negate the problem.

(c) Radar energy that strikes dense objects will be reflected and displayed on the operator's scope, thereby blocking out aircraft at the same range and greatly weakening or completely eliminating the display of targets at a greater range. Again, radar beacon and MTI are very effectively used to combat ground clutter and weather phenomena, and a method of circularly polarizing the radar beam will eliminate some weather returns. A negative characteristic of MTI is that an aircraft flying a speed that coincides with the canceling signal of the MTI (tangential or "blind" speed) may not be displayed to the radar controller.

(d) Relatively low-altitude aircraft will not be seen if screened by mountains or are below the radar beam due to earth curvature. The only solution to screening is the installation of strategically placed multiple radars, which has been done in some areas.

(e) There are several other factors which affect radar control. The amount of reflective surface of an aircraft will determine the size of the radar return. Therefore, a small light airplane or sleek jet fighter will be more difficult to see on radar than a large commercial jet or military bomber. Here again, the use of radar beacon is invaluable if the aircraft is equipped with an airborne transponder. All ARTCC in the conterminous U.S. and many airport surveillance radars have the capability to interrogate Mode C and display altitude information to the controller from appropriately equipped aircraft. However, there are a number of airport surveillance radars that are still two-dimensional (range and azimuth) only, and altitude information must be obtained from the pilot.

(f) At some locations within the ATC en route environment, secondary-radar-only (no primary radar) gap filler radar systems are used to give low-altitude radar coverage between two larger radar systems, each of which provides both primary and secondary radar coverage. In those geographical areas served by secondary radar only, aircraft without transponders cannot be provided with radar service. Additionally, transponder-equipped aircraft cannot be provided with radar advisories concerning primary targets and weather.

(g) The controller's ability to advise a pilot flying on instruments or in visual conditions of his proximity to another aircraft will be limited if the unknown aircraft is not observed on radar, if no flight plan information is available, or if the volume of traffic and workload prevent his issuing traffic information. The controller's first priority is given to establishing vertical, lateral, or longitudinal separation between aircraft flying IFR under the control of ATC.

(h) FAA radar units operate continuously at the locations shown in the Airport/Facility Directory, and their services are available to all pilots, both civil and military. Contact the associated FAA control tower or ARTCC on any frequency guarded for initial instructions, or in an emergency, any FAA facility for information on the nearest radar service.

2-2 Air Traffic Control Radar Beacon System (ATCRBS).

a. The ATCRBS, sometimes referred to as secondary surveillance radar, consists of three main components:

1. Interrogator. Primary radar relies on a signal being transmitted from the radar antenna site and for this signal to be reflected or "bounced back" from an object (such as an aircraft). This reflected signal is then displayed as a "target" on the controller's radarscope. In the ATCRBS, the interrogator, a ground-based radar transmitter-receiver, scans in synchronism with the primary radar and transmits discrete radio signals which repetitiously request all transponders, on the mode being used, to reply. The replies received are then mixed with the primary returns and both are displayed on the same radarscope.

2. Transponder. The airborne radar beacon transmitter-receiver automatically receives the signals from the interrogator and selectively replies with a specific pulse group (code) only to those interrogations being received on the mode to which it is set. These replies are independent of and much stronger than a primary radar return.

3. Radarscope. The radarscope used by the controller displays returns from both the primary radar system and the ATCRBS. These returns, called targets, are what the controller refers to in the control and separation of traffic.

b. The job of identifying and maintaining identification of primary radar targets is a long and tedious task for the controller. Some of the advantages of ATCRBS over primary radar are:

1. Reinforcement of radar targets.
2. Rapid target identification.
3. Unique display of selected codes.

c. A part of the ATCRBS ground equipment is the decoder. The equipment enables the controller to assign discrete transponder codes to each aircraft under his control. Normally only one code will be assigned for the entire flight. Assignments are made by the ARTCC computer on the basis of the National Beacon Code Allocation Plan. The equipment is also designed to receive MODE C altitude information from the aircraft.

d. It should be emphasized that aircraft transponders greatly improve the effectiveness of the radar systems.

2-3 Surveillance Radar.

a. Surveillance radars are divided into two general categories: Airport Surveillance Radar (ASR) and Air Route Surveillance Radar (ARSR).

1. ASR is designed to provide relatively short-range coverage in the general vicinity of an airport and to serve as an expeditious means of handling terminal area traffic through observation of precise aircraft locations on a radarscope. The ASR can also be used as an instrument approach aid.

2. ARSR is a long-range radar system designed primarily to provide a display of aircraft locations over large areas.

b. Surveillance radars scan through 360 degrees of azimuth and present target information on a radar display located in a tower or center. This information is used independently or in conjunction with other navigational aids in the control of air traffic.

TEST QUESTIONS

1. The only positive method of identifying a VOR is by its

A. Morse Code identification.
B. ambiguity indicator.
C. omni bearing selector.

2. Distance measuring equipment (DME) provides pilots with

A. horizontal distance.
B. slant-range distance.
C. vertical distance.

3. Which of the following may create erroneous bearing information when using the ADF?

A. Lightning.
B. Clouds.
C. Ground interference.

4. Removal of the coded identification indicates

A. voice-only capability.
B. facility is DME equipped.
C. station is unreliable and should not be used for navigation.

5. When radar cannot detect a distant target because the nearby target absorbs and scatters most of the outgoing and returning energy it is known as

A. attenuation.
B. transformation.
C. assimilation.

ANSWERS

1. A   2. B   3. A   4. C   5. A

8

AERONAUTICAL LIGHTING & OTHER AIRPORT VISUAL AIDS

SECTION 1. AIRPORT LIGHTING AIDS

1-1 Visual Glideslope Indicators.

  a. The VASI (Visual Approach Slope Indicator) is a system of lights so arranged to assist pilots in maintaining a safe glidepath during the approach to a runway. These lights are visible from 3-5 miles during the day and up to 20 miles or more at night. The visual glide path of the VASI provides safe obstruction clearance within plus or minus 10 degrees of the extended runway centerline up to 4 NM from the runway threshold. Descent, using the VASI, should not be initiated until the aircraft is visually aligned with the runway. Lateral course guidance is provided by the runway or runway lights.

  b. VASI installations may consist of either 2, 4, 6, 12, or 16 lights arranged in bars referred to as near, middle, and far bars. Most VASI installations consist of 2 bars, near and far, and may consist of 2, 4, or 12 light units. The near bars, also known as the downwind bars, may be located on one or both sides of the runway 600 feet from the threshold. The far or upwind bars may also be located on one or both sides of the runway 1300 feet from the threshold. The use of the VASI will result in a touchdown point located midway between the near and far bars. Some VASIs consist of three bars, near, middle, and far, which provide an additional visual glide path to accommodate high-cockpit aircraft. This installation may consist of either 6 or 16 light units. VASI installations consisting of 2, 4, or 6 light units are located on one side of the runway, usually the left. Where the installation consists of 12 or 16 light units, the units are located on both sides of the runway.

  c. Two-bar VASI installations provide one visual glide path which is normally set at 3 degrees. Three-bar VASI installations provide two visual glide paths. The lower glide path is provided by the near and middle bars and is normally set at 3 degrees, while the upper glide path, provided by the middle and far bars, is normally 1/4 degree higher. This higher glide path is intended for use only by high-cockpit aircraft to provide a sufficient threshold crossing height. Although normal glide path angles are 3 degrees, angles at some locations may be as high as 4.5 degrees to give proper obstacle clearance. Pilots of high-performance aircraft are cautioned that use of VASI angles in excess of 3.5 degrees may cause an increase in runway

113

length required for landing and rollout.

d. The basic principle of the VASI is that of color differentiation between red and white. Each light unit projects a beam of light having a white segment in the upper part of the beam and a red segment in the lower part of the beam. The light units are arranged so that the pilots using the VASIs during an approach will see the combination of lights shown. (See Figures 8-2, 8-3, and 8-4.)

e. Precision Approach Path Indicator (PAPI) uses light units similar to the VASI but are installed in a single row as compared to the two- or three-row VASI system. The row will contain either two or four light units. These systems have an effective visual range of about 5 miles during the day and up to 20 miles at night. The PAPI operates on the principle of color differentiation similar to the VASI. The row of light units is normally installed on the left side of the runway and the glide path indicators are as depicted. (See Figure 8-5.)

f. Tri-color visual approach slope indicators normally consist of a single light unit projecting a three-color visual approach path into the final approach area of the runway upon which the indicator is installed. The below glide path indication is red, the above glide path indication is amber, and the on glide path indication is green. These types of indicators have a useful range of approximately 1/2 to 1 mile during the day and up to 5 miles at night depending on the visibility conditions. (See Figure 8-1.)

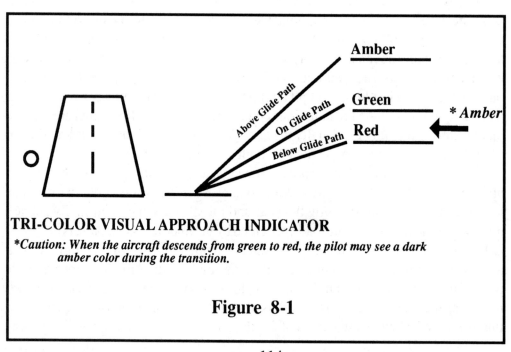

TRI-COLOR VISUAL APPROACH INDICATOR

*Caution: When the aircraft descends from green to red, the pilot may see a dark amber color during the transition.

Figure 8-1

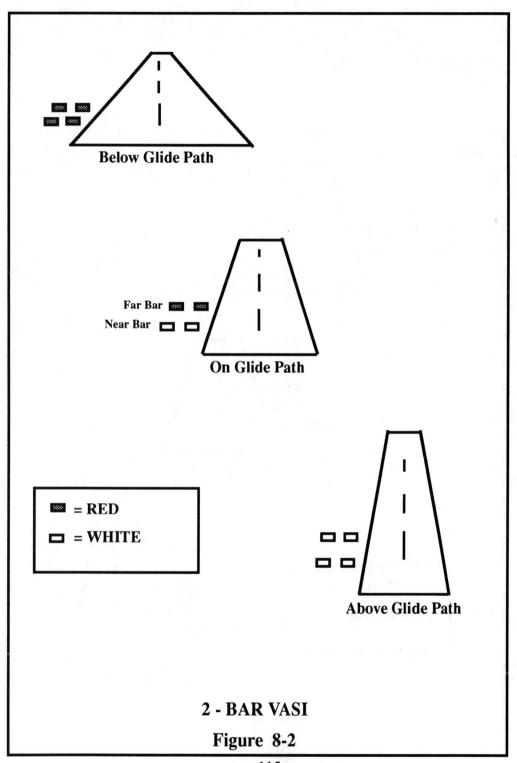

Below Glide Path

Far Bar
Near Bar

On Glide Path

■ = RED
▢ = WHITE

Above Glide Path

2 - BAR VASI

Figure 8-2

115

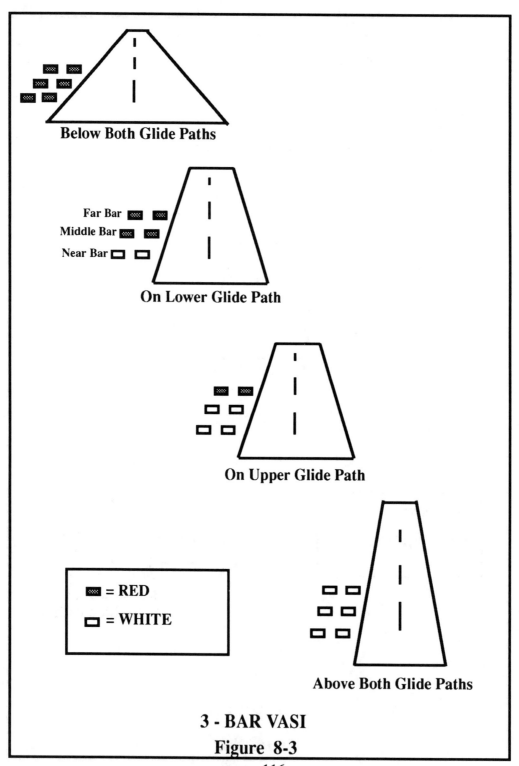

Below Both Glide Paths

Far Bar
Middle Bar
Near Bar

On Lower Glide Path

On Upper Glide Path

= RED
= WHITE

Above Both Glide Paths

3 - BAR VASI

Figure 8-3

116

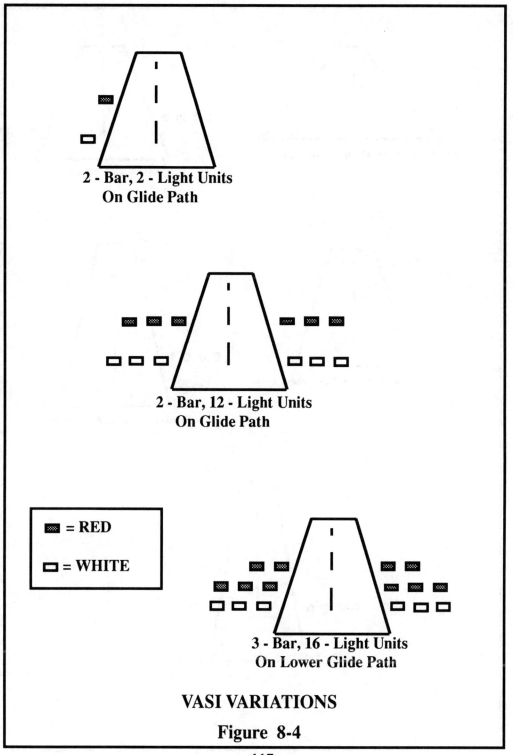

2 - Bar, 2 - Light Units
On Glide Path

2 - Bar, 12 - Light Units
On Glide Path

▨ = RED

☐ = WHITE

3 - Bar, 16 - Light Units
On Lower Glide Path

VASI VARIATIONS

Figure 8-4

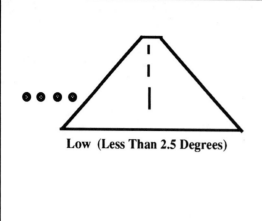
Low (Less Than 2.5 Degrees)

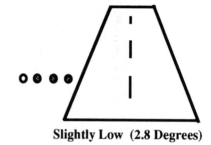
Slightly Low (2.8 Degrees)

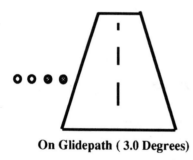
On Glidepath (3.0 Degrees)

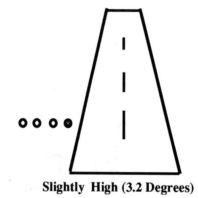
Slightly High (3.2 Degrees)

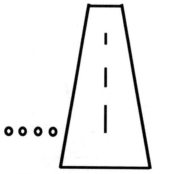
High (More Than 3.5 Degrees)

PAPI Indications
Figure 8-5

g. Pulsating visual approach slope indicators normally consist of a single light unit projecting a two-color visual approach path into final approach area of the runway upon which the indicator is installed. The below glide path indication is normally pulsating red and the above glide path indication is normally pulsating white. The on glide path indication is a steady white light. The useful range of this system is about 4 miles during the day and up to 10 miles at night. (See Figure 8-6.)

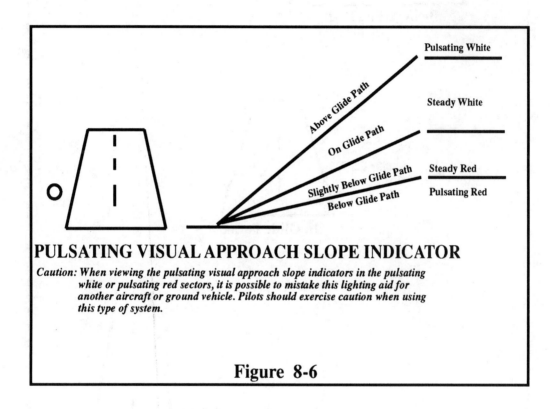

PULSATING VISUAL APPROACH SLOPE INDICATOR

Caution: When viewing the pulsating visual approach slope indicators in the pulsating white or pulsating red sectors, it is possible to mistake this lighting aid for another aircraft or ground vehicle. Pilots should exercise caution when using this type of system.

Figure 8-6

h. Alignment of elements systems are installed on some small general aviation airports and are a low-cost system consisting of painted plywood panels, normally black and white or fluorescent orange. Some of these systems are lighted for night use. The useful range of these systems is approximately 3/4 mile. To use the system the pilot positions his aircraft so the elements are in alignment. (See Figure 8-7.)

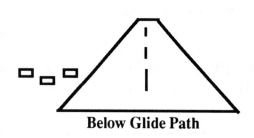
Below Glide Path

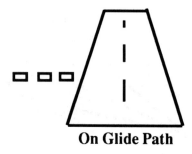
On Glide Path

Above Glide Path

ALIGNMENT OF ELEMENTS
Figure 8-7

1-2 Runway End Identifier Lights (REIL).

a. REILs are installed at many airfields to provide rapid and positive identification of the approach end of a particular runway. This system consists of a pair of synchronized flashing lights located laterally on each side of the runway threshold. REILs may either be omnidirectional or unidirectional facing the approach area. They are effective for:

1. Identification of a runway surrounded by a preponderance of other lighting.
2. Identification of a runway which lacks contrast with surrounding terrain.
3. Identification of a runway during reduced visibility.

1-3 Runway Edge Light Systems.

a. Runway edge lights are used to outline the edges of runways during periods of darkness or restricted visibility conditions. These light systems are classified according the intensity or brightness they are capable of producing.

(HIRL) - High-Intensity Runway Lights - Variable intensity control.
(MIRL) - Medium-Intensity Runway Lights - Variable intensity control.
(LIRL) - Low-Intensity Runway Lights - One intensity level.

b. The runway edge lights are normally white. On instrument runways, amber replaces white on the last 2,000 feet or half the runway length, whichever is less, to form a caution zone for landings.

c. The lights marking the ends of the runway emit red light toward the runway to indicate the end of the runway to a departing aircraft and emit green outward from the runway end to indicate the threshold to landing aircraft.

1-4 Control of Lighting Systems.

a. Operation of approach light systems and runway lighting is controlled by the control tower (ATCT). At some locations the Flight Service Station (FSS) may control the lights where there is no control tower in operation.

b. Pilots may request the lights be turned on or off. Runway edge lights, in-pavement lights, and approach lights also have intensity controls which may be varied to meet the pilot's request. Sequenced flashing lights (SFL) may be turned on and off. Some sequenced flashing light systems also have intensity control.

1-5 Pilot Control of Lighting.

a. At some unattended airports, runway lights, taxiway lights, etc. may not be left on continuously. In this situation a pilot needs the ability to turn on the appropriate lighting. Radio control of lighting is available at selected airports to provide airborne control of lights by keying the aircraft's microphone. Control of lighting systems is often available at locations without specified hours for lighting and where there is no control tower or FSS or when the tower or FSS is closed. All lighting systems which are radio controlled at an airport, whether on a single runway or multiple runways, operate on the same radio frequency.

b. With FAA approved systems, various combinations of medium-intensity approach lights, runway lights, taxi lights, VASI and/or REIL may be activated by radio control. On runways with both approach lighting and runway lighting, the approach lighting system takes precedence for air-to-ground radio control over the runway lighting. In this situation, the runway lighting is set at a predetermined intensity, based on expected visibility conditions. Runways without approach lighting may provide radio-controlled intensity adjustment for runway edge lights. Other lighting systems, including VASI, REIL, and taxiway lights may be either controlled with the runway edge lights or controlled independently of the runway edge lights.

c. The lighting system will consists of a 3-step, 2-step, or 1-step control system. A 3-step system allows the pilot 3 intensity levels (High, Medium, and Low). This system is responsive to 7, 5, and/or 3 microphone clicks each representing a separate intensity level. The 2-step system allows for two intensity levels while the 1-step system has only a single intensity. All lighting is illuminated for a period of 15 minutes from the most recent time of activation and may not be extinguished prior to the end of the 15 minute period (except for 1-step and 2-step REILs which may be turned off when desired by keying the mike 5 or 3 times respectfully).

d. Suggested use is to always initially key the mike 7 times; this assures that all controlled lights are turned on to the maximum available intensity. If desired, adjustment can then be made, where the capability is provided, to a lower intensity (or the REIL turned off) by keying 5 and/or 3 times. Due to the close proximity of airports using the same frequency, radio-controlled lighting receivers may be set at a low sensitivity requiring the aircraft to be relatively close to activate the system. Consequently, even when lights are on, always key mike as directed when overflying an airport of intended landing or just prior to entering the final segment of an approach. This will assure the aircraft is close enough to activate the system and a full 15 minute lighting duration is available. Approved lighting systems may be activated by keying the mike (within 5 seconds) as indicated below.

```
RADIO CONTROL SYSTEM

    KEY MIKE                              FUNCTION
7 times within 5 seconds..................Highest intensity available
5 times within 5 seconds..................Medium or lower intensity. Lower
                                          the REIL intensity or turn REIL  off.
3 times within 5 seconds..................Lowest intensity available. Lower
                                          REIL intensity or turn REIL off.
```

e. For all public use airports with FAA standard lighting systems as well as those with other than FAA approved systems, the Airport/Facility Directory contains types of lighting, runway, and frequency that is used to activate the system.

1-6 Airport (Rotating) Beacons.

a. The airport beacon has a vertical light distribution to make it most effective from 1 to 10 degrees above the horizon; however, it can be seen well above and below this peak spread. The beacon may be an omnidirectional capacitor-discharge device, or it may rotate at a constant speed which produces the visual effect of flashes at regular intervals. Flashes may be one or two colors alternately. The colors and color combinations of the beacons are:
  1. White & Green - Lighted land airport
  2. *Green alone - Lighted land airport
  3. White & Amber - Lighted water airport
  4. *Amber alone - Lighted water airport
  5. Green, Yellow, & White - Lighted heliport

NOTE - *Green alone or amber alone is used only in connection with a white-and-green or white-and-amber beacon display, respectively.

b. Military airport beacons flash alternately white and green, but are differentiated from beacons by dualpeaked (two quick) white flashes between the green flashes.

c. In control zones, operation of the airport beacon during the hours of daylight often indicates that the ground visibility is less than 3 miles and/or the ceiling is less than 1,000 feet. ATC clearance in accordance with FAR 91 is required for landing, takeoff, and flight in the traffic pattern. Pilots should not rely solely on the operation of the airport beacon to indicate if the weather conditions are IFR or VFR. At some locations with operating control towers, ATC personnel turn the beacon on or off when the controllers are in the tower. At many airports the airport beacon is turned on by a photoelectric cell or time clocks and the ATC personnel can not control them. There is no regulatory requirement for daylight operation and it is the pilot's responsibility to comply with proper preflight planning as required by FAR 91.103.

1-7 Taxiway Lights.

  a. Taxiway Edge Lights. - Taxiway edge lights are used to outline the edges of the taxiways during periods of darkness or restricted visibility conditions. These fixtures emit blue light.

  b. Taxiway Centerline Lights. - Taxiway centerline lights are used to facilitate ground traffic under low-visibility conditions. They are located along the taxiway centerline in a straight line on the straight portions, on the centerline of curved portions, and along designated taxiing paths in portions of runways, ramp, and apron areas. Taxiway centerline lights are steady burning and emit green light.

SECTION 2. AIR NAVIGATION AND OBSTRUCTION LIGHTING

2-1 Aeronautical Light Beacons.

a. An aeronautical light beacon is a visual NAVAID displaying flashes of white and/or colored light to indicate the location of an airport, a heliport, a landmark, a certain point of a federal airway in mountainous terrain, or an obstruction. The light used may be a rotating beacon or one or more flashing lights. The flashing lights may be supplemented by steady burning lights of lesser intensity.

b. The color or color combination displayed by a particular beacon and/or its auxiliary lights tell whether the beacon is indicating a landing place, landmark, point of the federal airways, or an obstruction. Coded flashes of the auxiliary lights, if employed, further identify the beacon site.

2-2 Code Beacons and Course Lights.

a. Code Beacons. - The code beacon, which can be seen from all directions, is used to identify airports and landmarks and to mark obstructions. The number of code beacon flashes are:

    1. GREEN CODED FLASHES not exceeding 40 flashes or character elements per minute, or constant flashes 12 to 15 per minute, for identifying land airports.

    2. YELLOW CODED FLASHES not exceeding 40 flashes or character elements per minute, or constant flashes 12 to 15 per minute, for identifying water airports.

    3. RED FLASHES, constant rate, 12 to 40 flashes per minute for marking hazards.

b. Course Lights. - The course light, which can be seen clearly from only one direction, is used only with rotating beacons of the Federal Airway System. Two course lights, back to back, direct coded flashing beams of light in either direction along the course of the airway.

NOTE. - Airway beacons are remnants of the "lighted" airways which antedated the present electronically equipped Federal Airways System. Only a few of these beacons exist today to mark airway segments in remote mountain areas. Flashes in Morse Code identify the beacon site.

2-3 Obstruction Lights.

a. Obstructions are marked/lighted to warn airmen of their presence during daytime and nighttime conditions. They may be marked/lighted in any of the

125

following combinations:

1. <u>Aviation red obstruction lights.</u> Flashing aviation red beacons and steady burning aviation red lights during nighttime operation. Aviation white and orange paint is used for daytime marking.

2. <u>High-intensity white obstruction lights.</u> Flashing high-intensity white lights during daytime with reduced intensity during twilight and nighttime operation. When this type system is used, the marking of structures with red obstruction lights and white and orange aviation paint may be omitted.

3. <u>Dual lighting.</u> A combination of flashing aviation red beacons and steady burning aviation red lights for nighttime operation and flashing high intensity white lights for daytime operation. Aviation white and orange paint may be omitted.

b. High-intensity flashing white lights are being used to identify some supporting structures of overhead transmission lines located across rivers, chasms, gorges, etc. These lights flash in a middle, top, lower light sequence at approximately 60 flashes per minute. The top light is normally installed near the top of the supporting structure, while the lower light indicates the approximate lower portion of the wire span. The lights are beamed toward the companion structure and identify the area of the wire span.

c. High-intensity, flashing white lights are also employed to identify tall structures, such as chimneys and towers, as obstructions to air navigation. The lights provide a 360-degree coverage about the structure at 40 flashes per minute and consist of from one to seven levels of lights depending upon the height of the structure. Where more than one level is used the vertical banks flash simultaneously.

SECTION 3. AIRPORT SIGNS AND MARKING AIDS

3-1 Airport Signs.

Signs are used on runways and taxiways to provide information. There are three types of signs which are color coded for specific uses.

a. Mandatory Instruction Signs. - These signs convey a message which, if not carried out, could create an unsafe condition. The signs have white inscriptions on a red background. Mandatory signs include:

1. Taxiway/Runway Intersections and Instrument Landing Critical Areas. These signs are used to augment holding position markings denoting entrance to a

runway or ILS/MLS critical areas.

2. Runway/Runway Intersections. These signs are used to identify intersecting runways and contain both runway threshold designations of intersecting runways.

3. Other Applications. Another use for this type of sign would be where it is desired to prohibit entry into a particular area, such as NO ENTRY.

b. Information Signs. These signs are used to provide location or destination information and have black inscriptions on a yellow background. Information signs include:

1. Taxiway Identification Signs. Taxiways are identified by letters of the alphabet insofar as possible. They are normally located at the intersection of taxiways or at an exit from a runway.

2. Designation Signs. The inscription indicates the destination and includes an arrow indicating the direction to be followed. There are two types of designation signs, outbound and inbound. Outbound destination signs are used to identify taxiing routes to the takeoff runways. Major destination areas are usually shown on inbound destination signs located at runway exits.

c. Runway Distance Remaining Signs. Runway distance remaining signs are located along the sides of a runway to indicate the remaining runway distance in increments of 1000 feet. The signs have white numbers on a black background and are lighted for nighttime and low-visibility operations.

NOTE. - Refer to Advisory Circular 150/5340-18, Standards for Airport Sign Systems, for detailed airport sign information.

3-2 Airport Marking Aids.

In the interest of safety, regularity, or efficiency of aircraft operations, the FAA has recommended, for the guidance of the public, the following airport markings.

NOTE.- Refer to Advisory Circular 150/5340-1, Marking of Paved Areas on Airports, for detailed airport marking information.

a. Runway Designators. - Runway numbers and letters are determined from the approach direction. The runway number is the whole number nearest one-tenth the magnetic azimuth of the centerline of the runway, measured clockwise from the magnetic north. The letter, or letters, differentiate between left (L), right (R), or center (C) parallel runways, as applicable:

1. For two parallel runways "L" and "R"
2. For three parallel runways "L," "C," and "R"

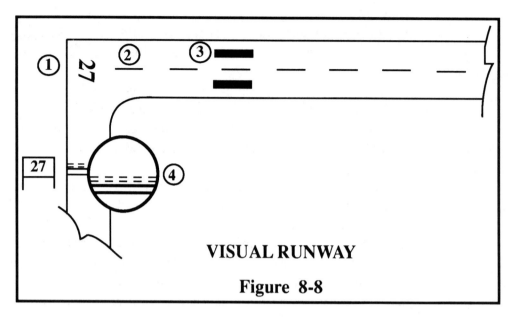

VISUAL RUNWAY

Figure 8-8

b. Visual Runway Marking. - Used for operations under Visual Flight Rules:
    1. Designation marking.
    2. Centerline marking.
    3. Fixed distance marking (on runways 4,000 feet or longer used by jet aircraft).
    4. Holding position markings (for taxiway/runway intersections).

    c. Threshold - The designated beginning of the runway that is available and suitable for the landing of aircraft.

d. Displaced Threshold - A threshold that is not at the beginning of the full-strength runway pavement. The paved area behind the displaced runway threshold may be available for taxiing, the landing rollout, and the takeoff of the aircraft. (See Figure 8-9).

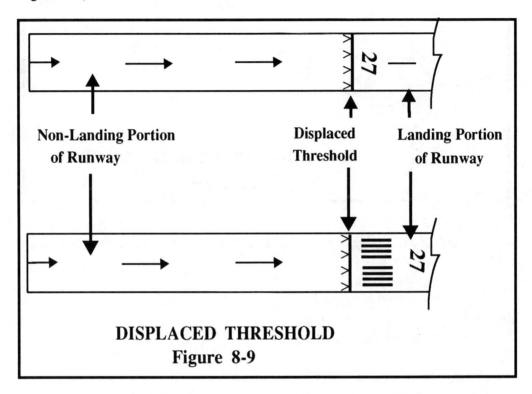

DISPLACED THRESHOLD
Figure 8-9

e. Stopway Areas - Area beyond the end of a runway suitable for use during an aborted takeoff. (See Figure 8-10).

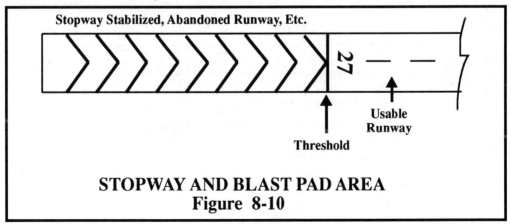

STOPWAY AND BLAST PAD AREA
Figure 8-10

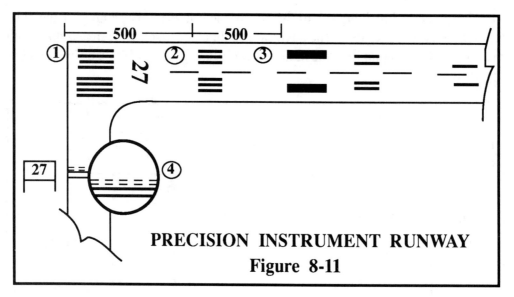

PRECISION INSTRUMENT RUNWAY
Figure 8-11

f. Precision Instrument Runway - Used on runways served by nonprecision visual approach aids and on runways having special operational requirements. (See Figure 8-11.)

      1. Threshold marking.
      2. Touchdown zone marking.
      3. Fixed-distance marking.
      4. Holding position marking.

    f. Closed Runway - A runway which is unusable and may be hazardous even though it may appear usable. (See Figure 8-12.)

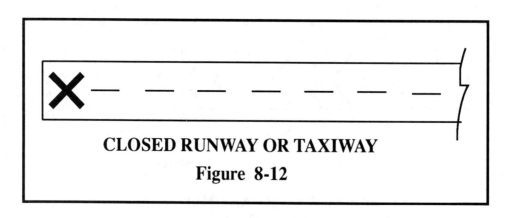

CLOSED RUNWAY OR TAXIWAY
Figure 8-12

g. STOL (Short Takeoff and Landing) Runway - In addition to the normal runway number marking, the letters STOL are painted on the approach end of the runway and a touchdown aim point is shown. (See Figure 8-13).

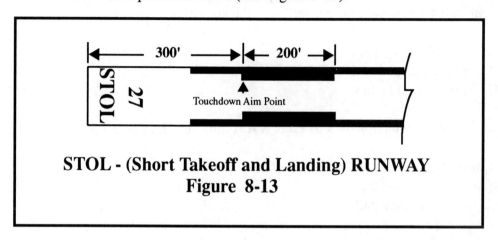

**STOL - (Short Takeoff and Landing) RUNWAY
Figure 8-13**

h. Taxiway Marking - The taxiway centerline is marked with a continuous yellow line. The taxiway edge may be marked with two continuous yellow lines 6 inches apart. Taxiway/runway holding lines consist of two continuous and two dashed lines, spaced 6 inches between the lines, perpendicular to the taxiway centerline; more recently, hold lines also consist of one or more signs at the edge of the taxiway, with white characters on a red sign face.

NOTE. - When instructed by ATC "Hold short of (runway, ILS, critical area, etc.)," the pilot should stop so that no part of the aircraft extends beyond the holding line. When approaching the holding line from the side with the continuous lines, a pilot should not cross the holding line without ATC clearance at a controlled airport or without making sure of adequate separation from other aircraft at uncontrolled airports. An aircraft exiting the runway is not clear until all parts of the aircraft have crossed the holding line.

TEST QUESTIONS

1. On a two-bar VASI, a red light depiction on the far bar combined with a white light depiction on the near bar indicates the aircraft is

A. above the glide path.
B. on the glide path.
C. below the glide path.

2. An amber depiction on a tri-color VASI indicates the aircraft is

A. above the glide path.
B. on the glide path.
C. below the glide path.

3. When three of the four lights on a PAPI are depicted as red, the pilot is

A. high.
B. slightly high.
C. slightly low.

4. A pulsating red light on a pulsating visual approach slope indicator indicates the pilot is

A. above the glide path.
B. on the glide path.
C. below the glide path.

5. Runway edge lights are normally

A. white.
B. blue.
C. green.

6. A white-and-green airport rotating beacon indicates

A. lighted heliport.
B. lighted seaport.
C. lighted land airport.

7. A closed runway is indicated by

A. a yellow line.
B. an X on the end of the runway.
C. red flashing lights at the end of the runway.

8. The taxiway centerline is marked with a continuous

A. yellow line.
B. white line.
C. red line.

ANSWERS

1. B 2. C 3. C 4. C 5. A 6. C 7. B 8. A

9

AIRSPACE

SECTION 1. GENERAL

1-1 General.

Because of the nature of some operations, restrictions are required for safety reasons. The complexity or density of aircraft movements in other airspace areas may result in additional aircraft and pilot requirements for operation within such airspace. It is important that pilots be familiar with the operational requirements for the various airspace segments.

SECTION 2. UNCONTROLLED AIRSPACE

2-1 General.

Uncontrolled airspace is that portion of the airspace that has not been designated as CONTROL ZONE, AIRPORT RADAR SERVICE AREA, TERMINAL CONTROL AREA, or POSITIVE CONTROL AREA.

2-2 VFR Requirements.

Rules governing VFR flight have been adopted to assist the pilot in meeting his responsibility to see and avoid other aircraft. Minimum weather conditions and distance from clouds required for VFR flight are contained within these rules (FAR 91.155). (See Figure 9-1.)

SECTION 3. CONTROLLED AIRSPACE

3-1 General.

A major portion of the airspace covering the conterminous U.S. is controlled.

Controlled airspace consists of those areas designated as CONTINENTAL CONTROL AREA CONTROL, CONTROL AREA, CONTROL ZONE, TERMINAL CONTROL AREA, AIRPORT RADAR SERVICE AREA, and TRANSITION AREA. Not all controlled airspace requires that the pilot be subjected to air traffic control. Restrictions in controlled airspace may involve particular equipment needed or more restrictive weather minimums. Safety, users' needs, and the volume of flight operations are some of the factors considered

VFR IN UNCONTROLLED AIRSPACE		
ALTITUDE	FLIGHT VISIBILITY	DISTANCE FROM CLOUDS
1,200 FEET OR LESS (AGL)	(DAY) 1 SM	CLEAR OF CLOUDS
	(NIGHT) 3 SM	500 FEET BELOW 1,000 FEET ABOVE 2,000 FEET HORIZ
MORE THAN 1,200 FEET (AGL) BUT LESS THAN 10,000 FEET (MSL).	(DAY) 1 SM	500 FEET BELOW 1,000 FEET ABOVE 2,000 FEET HORIZ
	(NIGHT) 3 SM	500 FEET BELOW 1,000 FEET ABOVE 2,000 FEET HORIZ
MORE THAN 1,200 FEET (AGL) AND AT OR ABOVE 10,000 FEET (MSL).	5 SM	1,000 FEET BELOW 1,000 FEET ABOVE 1 MILE HORIZ

FIGURE 9-1. VFR In Uncontrolled Airspace.

in the designation of controlled airspace. When so designated, the airspace is supported by ground-to-air communications, navigation aids, and air traffic services. (See Figure 9-2.)

3-2 Continental Control Area.

a. The Continental Control Area consists of the airspace of the 48 contiguous states, the District of Columbia, and Alaska, excluding the Alaska peninsula west of longitude 160 degrees 00 minutes 00 seconds W, at and above 14,500 feet (MSL), but does not include:

    1. The airspace less than 1,500 feet above the surface of the earth (AGL);

    2. Prohibited and Restricted Areas, other than the Restricted Areas listed in FAR-71 Subpart D.

3-3 Control Areas.

Control Areas consist of the airspace designated as Colored Federal airways, VOR Federal airways, Additional Control Areas, and Control Area Extensions, but do not include the Continental Control Area.

VFR IN CONTROLLED AIRSPACE		
ALTITUDE	FLIGHT VISIBILITY	DISTANCE FROM CLOUDS
1,200 FEET OR LESS (AGL)	3 SM	500 FEET BELOW 1,000 FEET ABOVE 2,000 FEET HORIZ
MORE THAN 1,200 FEET (AGL) BUT LESS THAN 10,000 FEET (MSL).	3 SM	500 FEET BELOW 1,000 FEET ABOVE 2,000 FEET HORIZ
MORE THAN 1,200 FEET (AGL) AND AT OR ABOVE 10,000 FEET (MSL).	5 SM	1,000 FEET BELOW 1,000 FEET BELOW 1 MILE HORIZ

FIGURE 9-2. VFR In Controlled Airspace.

Unless otherwise designated, Control Areas also include the airspace between a segment of a main VOR airway and its associated alternate segments. The vertical extent of the various categories of airspace contained in Control Areas is defined in FAR-71.

3-4 Positive Control Area.

Positive Control Area is airspace so designated as positive control area in FAR 71.193. This area includes specified airspace within conterminous U.S. from

18,000 feet to and including Flight Level 600 (60,000 feet), excluding Santa Barbara Island, Farallon Island, and that portion south of latitude 25 degrees 04 minutes north. In Alaska, it includes the airspace over the state from 18,000 feet to and including Flight Level 600 (60,000 feet), but not including the airspace less than 1,500 above the surface of the earth and the Alaskan Peninsula west of longitude 160 degrees 00 minutes W. Rules for operating in a Positive Control Area are found in FAR 91.135 and 91.215.

3-5 Transition Area.

a. Transition Areas are designated to contain IFR operations in controlled airspace during portions of the terminal operation and while transitioning between the terminal and en route environments.

b. Transition Areas are controlled airspace extending upward from 700 feet or more above the surface when designated in conjunction with an airport for which an instrument approach procedure has been prescribed; or from 1,200 feet or more above the surface when designated in conjunction with airway route structures or segments. Unless specified otherwise, Transition Areas terminate at the base of the overlying controlled airspace.

3-6 Control Zones.

a. Control Zones are regulatory in nature and established as controlled airspace. They extend upward from the surface and terminate at the base of the Continental Control Area. Control Zones that do not underlie the Continental Control Area have no upper limit. A Control Zone is based on a primary airport but may include one or more airports and is normally a circular area within a radius of 5 statute miles around the primary airport, except that it may include extensions necessary to include instrument departure and arrival paths.

b. Some basic requirements for designating a control zone are communications and weather observation reporting:

1. Communications capability with aircraft that normally operate within the control zone must exist down to the runway surface of the primary airport. Communications may be either direct from the ATC facility having jurisdiction over the control zone or by rapid relay through other communications facilities which are acceptable to that ATC facility.

2. Federally certificated weather observers take hourly and special weather observations at the primary airport in the control zone during the times and dates

a control zone is designated. The required weather observations must be forwarded expeditiously to the ATC facility having jurisdiction over the control zones.

c. Control Zones are depicted on the charts. For example, on the Sectional Charts the Control Zone is outlined by a broken blue line. If a control zone is effective only during certain hours of the day (a part-time control zone as prescribed in the regulation) it will be reflected on the charts.

3-7 Terminal Control Area (TCA).

a. A Terminal Control Area (TCA) consists of controlled airspace extending upward from the surface or higher to specified altitudes, within which all aircraft are subject to the operating rules and pilot/equipment requirements specified in Part 91 of the FARs. Each TCA location includes at least one primary airport around which the TCA is located.

b. TCAs are depicted on Sectional, World Aeronautical, En route Low Altitude, DOD Flip, and Terminal Area Charts.

TABLE 9-1. Areas Currently Designated As TCAs

Atlanta, GA - Hartsfield Airport
Boston, MA - Logan Airport
Charlotte, NC - Charlotte/Douglas International
Chicago, IL - O'Hare International Airport
Cleveland, OH - Cleveland Hopkins Airport
Dallas, TX - Fort Worth International Airport
Denver, CO - Stapleton International Airport
Detroit, MI - Detroit Metropolitan Wayne County
Honolulu, HI - Honolulu International
Houston, TX - Houston Intercontinental
Kansas City, MO - Kansas City International
Las Vegas, NV - McCarran International
Los Angeles, CA - Los Angeles International Airport
Memphis, TN - Memphis International
Miami, FL - Miami International Airport
Minneapolis, MN - Minneapolis-St. Paul/Wold-Chamberlain
New Orleans, LA - New Orleans International (Moisant Field)
Newark, NJ - Newark International Airport
New York, NY - New York Kennedy Airport

New York, NY - New York La Guardia Airport
Philadelphia, PA - Philadelphia International
Phoenix, AZ - Phoenix Sky Harbor International
Pittsburgh, PA - Greater Pittsburgh International
Orlando, FL - Orlando International
St. Louis, MO - Lambert-St. Louis International
Salt Lake City, UT - Salt Lake City International
San Diego, CA - San Diego International-Lindbergh Field
San Francisco, CA - San Francisco International Airport
Seattle, WA - Seattle-Tacoma International
Tampa, FL - Tampa International
Washington, D.C. - Washington National Airport
Maryland - Andrews Air Force Base

*Those shown in bold indicate that no person may takeoff or land at these particular TCAs unless the pilot-in-command holds at least a PRIVATE PILOT CERTIFICATE.

3-8 Terminal Control Area (TCA) Operation.

a. Operating Rules and Pilot/Equipment Requirements. - Regardless of weather conditions, an ATC authorization is required prior to operating within a TCA. Pilots should not request an authorization to operate within a TCA unless the requirements of FAR 91.215 and FAR 91.131 are met. Included among these requirements are:

1. Unless otherwise authorized by ATC, aircraft must be equipped with an operable two-way radio capable of communicating with ATC on appropriate frequencies for that Terminal Control Area.

2. No person may takeoff or land a civil aircraft at an airport within a TCA or operate a civil aircraft within a TCA unless the pilot-in-command holds at least a private pilot certificate or, in the case of a student pilot, the student has met the requirements of FAR 61.95. There are twelve TCAs at which student pilots are restricted from any participation. These are so noted in Table 9-1.

3. Unless otherwise authorized by ATC, each person operating a large turbine engine-powered airplane to or from a primary airport shall operate at or above the designated floors while within the lateral limits of the TCA.

4. Unless otherwise authorized by ATC, aircraft must be equipped with an operable VOR or TACAN receiver.

5. Unless otherwise authorized by ATC, aircraft must be equipped with a

140

4096 code transponder with automatic altitude reporting equipment.

NOTE. - ATC may, upon notification, immediately authorize a deviation from the altitude reporting equipment; however, a request for a deviation from the 4096 transponder equipment requirement must be submitted to the controlling ATC facility at least one hour before the proposed operation.

b. Flight Procedures.

1. Arriving aircraft must obtain authorization prior to entering a TCA and must contact ATC on the appropriate frequency, and in relation to geographical fixes shown on local charts. Although a pilot may be operating beneath the floor of the TCA on initial contact, communications with ATC should be established in relation to the points indicated for spacing and sequencing purposes.

2. Departing aircraft require a clearance to depart the TCA and should advise the clearance delivery position of their intended altitude and route of flight. ATC will normally advise VFR aircraft when leaving the geographical limits of the TCA. Radar service is not automatically terminated with this advisory unless specifically stated by the controller.

3. Aircraft not landing at or departing from the primary airport may obtain ATC clearance to transit the TCA when traffic conditions permit and provided the requirements of FAR 91.131 are met. Such VFR aircraft are encouraged, to the extent possible, to operate at altitudes above or below the TCA or transit through established VFR corridors. Pilots operating in VFR corridors are urged to use frequency 122.75 MHz for the exchange of aircraft position information.

4. VFR non-TCA aircraft are cautioned against operating too closely to TCA boundaries, especially where the floor of the TCA is 3,000 feet or less or where VFR cruise altitudes are at or near the floor of higher levels. Observance of this precaution will reduce the potential for encountering a TCA aircraft operating at TCA floor altitudes. Additionally, VFR non-TCA aircraft are encouraged to use the VFR Planning Chart as a tool for planning flight in proximity to a TCA. VFR Flyway Planning Charts are published on the back of the existing VFR Terminal Area Charts.

c. ATC Clearances and Separation. - An ATC authorization is required to enter and operate within a TCA. While operating within a TCA, pilots are provided the service and separation as in Stage III. In the event of radar outage, separation and sequencing of VFR aircraft will be suspended as this service is dependent on radar. The pilot will be advised that the service is not available and issued wind, runway information, and the time or place to contact the tower. Traffic information will be provided on a workload-permitting basis.

1. This program is not to be interpreted as relieving pilots of their responsibilities to see and avoid other traffic operating in basic VFR weather conditions, to adjust their operations and flight path as necessary to preclude serious

wake encounters, to maintain appropriate terrain and obstruction clearance, or to remain in weather conditions equal to or better than the minimums required by FAR 91.155. Whenever compliance with an assigned route, heading, and/or altitude is likely to compromise pilot responsibility respecting terrain and obstruction clearance, vortex exposure, and weather minimums, approach control should be so advised and a revised clearance or instruction obtained.

2. ATC may assign altitudes to VFR aircraft that do not conform to FAR 91.159. When altitude assignment is no longer needed for separation or when leaving the TCA, the instruction will be broadcast, "Resume appropriate VFR altitudes." Pilots must return to an altitude that conforms to FAR 91.159 as soon as practical.

3-9 Airport Radar Service Area (ARSA).

a. An Airport Radar Service Area (ARSA) consists of controlled airspace extending upward from the surface or higher to specified altitudes, within which all aircraft are subject to the operating rules and pilot and equipment requirements specified in FAR 91. ARSAs are described in FAR 71.

b. Dimensions.

1. ARSAs consist of a basic design with minor site specific variations. The ARSA airspace consists of two circles, both centered on the primary/ARSA airport. The enter circle has a radius of 5 nautical miles. The outer circle has a radius of 10 nautical miles. The airspace of the inner circle extends from the surface of the ARSA airport up to 4,000 feet above the airport. The airspace between the 5NM and the 10NM rings begins at 1,200 feet above ground level and extends to the same altitude cap as the inner circle.

2. The normal radius of the outer area will be 20 NM, with some variations based on site-specific requirements. The outer area extends outward from the primary/ARSA airport and extends from the lower limits of the radar/radio coverage up to the ceiling of the approach control's delegated airspace, excluding the ARSA and other airspace as appropriate.

c. ARSAs are charted on Sectional Charts and some Terminal Control Area Charts. (See ARSA Table below.)

ALABAMA
    Birmingham
    Huntsville
    Mobile

ALASKA
    Anchorage

ARIZONA
    Davis-Monthan AFB
    Tucson

142

ARKANSAS
Little Rock

CALIFORNIA
Beale AFB
Burbank
Castle AFB (Merced)
El Toro MCAS
Fresno
March AFB
Mather AFB
McClellan AFB
Monterey
Norton AFB
Oakland
Ontario
Sacramento
San Jose
Santa Barbara

COLORADO
Colorado Springs

CONNECTICUT
Windsor Locks (Bradley)

DISTRICT OF COLUMBIA
Washington (Dulles)

FLORIDA
Pensacola
Whiting NAS
Pensacola NAS
Daytona Beach
Ft. Lauderdale
Ft. Meyers (Southwest Florida Regional)
Jacksonville
West Palm Beach
Sarasota
Tallahassee (Muni)

GEORGIA
Columbus
Savannah

HAWAII
Kahului

IDAHO
Boise

ILLINOIS
Champaign
Chicago (Midway)
Moline
Peoria
Springfield

INDIANA
Evansville
Fort Wayne
Indianapolis
South Bend

IOWA
Cedar Rapids
Des Moines

KANSAS
Wichita

KENTUCKY
Covington (Cincinnati, OH)
Lexington
Louisville

LOUISIANA
Barksdale AFB
Baton Rouge
Lafayette
Shreveport

MAINE
Portland

MARYLAND
Baltimore

MICHIGAN
Flint
Grand Rapids
Lansing

MISSISSIPPI
Columbus AFB
Jackson

NEBRASKA
Lincoln
Omaha
Offutt AFB

NEVADA
Reno

NEW JERSEY
Alantic City (Intl)

NEW MEXICO
Albuquerque

NEW YORK
Albany
Buffalo
Islip
Rochester
Syracuse

NORTH CAROLINA
Fayetteville
Greensboro
Pope AFB (Fayetteville)
Raleigh/Durham

OHIO
Akron
Columbus
Cincinnati (Covington, KY)
Dayton
Toledo

OKLAHOMA
Oklahoma City
Tinker AFB

Tulsa

OREGON
Portland

PENNSYLVANIA
Allentown

PUERTO RICO
San Juan

RHODE ISLAND
Providence

SOUTH CAROLINA
Charleston (AFB/Intl)
Columbia
Greer
Shaw AFB

TENNESSEE
Chattanooga
Knoxville
Nashville

TEXAS
Abilene
Amarillo
Austin
Corpus Christi
Dallas (Love)
Dyess AFB (Abilene)
El Paso
Houston (William P. Hobby)
Laughlin AFB
Lubbock
Midland
San Antonio

VERMONT
Burlington

VIRGINIA
Norfolk
Richmond

Roanoke

WASHINGTON
Spokane (Intl)
Spokane (Fairchild AFB)
Whidbey Island (NAS)

WEST VIRGINIA
Charleston

WISCONSIN
Green Bay
Madison
Milwaukee

3-10 Airport Radar Service Area (ARSA) Operation.

a. Operating Rules and Pilot/Equipment Requirements.
1. Pilot Certification: No specific certification required.
2. Equipment:
(a) Two-way radio.
(b) A Mode C (altitude encoding) transponder.
3. Arrivals and Overflights: Two-way radio communication must be established with the ATC facility having jurisdiction over the ARSA prior to entry and thereafter as instructed by ATC. Normally two-way radio communication is officially established when the controller acknowledges the aircraft call sign.
4. Departures:
(a) At the primary airport or a satellite airport with an operating control tower, two-way radio communication must be established and maintained with the control tower in accordance with Title 14 Part 91.129 and thereafter as instructed by ATC.
(b) At satellite airports without an operating control tower, two-way radio communication must be established as soon as practicable after departing with ATC facility having jurisdiction over the ARSA and thereafter, as instructed by ATC.
5. Traffic Patterns: Pilots must comply with FAA arrival or departure traffic patterns.
6. Ultralight Vehicles: Ultralight vehicle operations are not permitted in an ARSA unless otherwise authorized by the ATC facility having jurisdiction over the ARSA.

145

b. ATC Services.

　　1. Within The ARSA:

　　　　(a) Sequencing of all arriving aircraft to the primary/ARSA airport.

　　　　(b) Standard IFR separation between IFR aircraft.

　　　　(c) Between IFR and VFR aircraft - traffic advisories and conflict resolution so that radar targets do not touch, or 500 feet vertical separation.

　　　　(d) Between VFR traffic - traffic advisories and as appropriate, safety alerts.

　　2. Within the Outer Area:

　　　　(a) The same services are provided for aircraft operating within the outer area, as within the ARSA, when two-way communication and radar contact is established.

　　　　(b) While pilot participation in this area is strongly encouraged, it is not a VFR requirement.

　　3. Beyond the Outer Area:

　　　　(a) Standard IFR separation

　　　　(b) Basic radar service.

　　　　(c) StageII/Stage III service, where appropriate.

　　　　(d) Safety alert, where appropriate.

c. Since this is a radar program, ARSA services will only be provided within radar/radio coverage. In the event of a radar outage, separation and sequencing of VFR aircraft will be suspended. The pilot will be advised that the service is not available and will be issued wind information, runway information, and the time to contact the tower.

d. While pilot participation is required within the ARSA, it is voluntary within the outer area and may be discontinued, within the outer area, at the pilot's request.

e. ARSA services will be provided in the outer area unless the pilot requests termination of the service.

f. Service provided beyond the outer area will be on a workload-permitting basis and can be terminated by the controller if workload dictates.

g. In some locations an ARSA may overlap the airport traffic area of a secondary airport. In order to allow that control tower to provide service to aircraft, portions of the overlapping ARSA may be procedurally excluded when the secondary airport tower is in operation. Aircraft operating in these procedurally excluded areas will only be provided airport traffic control services when in communication with the secondary airport tower. ARSA service to the aircraft inbound to these airports will be discontinued when the aircraft is instructed to contact the tower.

h. Aircraft departing secondary-controlled airports will not receive ARSA service

146

until they have been radar identified and two-way communication has been established with the ARSA facility.

i. ARSA service to aircraft proceeding to a satellite airport will be terminated at a sufficient distance to allow time to change to the appropriate tower or advisory frequency.

j. Some ARSA facilities shut down for portions of the night. When this occurs, the effective hours of the ARSA will be the same as the operating hours of the serving facility.

k. This program is not to be interpreted as relieving pilots of their responsibilities to see and avoid other traffic operating in basic VFR weather conditions, to adjust their operations and flight path as necessary to preclude serious wake encounters, to maintain appropriate terrain and obstruction clearance, or to remain in weather conditions equal to or better than the minimums required by FAR 91.155. Whenever compliance with an assigned route, heading, and/or altitude is likely to compromise pilot responsibility respecting terrain and obstruction clearance, vortex exposure, or weather minimums, approach control should be so advised and revised clearance or instruction obtained.

l. Pilots of arriving aircraft should contact the ARSA facility on the published frequency and give their position, altitude, radar beacon (if transponder equipped), destination and request ARSA service. Radio contact should be initiated far enough from the ARSA boundary to preclude entering the ARSA before radio communication is established.

m. If the controller responds to a radio call with "aircraft callsign," radio communications have been established and the pilot may enter the ARSA. If workload or traffic considerations prevent immediate provisions of the ARSA services, the controller will inform the pilot to remain outside the ARSA until conditions permit the services to be provided.

EXAMPLE:

"BUCKEYE 33 stand by." - (Pilot is permitted to enter the ARSA.)

"BUCKEYE 33 remain outside the ARSA and stand by." - (Pilot is not permitted to enter the ARSA.)

NOTE. - It is important to understand that if the controller responds to the initial radio call without using the aircraft callsign, radio communications have not officially been established and the pilot may not enter the ARSA.

EXAMPLE:

"Aircraft calling Don Scott tower, stand by." (Pilot is not permitted to enter the ARSA.)

SECTION 4. SPECIAL USE AIRSPACE

4-1 General.

Special use airspace consists of that airspace wherein activities must be confined because of their nature, or wherein limitations are imposed upon aircraft operations that are not a part of those activities, or both. Except for controlled firing areas, special use airspace areas are depicted on aeronautical charts.

4-2 Prohibited Areas.

Prohibited Areas contain airspace of defined dimensions identified by an area on the surface of the earth within which the flight of aircraft are prohibited. Such areas are established for security and other reasons associated with the national welfare. For example, a Prohibited Area exists over the White House in Washington, D.C. These areas are published in the Federal Register and are depicted on aeronautical charts.

4-3 Restricted Areas.

a. Restricted Areas contain airspace identified by an area on the surface of the earth within which the flight of aircraft, while not wholly prohibited, is subject to restrictions. Activities within these areas must be confined because of their nature or limitations imposed upon aircraft operations that are not a part of those activities or both. Restricted areas denote the existence of unusual, often invisible, hazards to aircraft such as artillery firing, aerial gunnery, or guided missiles. Penetration of Restricted Areas without authorization from the using or controlling agency may be extremely hazardous to the aircraft and its occupants. Restricted Areas are published in the Federal Register and constitute FAR 73.

b. In many cases, the dimensions of the Restricted Area are such that the pilot may be able to avoid the airspace altogether. If the pilot finds it necessary to penetrate

148

a Restricted Area, she must receive permission from the controlling agency before entering.

   c. Restricted airspace is depicted on aeronautical charts. The area is generally denoted by a specific number (e.g., R-5503). The name of the controlling agency is generally listed at the bottom of the aeronautical chart in conjunction with the associated number.

4-4 Warning Areas.

Warning Areas are airspace which may contain hazards to nonparticipating aircraft in international airspace. Warning Areas are established beyond the 3 mile limit. Though the activities conducted within Warning Areas may be as hazardous as those within a Restricted Area, Warning Areas cannot be legally designated as Restricted Areas because they are over international waters. Penetration of Warning Areas during periods of activity may be hazardous to the aircraft and its occupants. Official descriptions of Warning Areas may be obtained on request to the FAA, Washington, D.C.

4-5 Military Operations Areas (MOAs).

   a. MOAs consist of airspace of defined vertical and lateral limits established for the purpose of separating certain military training activities from IFR traffic. Whenever the MOA is being used, nonparticipating IFR traffic may be cleared through the MOA if IFR separation can be provided by ATC. Otherwise, ATC will reroute or restrict nonparticipating IFR traffic.

   b. Most training activities necessitate acrobatic or abrupt flight maneuvers. Military pilots conducting flight in Department of Defense aircraft within a designated and active Military Operations Area are exempted from the provisions of FAR 91.303 (c) and (d) which prohibit acrobatic flight within Federal Airways and Control Zones.

   c. Pilots operating under VFR should exercise extreme caution while operating within the MOA when military activity is being conducted. The activity status (active/inactive) of MOAs may change frequently. Therefore, pilots should contact any FSS within 100 miles of the area to obtain accurate, real-time information concerning the hours of MOA operation. Prior to entering an active MOA, pilots should contact the controlling agency for traffic advisories.

149

d. MOAs are depicted on Sectional, VFR Terminal, Area, and En Route Low Altitude Charts.

4-6 Alert Areas.

Alert Areas are depicted on aeronautical charts to inform nonparticipating pilots of areas that may contain a high volume of pilot training or an unusual type of aerial activity. Pilots should be particularly alert when flying in these areas. All activity within an Alert Area should be conducted in accordance with FARs, without waiver, and pilots of participating aircraft as well as pilots transiting the area shall be equally responsible for collision avoidance. Information concerning these areas may be obtained upon request to the FAA, Washington, D.C.

4-7 Controlled Firing Areas.

Controlled Firing Areas contain activities which, if not conducted in a controlled environment, could be hazardous to nonparticipating aircraft. The distinguishing feature of the Controlled Firing Area, as compared to other special use airspace, is that its activities are suspended immediately when spotter aircraft, radar, or ground lookout positions indicate that an aircraft may be approaching the area. There is no need to chart Controlled Firing Areas since they do not cause a nonparticipating aircraft to change its flight path.

SECTION 5. OTHER AIRSPACE AREAS

5-1 Airport Traffic Areas.

 a. Unless otherwise specifically designated (FAR 93), Airport Traffic Areas consist of airspace within a horizontal radius of 5 statute miles from the geographic center of any airport at which a control tower is operating, extending from the surface up to, but not including, an altitude of 3,000 feet above the elevation of the airport.
 b. FAR 91.127 requires that unless a pilot is landing at or taking off from an airport in the Airport Traffic Area or authorized otherwise by ATC, the pilot must avoid the area. Generally it is the pilot's responsibility to obtain any necessary authorization. Pilots operating under IFR or receiving radar services from an ATC facility

are not expected to obtain their own authorizations through each area. Rather, the ATC facility providing the service will coordinate with the appropriate control towers for the approval to transit each area.

   c. FAR 91.129 requires that unless otherwise authorized by ATC, a pilot operating to or from an airport served by an operating control tower must maintain two-way radio communications with the control tower while in the Airport Traffic Area that includes the movement areas of that airport. FAR 91. 117 sets the maximum indicated airspeeds for operations in the Airport Traffic Area at 200 knots. Airport Traffic Areas are indicated on aeronautical charts by the blue airport symbol, but the actual boundary is not depicted.

5-2 Airport Advisory Area.

   a. The Airport Advisory Area is the area within 10 statute miles of an airport where a control tower is not operating but where a Flight Service Station (FSS) is located. At such stations, the FSS provides advisory service to arriving and departing aircraft.

   b. It is not mandatory that pilots participate in the Airport Advisory Service program, but it is strongly recommended that they do.

5-3 Military Training Routes (MTRs).

   a. National security depends largely on the deterrent effect of our airborne military forces. To be proficient, the military services must train in a wide range of airborne tactics. One phase of this training involves low-level combat tactics. The required maneuvers and high speeds are such that they may occasionally make the see-and-avoid aspect of VFR flight more difficult without increased vigilance in areas containing such operations. In an effort to ensure the greatest practical level of safety for all flight operations, the MTR program was conceived.

   b. The MTR program is a joint venture by the FAA and the Department of Defense (DOD). MTRs are mutually developed for use by the military for the purpose of conducting low-altitude, high-speed training. The routes above 1,500 feet above ground level (AGL) are developed to be flown, to the maximum extent possible, under Instrument Flight Rules (IFR). The routes at or below 1,500 feet (AGL) are generally developed to be flown under Visual Flight Rules (VFR).

   c. Generally, MTRs are established below 10,000 feet MSL for operations at speeds in excess of 250 knots. However, route segments may be defined at higher altitudes for purposes of route continuity. For example, route segments may be designed for descent, climbout, and mountainous terrain. There are IFR and VFR routes as follows:

1. IFR Military Training Routes (IR) - Operations on these routes are conducted in accordance with Instrument Flight Rules regardless of weather conditions.

2. VFR Military Training Routes (VR) - Operations on these routes are conducted in accordance with Visual Flight Rules.

d. Route Identification.

1. (IR) and (VR) at or below 1,500 feet AGL (with no segment above 1,500 feet) will be identified by a four-digit number.

EXAMPLE: IR 1001 - An IFR Military Training Route operating at or below 1,500 feet AGL.

VR 1002 - A VFR Military Training Route operating at or below 1,500 feet AGL.

2. (IR) and (VR) above 1,500 feet AGL (segments of these routes may be below 1,500 feet AGL) will be identified by a three-digit number.

EXAMPLE: IR 001 - An IFR Military Training Route operating above 1,500 feet AGL.

VR 002 - A VFR Military Training Route operating above 1,500 feet AGL.

3. Alternate IR/VR routes or route segments are identified by using the basic/principal route designation followed by a letter suffix   (IR001A, VR002B, etc.).

e. Route Charting -

1. VFR Planning Chart - This chart will depict routes (military training activities such as IR and VR regardless of altitude), MOAs, and Restricted, Warning, and Alert Areas.

2. Area Planning Chart (DOD Flight Information Publications - FLIP)- This chart is published by the DOD primarily for military users and contains detailed information on both IR and VR routes. The FLIP contains charts and narrative descriptions of these routes. This publication is available to the general public by single copy or annual subscription by writing:

Director, DMACSC
Attention: DOCP
Washington, D.C. 20315-0020

f. Nonparticipating aircraft are not prohibited from flying within an MTR; however, extreme vigilance should be exercised when conducting flight through or near these routes. Pilots should contact FSSs within 100 nautical miles of a particular MTR to obtain current information or route usage in their vicinity. Information available includes times of scheduled activity, altitudes in use on each route segment, and actual route width. Route width varies for each MTR and can extend several miles on either side of the charted MTR centerline. Route width information for IR and VR MTRs is also available in the FLIP along with additional MTR (SR/AR) information. When requesting MTR information, pilots should give the FSS their position, route of flight, and destination in order to reduce frequency congestion and permit the FSS specialist to identify the MTR routes which could be a factor.

5-4 Temporary Flight Restrictions.

a. General - This paragraph describes the types of conditions under which the FAA may impose temporary flight restrictions. It also explains which FAA elements have been delegated authority to issue a temporary flight restrictions NOTAM and lists the types of responsible agencies/offices from which the FAA will accept requests to establish temporary flight restrictions. The FAR is explicit as to what operations are prohibited, restricted, or allowed in a temporary flight restrictions area. Pilots are responsible to comply with FAR 91.137 when conducting flight in an area where a temporary flight restrictions area is in effect and should check appropriate NOTAMs during flight planning.

b. The purpose for establishing a temporary flight restrictions area is to:

1. Protect persons or property in the air or on the surface from an existing or imminent hazard associated with an incident on the surface when the presence of low-flying aircraft would magnify, alter, spread, or compound the hazard (91.137(a)(1));

2. Provide a safe environment for the operation of disaster relief aircraft (FAR 91.137(a)(2));

3. Or prevent an unsafe congestion of sight-seeing aircraft above an incident or event which may generate a high degree of public interest (FAR 91.137(a)(3)).

c. Except for hijacking situations, when the provisions of FAR 91.137(a)(1) or 91.137(a)(2) are necessary, a temporary flight restrictions area will only be established by or through the area manager at the air route traffic control center

(ARTCC) having jurisdiction over the area concerned. A temporary flight restrictions NOTAM involving the conditions of FAR 91.137(a)(3) will be issued at the direction of the regional air traffic division manager having oversight of the airspace concerned. When hijacking situations are involved, a temporary flight restrictions area will be implemented through the FAA Washington Headquarters Office of Civil Aviation Security. The appropriate FAA air traffic element, upon receipt of such a request, will establish a temporary flight restrictions area under FAR 91.137(a)(1).

   d. The FAA accepts recommendations for the establishment of a temporary flight restrictions area under FAR 91.137(a)(1) from military major command headquarters, regional directors of the Office of Emergency Planning, Civil Defense state directors, state governors, or other similar authority. For the situations involving FAR 91.137(a)(2), the FAA accepts recommendations from military commanders serving as regional, subregional, or Search and Rescue (SAR) coordinators; by military commanders directing or coordinating air operations associated with disaster relief; or by civil authorities directing or coordinating organized relief air operations (including representatives of the Office of Emergency Planning, U.S. Forest Service, and state aeronautical agencies). Appropriate authorities for a temporary flight restrictions establishment under FAR 91.137(a)(3) are any of those listed above or by state, county, or city government entities.

   e. The type of restrictions issued will be kept to a minimum by the FAA consistent with achievement of the necessary objective. Situations which warrant the extreme restrictions of FAR 91.137(a)(1) include, but are not limited to: toxic gas leaks or spills, flammable agents, or fumes which if fanned by rotor or propeller wash could endanger persons or property on the surface, or if entered by an aircraft could endanger persons or property in the air; imminent volcano eruptions which could endanger airborne aircraft and occupants; nuclear accident or incident; and hijackings. Situations which warrant the restrictions associated with FAR 91.137(a)(2) include: forest fires which are being fought by releasing fire retardants from aircraft; and aircraft relief activities following a disaster (earthquake, tidal wave, flood, etc.). FAR 91.137(a)(3) restrictions are established for events and incidents that would attract an unsafe congestion of sight-seeing aircraft.

   f. The amount of airspace needed to protect persons and property or provide a safe environment for rescue/relief aircraft operations is normally limited to within 2,000 feet above the surface and within a 2-nautical-mile radius. Incidents occurring within an Airport Traffic Area (ATA) or Terminal Control Area (TCA) will normally be handled through existing procedures and should not require the issuance of temporary flight restrictions NOTAM.

g. The FSS nearest the incident site is normally the coordination facility. When FAA communications assistance is required, the designated FSS will function as the primary communications facility for coordination between emergency control authorities and affected aircraft. The ARTCC may act as liaison for the emergency control if adequate communications cannot be established between the designated FSS and the relief organization. For example, the coordination facility may relay authorizations from the on-scene emergency response official in cases where news media aircraft operations are approved at the altitudes used by relief aircraft.

h. ATC may authorize operations in a temporary flight restrictions area under its own authority only when flight restrictions are established under FAR 91.137(a)(2) and 91.137(a)(3) and only when such operations are conducted under instrument flight rules (IFR). The appropriate ARTCC/air traffic control tower manager will, however, ensure that such authorized flights do not hamper activities or interfere with the event for which restrictions are implemented. However, ATC will not authorize local IFR flights into the temporary flight restrictions area.

i. To preclude misunderstanding, the implementing NOTAM will contain specific and formatted information. The facility establishing the temporary flight restrictions area will format a NOTAM beginning with the phrase "flight restrictions" followed by: the location of the temporary flight restrictions area; the effective period; the area defined in statute miles; the altitudes affected; the FAA coordination facility and commercial telephone number; the reason for the temporary flight restrictions; the agency directing any relief activities and its commercial telephone number; and other information considered appropriate by the issuing authority.

EXAMPLE - FAR 91.137(a)(1):
> The following NOTAM prohibits all aircraft operations except those specified in the NOTAM. FLIGHT RESTRICTIONS MATTHEWS, VIRGINIA, EFFECTIVE IMMEDIATELY UNTIL 1200 GMT JANUARY 20, 1987. PURSUANT TO FAR 91.137(A)(1) TEMPORARY FLIGHT RESTRICTIONS ARE IN EFFECT. RESCUE OPERATIONS IN EFFECT. ONLY RELIEF AIRCRAFT OPERATIONS UNDER THE DIRECTION OF THE DEPARTMENT OF DEFENSE ARE AUTHORIZED IN THE AIRSPACE AT AND BELOW 5,000 FEET MSL WITHIN A TWO-MILE RADIUS OF LASER AFB, MATTHEWS, VIRGINIA. COMMANDER, LASER AFB, IN CHARGE (897)-946-5543. STEENSON FSS IS THE FAA COORDINATION FACILITY (792)-555-6141.

EXAMPLE - FAR 91.137(a)(2):

The following NOTAM permits the on-site emergency response official to authorize media aircraft operations below the altitudes used by the relief aircraft. FLIGHT RESTRICTIONS 25 MILES EAST OF BRANSOME, IDAHO, EFFECTIVE IMMEDIATELY UNTIL 2359 GMT JANUARY 20, 1987. PURSUANT TO FAR 91.137(a)(2) TEMPORARY FLIGHT RESTRICTIONS ARE IN EFFECT WITHIN A FOUR-MILE RADIUS OF THE INTERSECTIONS OF COUNTY ROADS 564 AND 315 AT AND BELOW 3,500 FEET MSL TO PROVIDE A SAFE ENVIRONMENT FOR THE FIRE FIGHTING AIRCRAFT OPERATIONS. DAVIS COUNTY SHERIFF'S DEPARTMENT (792)-555-1818 IS THE FAA COORDINATION FACILITY.

EXAMPLE - FAR 91.137(a)(3)

The following NOTAM prohibits sight-seeing aircraft operations. FLIGHT RESTRICTIONS BROWN, TENNESSEE, DUE TO OLYMPIC ACTIVITY. EFFECTIVE 1100 GMT JUNE 18, 1987, UNTIL 0200 GMT JULY 19, 1987. PURSUANT TO FAR 91.137(a)(3) TEMPORARY FLIGHT RESTRICTIONS ARE IN EFFECT WITHIN A THREE-MILE RADIUS OF THE BASSAT SPORTS COMPLEX AT AND BELOW 2,500 FEET MSL. NORTON FSS (423)-555-6742 IS THE FAA COORDINATION FACILITY.

5-5 Flight Limitations/Prohibitions.

a. Flight limitations in the proximity of space flight operations are designated in a Notice to Airmen (NOTAM). FAR 91.143 provides protection from potentially hazardous situations for pilots and space flight crews and costly delays of shuttle operations.

b. Flight restrictions in the proximity of Presidential and other parties are put into effect because numerous aircraft and large assemblies of persons may be attracted to areas to be visited or traveled by the President or Vice President, heads of foreign states, and other public figures. Such conditions may create a hazard to aircraft engaged in air commerce and to persons or property on the ground. In addition, responsible agencies of the United States government may determine that certain regulatory actions should be taken in the interest of providing protection of these public figures. FAR 91.141 provides for the issuance of a regulatory NOTAM to establish flight restrictions where required in such cases.

5-6 Parachute Jump Aircraft Operations.

a. Procedures related to parachute jump areas are contained in FAR 105. Tabulations of parachute jump areas in the U.S. are contained in the Airport/Facility Directory.

b. Pilots of aircraft engaged in parachute jump operations are reminded that all reported altitudes must be with reference to mean sea level, or flight level, as appropriate, to enable ATC to provide meaningful traffic information.

TEST QUESTIONS

1. What is the minimum flight visibility required for VFR flight in controlled airspace above 1,200 feet AGL and below 10,000 feet MSL?

A. 1 mile.
B. 2 miles.
C. 3 miles.

2. The Continental Control Area begins at

A. 12,500 feet.
B. 14,500 feet.
C. 18,000 feet.

3. The Postive Control Area begins at

A. 12,500 feet.
B. 14,500 feet.
C. 18,000 feet.

4. A broken blue line on a sectional chart depicts a(n)

A. Control Zone.
B. Airport Traffic Area.
C. Terminal Control Area.

5. Which of the following is required to operate within a Terminal Control Area (TCA)?

A. ADF
B. RMI
C. 4096 code transponder.

6. The inner circle of an Airport Radar Service Area (ARSA) extends up to

A. 1,200 feet AGL.
B. 4,000 feet AGL.
C. 4,000 feet MSL.

7. What pilot certification is required to operate in an ARSA?

A. Private pilot certificate.
B. Instrument rating.
C. No specific certificate required.

8. In order to penetrate a Restricted Area the pilot must

A. possess at least a private pilot certificate.
B. obtain permission before entering.
C. have an operable 4096 code transponder on board the aircraft.

9. An Airport Traffic Area (ATA) has a horizontal radius of

A. 3 nautical miles.
B. 5 nautical miles.
C. 5 statute miles.

10. A Military Training Route (MTR) identified by a four-digit number indicates operations on that route will occur

A. at or above 1,500 feet AGL.
B. at or below 1,500 feet AGL.
C. above 1,200 feet AGL.

ANSWERS

1. C 2. B 3. C 4. A 5. C 6. B 7. C 8. B 9. C 10. B

AIR TRAFFIC CONTROL

SECTION 1. SERVICES AVAILABLE TO PILOTS

1-1 Air Route Traffic Control Centers.

Centers are established primarily to provide Air Traffic Service to aircraft operating on IFR flight plans within controlled airspace, and principally during the en route phase of flight.

1-2 Control Towers.

Towers have been established to provide for a safe, orderly, and expeditious flow of traffic on and in the vicinity of an airport. When the responsibility has been so delegated, towers also provide for the separation of IFR aircraft in the terminal areas.

1-3 Flight Service Stations (FSS).

Flight Service Stations (FSS) are air traffic facilities that provide pilot briefings, en route communications, and VFR search and rescue services; assist lost aircraft and aircraft in emergency situations; relay ATC clearances; originate Notices to Airmen (NOTAMs); broadcast aviation weather and NAS information; receive and process IFR flight plans; and monitor NAVAIDs. In addition, at selected locations FSSs provide En Route Flight Advisory Service (EFAS), which is known as Flight Watch, and take weather observations, issue airport advisories, and advise Customs and Immigration of transborder flights.

1-4 Recording and Monitoring.

 a. Calls to Air Traffic Control (ATC) facilities (ARTCCs, Towers, FSSs, Central Flow, and Operations Centers) over radio and ATC operational telephone lines (lines used for operational purposes such as controller instructions, briefings, opening and closing flight plans, issuances of IFR clearances and amendments, counterhijacking activities, etc.) may be monitored and recorded for accident prevention, search and rescue purposes, specialist training and evaluation, and technical evaluation and repair of control and communications systems.

b. Where the public access telephone is recorded, a beeper tone is not required. In the place of the "beep" tone the FCC has substituted a mandatory requirement that persons to be recorded be given notice they are to be recorded and that they must give their consent (if the recording is to continue). Notice is given by this entry, consent to record is assumed by the individual placing a call to the operational facility.

1-5 Pilot Visits to Air Traffic Facilities.

Pilots are encouraged to visit air traffic facilities (Towers, Centers, and FSSs) and participate in Operation Raincheck. Operation Raincheck is a program designed to familiarize pilots with the ATC system, its functions, responsibilities, and benefits. On rare occasions facilities may not be able to approve a visit because of ATC workload or other reasons. It is therefore requested that pilots contact the facilities prior to the visit and advise of the number of persons in the group, the time and date of the proposed visit, and the primary interest of the group. With this information available, the facility can prepare an itinerary and have someone available to guide the group through the facility.

1-6 Approach Control Service for VFR Arriving Aircraft.

a. Numerous approach control facilities have established programs for arriving VFR aircraft to contact approach control for landing information. This information includes: wind, runway, and altimeter setting at the airport of intended landing. This information may be omitted if contained in the ATIS broadcast and the pilot states the appropriate ATIS code.

NOTE. - Pilot use of "have numbers" does not indicate receipt of the ATIS broadcast. In addition, the controller will provide traffic advisories on a workload-permitting basis.

b. Such information will be furnished upon initial contact with the concerned approach control facility. The pilot will be requested to change to the tower frequency at a predetermined time or point, to receive further landing information.

c. Where available, use of this procedure will not hinder the operation of VFR flights by requiring excessive spacing between aircraft or devious routing.

d. Compliance with this procedure is not mandatory but pilot participation is encouraged.

1-7 Traffic Advisory Practices at Airports Without Operating Control Towers.

   a. Airport Operations Without Operating Control Towers.

   1. There is no substitute for alertness while in the vicinity of an airport. It is essential that pilots be alert and look for other traffic and exchange traffic information when approaching or departing an airport without an operating control tower. This is of particular importance since other aircraft may not have communication capability or, in some cases, pilots may not communicate their presence or intentions when operating into or out of such airports. To achieve the greatest degree of safety, it is essential that all radio-equipped aircraft transmit/ receive on a common frequency identified for the purpose of airport advisories.

   2. An airport may have a full- or part-time tower or flight service station (FSS) located on the airport, a full- or part-time UNICOM station or no aeronautical station at all. There are three ways for pilots to communicate their intention and obtain airport/ traffic information when operating at an airport that does not have an operating control tower: by communicating with an FSS or a UNICOM operator, or by making a self-announced broadcast.

   b. Communicating on a Common Frequency.

   1. The key to communicating at an airport without an operating control tower is selection of the correct common frequency. The acronym CTAF, which stands for Common Traffic Advisory Frequency, is synonymous with this program. A CTAF is a frequency designated for the purpose of carrying out airport advisory practices while operating to or from an airport without an operating control tower. The CTAF may be a UNICOM, MULTICOM, FSS, or tower frequency and is identified in the appropriate aeronautical publication.

   2. The CTAF frequency for a particular airport is contained in the Airport/ Facility Directory (A/FD), Alaskan Supplement, Alaskan Terminal Publication, Instrument Approach Procedure Charts, and Standard Instrument Departure Charts (SID) charts. Also, the CTAF frequency can be obtained by contacting any FSS. Use of the appropriate CTAF, combined with a visual alertness and application of the following recommended good operating practices, will enhance safety of flights into and out of all uncontrolled airports.

   c. Recommended Traffic Advisory Practices.

All inbound traffic should monitor and communicate as appropriate on the designated CTAF from 10 miles out up to landing. Departing aircraft should monitor/communicate on the appropriate frequency from start-up, during taxi, and until 10 miles from the airport unless the FARs or local procedures require otherwise.

d. Airport Advisory Service Provided by an FSS.

1. Airport Advisory Service (AAS) is a service provided by an FSS physically located on an airport that does not have a control tower or where the tower is open on a part-time basis. The CTAF for FSSs which provide the service will be disseminated in appropriate aeronautical publications.

2. In communicating with a CTAF FSS, establish two-way communications before transmitting inbound/outbound intentions or information. At approximately 10 miles from the airport, an inbound aircraft should: report altitude and aircraft type, location relative to the airport; state whether landing or overflight; and request airport advisory. Departing aircraft should state the aircraft type, full identification number, type of flight planned (ie., VFR or IFR), and the planned destination or direction of flight. Report before taxiing and before taxiing onto the runway for departure. If communications with a UNICOM are necessary after initial report to FSS, return to FSS frequency for traffic update.

EXAMPLE: (Inbound)
> DAYTON RADIO, CESSNA ONE SEVEN ZERO SIERRA UNIFORM IS TEN MILES SOUTH, THREE THOUSAND FIVE HUNDRED, LANDING DAYTON. REQUEST AIRPORT ADVISORY.

EXAMPLE: (Outbound)
> DAYTON RADIO, CESSNA ONE SEVEN ZERO SIERRA UNIFORM, READY TO TAXI, VFR DEPARTING TO THE SOUTHWEST. REQUEST AIRPORT ADVISORY.

3. A CTAF FSS provides wind direction and velocity, favored or designated runway, altimeter setting, known traffic, Notices to Airmen, airport taxi routes, airport traffic pattern information, and instrument approach procedures. The elements are varied so as best to serve the current traffic situation. Some airport managers have specified that under certain wind or other conditions, designated runways should be used. Pilots should advise the FSS of the runway they intend to use. CAUTION: All aircraft in the vicinity of an airport may not be in communication with the FSS.

e. Information Provided by Aeronautical Advisory Stations.

1. UNICOM is a nongovernment air/ground radio communication station

which may provide airport information at public use airports where there is no tower or FSS.

   2. On pilot request, UNICOM stations may provide pilots with weather information, wind direction, the recommended runway, or other necessary information. If the UNICOM frequency is designated as the CTAF, it will be identified in the appropriate aeronautical publications.

   3. Should airport advisory service by an FSS, or Aeronautical Advisory Station (UNICOM) be unavailable, wind and weather information may be obtainable from nearby controlled airports via Automatic Terminal Information Service (ATIS) or Automated Weather Observing System (AWOS) frequency.

 f. Self-Announce Position and/or Intentions.

   1. General. Self-announced is a procedure whereby pilots broadcast their intentions or intended flight activity or ground operation on the designated CTAF. This procedure is used primarily at airports which do not have an FSS on the field. The self-announced procedure should also be used if a pilot is unable to communicate with the FSS on the designated CTAF.

   2. If an airport has a tower and it is temporarily closed, or operated on a part-time basis and there is no FSS on the field or the FSS is closed, use the CTAF to self-announce your position or intentions.

   3. Where there is no tower, FSS, or UNICOM station on the airport, use MULTICOM frequency 122.9 for self-announce procedures. Such airports will be identified in appropriate aeronautical information publications.

   4. Recommended Self-announce Phraseologies. It should be noted that aircraft operating to or from another nearby airport may be making self-announce broadcasts on the same UNICOM or MULTICOM frequency. To help identify one airport from another, the airport name should be spoken at the beginning and end of each self-announce transmission.

EXAMPLE: (Inbound)
   UNION COUNTY TRAFFIC, CESSNA ONE SEVEN ZERO SIERRA
   UNIFORM, FIVE MILES SOUTH, TWO THOUSAND FEET, ENTER-
   ING LEFT DOWNWIND, RUNWAY TWO SEVEN FULL STOP,
   UNION COUNTY.

EXAMPLE: (Outbound)
   UNION COUNTY TRAFFIC, CESSNA ONE SEVEN ZERO SIERRA
   UNIFORM, MAIN RAMP, TAXIING TO RUNWAY TWO SEVEN
   UNION COUNTY. UNION COUNTY TRAFFIC CESSNA ONE SEVEN

ZERO SIERRA UNIFORM DEPARTING RUNWAY TWO SEVEN. WILL BE DEPARTING THE PATTERN SOUTHWEST, CLIMBING TO TWO THOUSAND FIVE HUNDRED UNION COUNTY.

g. UNICOM Communications Procedures.

1. In communicating with a UNICOM station, the following practices will help reduce frequency congestion, facilitate a better understanding of pilot intentions, help identify the location of aircraft in the traffic pattern, and enhance safety of flight:

(a). Select the correct UNICOM frequency.

(b). State the identification of the UNICOM station you are calling in each transmission.

(c). Speak slowly and distinctly.

(d). Report approximately 10 miles from the airport stating altitude, aircraft type, aircraft identification, location relative to airport, your intentions, and request wind information and active runway.

(e). Report on downwind, base, and final approach.

(f). Report clear of runway.

2. Recommended UNICOM phraseologies:

EXAMPLE: (Inbound)

DELAWARE UNICOM, CESSNA ONE SEVEN ZERO SIERRA UNIFORM TEN MILES SOUTH DESCENDING OUT OF FOUR THOUSAND FEET, LANDING DELAWARE, REQUESTING WIND AND RUNWAY INFORMATION. DELAWARE TRAFFIC, CESSNA ONE ZERO SEVEN SIERRA UNIFORM ENTERING DOWNWIND, FOR FULL STOP RUNWAY TWO SEVEN, DELAWARE. DELAWARE TRAFFIC, CESSNA ONE SEVEN ZERO SIERRA UNIFORM CLEAR OF RUNWAY TWO SEVEN, DELAWARE.

EXAMPLE: (Outbound)

DELAWARE UNICOM, CESSNA ONE SEVEN ZERO SIERRA UNIFORM, ON MAIN RAMP, TAXIING TO RUNWAY TWO SEVEN, REQUEST WIND AND TRAFFIC INFORMATION, DELAWARE. DELAWARE TRAFFIC, CESSNA ONE SEVEN ZERO SIERRA UNIFORM, DEPARTING RUNWAY TWO SEVEN, DEPARTING THE PATTERN TO THE NORTHWEST, DELAWARE.

1-8 Automatic Terminal Information System (ATIS).

a. ATIS is the continuous broadcast of recorded noncontrol information in selected high-activity terminal areas. Its purpose is to improve controller effectiveness and to relieve frequency congestion by automating the repetitive transmission of essential but routine information. Pilots are urged to cooperate in the ATIS program as it relieves frequency congestion on approach control, ground control, and local control frequencies. The Airport Facility/Directory indicates airports for which ATIS is provided.

b. ATIS information includes the time of the latest weather sequence, ceiling, visibility (if the weather is above ceiling/sky condition of 5,000 feet and visibility is 5 miles or greater, inclusion of the ceiling/sky condition, visibility, and obstructions to vision in the ATIS message is optional), obstructions to visibility, temperature, dewpoint (if available), wind direction (magnetic) and velocity, altimeter, other pertinent remarks, instrument approach, and runways in use is continuously broadcast on the voice feature of a TVOR, VOR, VORTAC located on or near the airport, or in a discrete VHF/UHF frequency. The departure runway will only be given if different from the landing runway except at locations having a separate ATIS for departure. Where VFR arrival aircraft are expected to make initial contact with approach control, this fact and the appropriate frequencies may be broadcast on ATIS. Pilots of aircraft arriving or departing the terminal area can receive the continuous ATIS broadcasts at times when the cockpit duties are least pressing and listen to as many repeats as desired. ATIS broadcasts shall be updated upon the receipt of any official weather, regardless of content change and reported values. A new recording will also be made when there is a change in other pertinent data runway change, instrument approach in use, etc.

EXAMPLE:

DULLES INTERNATIONAL INFORMATION SIERRA. 1300 ZULU WEATHER. MEASURED CEILING THREE THOUSAND OVERCAST. VISIBILITY THREE, SMOKE. TEMPERATURE SIX EIGHT. WIND THREE FIVE ZERO AT EIGHT. ALTIMETER TWO NINER NINER TWO. ILS RUNWAY TWO SEVEN LEFT APPROACH IN USE. LANDING AND DEPARTING RUNWAY TWO SEVEN LEFT AND TWO SEVEN RIGHT. JOEY VOR OUT OF SERVICE. ADVISE ON INITIAL CONTACT YOU HAVE INFORMATION SIERRA.

c. Pilots should listen to ATIS broadcasts whenever ATIS is in operation.

d. Pilots should notify controllers on initial contact that they have received the ATIS broadcast by repeating the alphabetical code word appended to the broadcast.

EXAMPLE:
    INFORMATION SIERRA RECEIVED.

e. When pilots acknowledge that they have received the ATIS broadcast, controllers may omit those items contained in the broadcast if they are current. Rapidly changing conditions will be issued by ATC and the ATIS will contain words as follows:

EXAMPLE:
    LATEST CEILING, VISIBILITY, ALTIMETER, WIND,
    (OTHER CONDITIONS), WILL BE ISSUED BY APPROACH CON-
    TROL/TOWER.

NOTE. - The absence of a sky condition or ceiling and/or visibility on ATIS indicates a sky condition or ceiling of 5,000 feet or above and visibility of 5 miles or more. A remark may be made on the broadcast, "The weather is better than 5,000 and 5," or the existing weather may be broadcast.

f. Controllers will issue pertinent information to pilots who do not acknowledge receipt of a broadcast or who acknowledge receipt of a broadcast which is not current.

g. To serve frequency limited aircraft, FSSs are equipped to transmit on the omnirange frequency at most en route VORs used as ATIS voice outlets. Such communication interrupts the ATIS broadcast. Pilots of aircraft equipped to receive on other FSS frequencies are encouraged to do so in order that these override transmissions may be kept to an absolute minimum.

h. While it is good operating practice for pilots to make use of the ATIS broadcast where it is available, some pilots use the phrase "have numbers" in communications with the control tower. Use of this phrase indicates the pilot has received wind, runway and altimeter information ONLY and the tower does not have to repeat this information. It does not indicate receipt of the ATIS broadcast and should never be used for this purpose.

1-9 Radar Traffic Information Service.

This is a service provided by radar ATC facilities. Pilots receiving this service are advised of any radar target observed on the radar display which may be in such proximity to the position of their aircraft or its intended route of flight that it

168

warrants their attention. This service is not intended to relieve the pilots of their responsibility for continual vigilance to see and avoid other aircraft.

a. Purpose of the Service.

1. The issuance of traffic information as observed on a radar display is based on the principle of assisting and advising pilots that a particular radar target's position and track indicates it may intersect or pass in such proximity to their intended flight path that it warrants their attention. This is to alert pilots to the traffic so that they can be on the lookout for it and thereby be in a better position to take appropriate action should the need arise.

2. Pilots are reminded that the surveillance radar used by ATC does not provide altitude information unless the aircraft is equipped with Mode C and the Radar Facility is capable of displaying altitude information.

b. Provisions of the Service.

1. Many factors, such as limitations of the radar, volume of traffic, controller workload, and communications frequency congestion could prevent the controller from providing this service. The controller possesses complete discretion for determining whether he is able to provide or continue to provide this service in a specific case. His reason against providing or continuing to provide the service in a particular case is not subject to question nor need it be communicated to the pilot. In other words, the provision of this service is entirely dependent on whether the controller believes he is in a position to provide it. Traffic information is routinely provided to all aircraft operating on IFR Flight Plans except when the pilot advises he does not desire the service, or the pilot is operating within positive controlled airspace. Traffic information may be provided to flights not operating on IFR Flight Plans when requested by pilots of such flights.

NOTE. - Radar ATC facilities normally display and monitor both primary and secondary radar when it is available, except that secondary radar may be used as the sole display source in Positive Control Airspace (PCA), and under some circumstances outside of PCA (beyond primary coverage and en route areas where only secondary is available). Secondary radar may also be used outside PCA as the sole display source when the primary radar is temporarily unusable or out of service. Pilots in contact with the affected ATC facility are normally advised when a temporary outage occurs; e.g., "primary radar out of service; traffic advisories available on transponder aircraft only." This means simply that only the aircraft which have transponders installed and in use will be depicted on ATC radar indicators when the primary radar is out of service

2. When receiving VFR radar advisory service, pilots should monitor the assigned frequency at all times. This is to preclude controllers' concern for radio failure or emergency assistance for aircraft under his jurisdiction. VFR radar advisory service does not vector away from conflicting traffic unless requested by the pilot. When advisory service is no longer desired, advise the controller before changing frequencies and then change your transponder code to 1200, if applicable.

169

Pilots should also inform the controller when changing VFR cruising altitude. Except in programs where radar service is automatically terminated, the controller will advise the aircraft when radar is terminated.

NOTE. - Participation by VFR pilots in formal programs implemented at certain terminal locations constitutes pilot request. This also applies to participating pilots at those locations where arriving VFR flights are encouraged to make their first contact with the tower on the approach control frequency.

c. Issuance of Traffic Information - Traffic information will include the following concerning a target which may constitute traffic for an aircraft that is:

    1. Radar identified:

        (a) Azimuth from the aircraft in terms of the 12 hour clock, or

        (b) When rapidly maneuvering civil test or military aircraft prevent accurate issuance of traffic as in (a) above, specify the direction from an aircraft's position in terms of the eight cardinal compass points (N,NE, E, SE, S, SW, W, NW). This method shall be terminated at the pilot's request.

        (c) Distance from the aircraft in nautical miles;

        (d) Direction in which the target is proceeding; and

        (e) Type of aircraft and altitude if known.

EXAMPLE:
      TRAFFIC 10 O'CLOCK, 3 MILES, WEST-BOUND (TYPE AIRCRAFT AND ALTITUDE, IF KNOWN, OF THE OBSERVED TRAFFIC).

The altitude may be known, by means of Mode C, but not verified with the pilot for accuracy. (To be valid for separation purposes by ATC, the accuracy of Mode C readouts must be verified. This is usually accomplished upon initial entry into the radar system by a comparison of the readout to pilot stated altitude, or the field elevation in the case of continuous readout being received from an aircraft on the airport.) When necessary to issue traffic advisories containing unverified altitude information, the controller will isue the advisory in the same manner as if it were verified due to the accuracy of these readouts. The pilot may upon receipt of traffic information request a vector (heading) to avoid such traffic. The vector will be provided to the extent possible as determined by the controller, provided the aircraft to be vectored is within the airspace under the jurisdiction of the controller.

2. Not radar identified:
    (a) Distance and direction with respect to a fix;
    (b) Direction in which the target is proceeding; and
    (c) Type of aircraft and altitude if known.

EXAMPLE:
    TRAFFIC 8 MILES SOUTH OF THE AIRPORT NORTHEAST BOUND,
    (TYPE AIRCRAFT AND ALTITUDE IF KNOWN).

d. The examples depicted in the following figures point out the possible error in the position of this traffic when it is necessary for a pilot to apply drift correction to maintain this track. This error could also occur in the event a change in course is made at the time radar traffic information is issued.

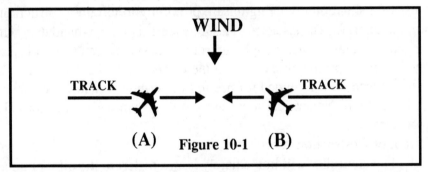

Figure 10-1

1. In the figure above traffic information would be issued to the pilot of aircraft "A" as 12 o'clock. The actual position of the traffic as seen by the pilot of aircraft "A" would be 2 o'clock. Traffic information issued to aircraft "B" would also be given as 12 o'clock, but in this case, the pilot of "B" would see his traffic at 10 o'clock.

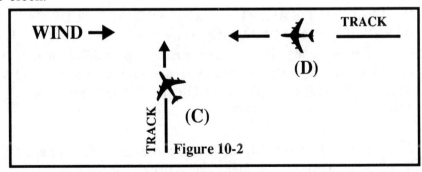

Figure 10-2

2. In the figure above traffic information would be issued to the pilot of aircraft "C" as 2 o'clock. The actual position of the traffic as seen by the pilot of

171

aircraft "C" would be 3 o'clock. Traffic information issued to aircraft "D" would be at an 11 o'clock position. Since it is not necessary for the pilot of aircraft "D" to apply wind correction (crab) to make good his track, the actual position of the traffic issued would be correct. Since the radar controller can only observe aircraft track (course) on his radar screen, he must issue traffic advisories accordingly, and pilots should give due consideration to this fact when looking for reported traffic.

1-10 Safety Alert.

A safety alert will be issued to pilots of aircraft being controlled by ATC if the controller is aware the aircraft is at an altitude which, in the controller's judgement, places the aircraft in unsafe proximity to terrain, obstructions, or other aircraft. The provision of this service is contingent upon the capability of the controller to have awareness of a situation involving unsafe proximity to terrain, obstructions, and uncontrolled aircraft. The issuance of a safety alert cannot be mandated, but it can be expected on a reasonable, though intermittent basis. Once the alert is issued, it is solely the pilot's prerogative to determine what course of action, if any, he will take. This procedure is intended for use in time-critical situations where aircraft safety is in question. Noncritical situations should be handled via the normal traffic alert procedures.

   a. Terrain or Obstruction Alert:

   1. The controller will immediately issue an alert to the pilot of an aircraft under his control when he recognizes that the aircraft is at an altitude which, in his judgment, may be in unsafe proximity to terrain/obstructions. The primary method of detecting unsafe proximity is through Mode C automatic altitude reports.

EXAMPLE:
   "LOW ALTITUDE ALERT, CHECK YOUR ALTITUDE IMMEDI-
   ATELY. THE (MEA/MVA/MOCA) IN YOUR AREA IS (ALTITUDE).
   If past the final approach fix (nonprecision approach) or the outer marker
   or fix used in lieu of the outer marker (precision approach), "LOW
   ALTITUDE ALERT, CHECK YOUR ALTITUDE IMMEDIATELY.
   THE (MDA/DH) IS (ALTITUDE)."

   2. Terminal ARTS IIA, III, and IIIA facilities have an automated function which, if operating, alerts a controller when a tracked Mode C equipped aircraft under his control is below or predicted to be below a predetermined minimum safe altitude. This function, called Minimum Safe Altitude Warning (MSAW), is

designed solely as a controller aid in detecting potentially unsafe aircraft proximity to terrain/obstructions. The ARTS IIA, III, and IIIA facility will, when MSAW is operating, provide MSAW monitoring for all aircraft with an operating Mode C altitude encoding transponder that are tracked by the system and are:

   (a) Operating on an IFR flight plan, or

   (b) Operating on VFR and have requested MSAW monitoring.

   3. Terminal AN/TPX-42A (number beacon decoder system) facilities have an automated function called Low Altitude Alert System (LAAS). Although not as sophisticated as MSAW, LAAS alerts the controller when a Mode C transponder-equipped aircraft operating on an IFR flight plan is below a predetermined minimum safe altitude.

NOTE. - Pilots operating VFR may request MSAW or LAAS monitoring if their aircraft are equipped with Mode C transponders.

EXAMPLE:
   CESSNA THREE ZERO SIERRA UNIFORM REQUEST (MSAW/ LAAS).

   b. Aircraft Conflict Alert.

   1. The controller will immediately issue an alert to the pilot of an aircraft under his control if he is aware of another aircraft which is not under his control that is at an altitude which, in the controller's judgment, places both aircraft in unsafe proximity to each other. With the alert, when feasible, the controller will offer the pilot the position of the traffic (if time permits) and an alternate course(s) of action. Any alternate course of action the controller may recommend to the pilot will be predicated only on other traffic under his control.

EXAMPLE:
   CESSNA ONE ZERO SIERRA UNIFORM, TRAFFIC ALERT (POSI-TION OF TRAFFIC IF TIME PERMITS) ADVISE YOU TURN (RIGHT/ LEFT) HEADING (DEGREES) AND/OR CLIMB/DESCEND TO (AL-TITUDE) IMMEDIATELY.

1-11 Radar Assistance to VFR Aircraft.

   a. Radar equipped FAA ATC facilities provide radar assistance and navigation service (vectors) to VFR aircraft provided the aircraft can communicate with the facility, are within radar coverage, and can be radar identified.

b. Pilots should clearly understand that authorization to proceed in accordance with such radar navigational assistance does not constitute authorization for the pilot to violate FARs. In effect, assistance provided is on the basis that navigational guidance information issued is advisory in nature and the job of flying the aircraft safely, remains with the pilot.

c. In many cases, the controller will be unable to determine if flight into instrument conditions will result from his instructions. To avoid possible hazards resulting from being vectored into IFR conditions, pilots should keep the controller advised of weather conditions in which he is operating and along the course ahead.

d. Radar navigation assistance (vectors) may be initiated by the controller when one of the following conditions exist:

    1. The controller suggests the vector and the pilot concurs.

    2. A special program has been established and vectoring service has been advertised.

    3. In the controller's judgment, the vector is necessary for air safety.

e. Radar navigation assistance (vectors) and other radar-derived information may be provided in response to pilot requests. Many factors such as limitations of radar, volume of traffic, communications frequency, congestion, and controller workload could prevent the controller from providing it. The controller has complete discretion for determining if he is able to provide the service in a particular case. His decision not to provide the service in a particular case is not subject to question.

1-12 Terminal Radar Programs for VFR Aircraft.

a. Basic Radar Service.

    1. In addition to the use of radar for the control of IFR traffic, all commissioned radar facilities provide traffic advisories and limited vectoring (on a workload permitting basis) to VFR aircraft.

NOTE. - When the Stage services were developed, two basic radar services (traffic advisories and limited vectoring) were identified as Stage I. This definition became, over the years, unnecessary. Therefore, the term Stage I has been eliminated from use in the field and the handbooks. These basic services will still be provided by all commissioned terminal radar facilities whether they are Stage II, III, or neither.

    2. Vectoring service may be provided when requested by the pilot or with pilot concurrence when suggested by ATC.

    3. Pilots of arriving aircraft should contact approach control on the publicized frequency and give their position, altitude, radar beacon code (if transponder equipped), destination, and request traffic information.

4. Approach control will issue wind and runway, except when the pilot states "have numbers" or this information is contained in the ATIS broadcast and the pilot indicates he has received the ATIS information. Traffic information is provided on a workload-permitting basis. Approach control will specify the time and place at which the pilot is to contact the tower on local control frequency for further landing information. Upon being told to contact the tower, radar service is automatically terminated.

b. Stage II Service (Radar Advisory and Sequencing for VFR Aircraft).

1. This service has been implemented at certain terminal locations. (See locations listed in the Airport/Facility Directory.) The purpose of the service is to adjust the flow of arriving VFR and IFR aircraft into the traffic pattern in a safe and orderly manner and to provide radar traffic information to departing VFR aircraft. Pilot participation is urged but is not mandatory.

2. Pilots of arriving VFR aircraft should initiate radio contact on the publicized frequency with approach control when approximately 25 miles from the airport at which Stage II services are being provided. On initial contact by VFR aircraft, approach control will assume that Stage II service is requested. Approach control will provide the pilot with wind and runway (except when the pilot states "have numbers" or that he has received the ATIS information), routings, etc., as necessary for proper sequencing with other participating VFR and IFR traffic en route to the airport. Traffic information will be provided on a workload-permitting basis. If an arriving aircraft does not want the service, the pilot should state "negative stage II" or make a similar comment, on initial contact with approach control.

3. After radar contact is established, the pilot may use pilot navigation to enter the traffic pattern or, depending on traffic conditions, may be instructed by ATC to fly specific headings to position the flight behind a preceding aircraft in the approach sequence. When a flight is positioned behind the preceding aircraft and the pilot reports having that aircraft in sight, the pilot will be instructed to follow the preceding aircraft. THE ATC INSTRUCTION TO FOLLOW THE PRECEDING AIRCRAFT DOES NOT AUTHORIZE THE PILOT TO COMPLY WITH ANY ATC CLEARANCE OR INSTRUCTION ISSUED TO THE PRECEDING AIRCRAFT. If other "nonparticipating" or "local" aircraft are in the traffic pattern, the tower will issue a landing sequence. Radar service will be continued to the runway.

4. Standard radar separation will be provided between IFR aircraft until such time as the aircraft is sequenced and the pilot sees the traffic he is to follow.

Standard radar separation between VFR or between VFR and IFR aircraft will not be provided.

5. Pilots of departing VFR aircraft are encouraged to request radar traffic information by notifying ground control on initial contact with their request and proposed direction of flight.

EXAMPLE:

OHIO STATE GROUND CONTROL, NOVEMBER ONE EIGHT SIX, READY TO TAXI, VFR SOUTHBOUND, HAVE INFORMATION BRAVO AND REQUEST RADAR TRAFFIC INFORMATION.

NOTE. Following takeoff, the tower will advise when to contact departure control.

6. Pilots of aircraft transiting the area and in radar contact/communication with approach control will receive traffic information on a controller workload-permitting basis. Pilots of such aircraft should give their position, altitude, radar beacon code (if transponder equipped), destination, and/ or route of flight.

c. Stage III Service (Radar Sequencing and Separation Service for VFR Aircraft).

1. This service has been implemented at certain terminal locations. The service is advertised in the Airport/Facility Directory. The purpose of this service is to provide separation between all participating VFR aircraft and all IFR aircraft operating within the airspace defined as the Terminal Radar Service Area (TRSA). Pilot participation is urged but it is not mandatory.

2. If any aircraft does not want the service, the pilot should state '"negative stage III" or make a similar comment, on initial contact with approach control or ground control, as appropriate.

3. TRSAs are depicted on sectional aeronautical charts and listed in the Airport/Facility Directory.

4. While operating within a TRSA, pilots are provided Stage III service and separation as prescribed in this paragraph. In the event of a radar outage, separation and sequencing of VFR aircraft will be suspended as this service is dependent on radar. The pilot will be advised that the service is not available and issued wind, runway information, and the time or place to contact the tower. Traffic information will be provided on a workload-permitting basis.

5. Visual separation is used when prevailing conditions permit, and it will be applied as follows:

(a) When a VFR flight is positioned behind a preceding aircraft and the pilot reports having that aircraft in sight, the pilot will be instructed by ATC to follow the preceding aircraft. THE ATC INSTRUCTION TO FOLLOW THE PRECEDING AIRCRAFT DOES NOT AUTHORIZE THE PILOT TO COMPLY WITH ANY ATC CLEARANCE OR INSTRUCTION ISSUED TO THE PRECEDING AIRCRAFT. Radar service will be continued to the runway.

(b) When an IFR aircraft is being sequenced with other traffic and the pilot reports seeing the aircraft that the pilot is to follow, the pilot may be instructed by ATC to follow it and will be cleared for a "visual approach." THE ATC INSTRUCTION TO FOLLOW THE PRECEDING AIRCRAFT DOES NOT AUTHORIZE THE PILOT TO COMPLY WITH ANY ATC CLEARANCE OR INSTRUCTION ISSUED TO THE PRECEDING AIRCRAFT.

(c) If other "nonparticipating" or "local" aircraft are in the traffic pattern, the tower will issue a landing sequence.

(d) Departing VFR aircraft may be asked if they can visually follow a preceding departure out of the TRSA. If the pilot concurs, he will be directed to follow it until leaving the TRSA.

6. Until visual separation is obtained, standard vertical or radar separation will be provided.

(a) 1,000 feet vertical separation may be used between IFR aircraft.

(b) 500 feet vertical separation may be used between VFR aircraft, or between a VFR and an IFR aircraft.

(c) Radar separation varies depending on size of aircraft and aircraft distance from the radar antenna. The minimum separation used will be 1 1/2 miles for most VFR aircraft under 12,500 pounds GWT. If being separated from larger aircraft, the minimum is increased appropriately.

7. Pilots operating VFR under Stage III in a TRSA -

(a) Must maintain an altitude when assigned by ATC unless the altitude assignment is to maintain at or below a specified altitude. ATC may assign altitudes for separation that do not conform to FAR 91.159. When the altitude assignment is no longer needed for separation or when leaving the TRSA, the instruction will be broadcast, "resume appropriate VFR altitudes." Pilots must then return to an altitude that conforms to FAR 91.159 as soon as practicable.

(b) When not assigned an altitude, the pilot should coordinate with ATC prior to any altitude change.

8. Within the TRSA, traffic information on observed but unidentified targets will, to the extent possible, be provided all IFR and participating VFR aircraft. At the request of the pilot, he will be vectored to avoid the observed traffic, insofar as possible, provided the aircraft to be vectored is within the airspace under the jurisdiction of the controller.

9. Departing aircraft should inform ATC of their intended destination and/ or route of flight and proposed cruising altitude.

10. ATC will normally advise participating VFR aircraft when leaving the geographical limits of the TRSA. Radar service is not automatically terminated with this advisory unless specifically stated by the controller.

d. Pilot Responsibility: These programs are not to be interpreted as relieving pilots of their responsibilities to see and avoid other traffic operating in basic VFR weather conditions, to adjust their operations and flight path as necessary to preclude serious wake encounters, to maintain appropriate terrain and obstruction clearance, or to remain in weather conditions equal to or better than the minimums required by FAR 91.155. Whenever compliance with a route, heading, and/or altitude is likely to compromise pilot responsibility respecting terrain and obstruction clearance, vortex exposure, and weather minimums, approach control should be so advised and a revised clearance or instruction obtained.

1-13 Tower En Route Control (TEC).

a. TEC is an ATC program to provide a service to aircraft proceeding to and from metropolitan areas. It links designated approach control areas by a network of identified routes made up of the existing airway structure of the National Airspace System. The FAA initiated an expanded TEC program to include as many facilities as possible. The program's intent is to provide an overflow resource in the low-altitude system which would enhance ATC services. A few facilities have historically allowed turbojets to proceed between certain city pairs, such as Milwaukee and Chicago, via tower en route, and these locations may continue this service. However, the expanded TEC program will be applied, generally, for nonturbojet aircraft operating at and below 10,000 feet. The program is entirely within the approach control airspace of multiple terminal facilities. Essentially, it is for relatively short flights. Participating pilots are encouraged to use TEC for flights of 2 hours duration or less. If longer flights are planned, extensive coordination may be required within the multiple complex which could result in unanticipated delays.

b. Pilots requesting TEC are subject to the same delay factor at the destination airport as other aircraft in the ATC system. In addition, departure and en route delays may occur depending upon individual facility workload. When a major metropolitan airport is incurring significant delays, pilots in the TEC program may want to consider an alternative airport experiencing no delay.

c. There are no unique requirements upon pilots to use the TEC program. Normal flight plan filing procedures will ensure proper flight plan processing. Pilots should include the acronym TEC in the remarks section of the flight plan when requesting tower en route.

d. All approach controls in the system may not operate up to the maximum TEC altitude of 10,000 feet. IFR flight may be planned to any satellite airport in proximity to the major primary airport via the same routing.

1-14 Transponder Operation.

a. General.

1. Pilots should be aware that proper application of transponder operating procedures will provide both VFR and IFR aircraft with a higher degree of safety in the environment where high-speed closure rates are possible. Transponders substantially increase the capability of radar to see an aircraft and the Mode C feature enables the controller to quickly determine where potential traffic conflicts may exist. Even VFR pilots who are not in contact with ATC will be afforded greater protection from IFR aircraft and VFR aircraft which are receiving traffic advisories. Nevertheless, pilots should never relax their visual scanning vigilance for other aircraft.

2. Air Traffic Control Radar Beacon System (ATCRBS) is similar to and compatible with military coded radar beacon equipment. Civil Mode A is identical to military Mode 3.

3. Civil and military transponders should be adjusted to the "on" or normal operating position as late as practicable prior to takeoff and to ''off'' or "standby" as soon as practicable after completing landing roll, unless the change to "standby" has been accomplished previously at the request of ATC. IN ALL CASES, WHILE IN CONTROLLED AIRSPACE EACH PILOT OPERATING AN AIRCRAFT EQUIPPED WITH AN OPERABLE ATC TRANSPONDER MAINTAINED IN ACCORDANCE WITH FAR 91.413 SHALL OPERATE THE TRANSPONDER, INCLUDING MODE C IF INSTALLED, ON THE APPROPRIATE CODE OR AS ASSIGNED BY ATC. IN UNCONTROLLED AIRSPACE, THE TRANSPONDER SHOULD BE OPERATING WHILE AIRBORNE UNLESS OTHERWISE REQUESTED BY ATC.

4. If a pilot on an IFR flight cancels his IFR flight plan prior to reaching his destination, he should adjust his transponder according to VFR operations.

5. If entering a U.S. domestic control area from outside the U.S., the pilot should advise on first radio contact with a U.S. radar ATC facility that such equipment is available by adding " transponder" to the aircraft identification.

6. It should be noted by all users of the ATC transponders that the coverage

they can expect is limited to "line of sight." Low altitude or aircraft antenna shielding by the aircraft itself may result in reduced range. Range can be improved by climbing to a higher altitude. It may be possible to minimize antenna shielding by locating the antenna where dead spots are only noticed during abnormal flight attitudes.

b. Transponder Code Designations.

1. For ATC to utilize one or a combination of the 4096 discrete codes, FOUR DIGIT CODE DESIGNATION will be used; e.g., code 2100 will be expressed as TWO ONE ZERO ZERO. Due to the operational characteristics of the rapidly expanding automated air traffic control system, THE LAST TWO DIGITS OF THE SELECTED TRANSPONDER CODE SHOULD ALWAYS READ "00" UNLESS SPECIFICALLY REQUESTED BY ATC TO BE OTHERWISE.

c. Automatic Altitude Reporting (Mode C).

1. Some transponders are equipped with a Mode C automatic altitude reporting capability. This system converts aircraft altitude in 100-foot increments to coded digital information which is transmitted together with Mode C framing pulses to the interrogating radar facility. The manner in which transponder panels are designed differs; therefore, a pilot should be thoroughly familiar with the operation of his transponder so that ATC may realize its full capabilities.

2. Adjust transponder to reply on the Mode A/3 code specified by ATC and, if equipped, to reply on Mode C with altitude reporting capability activated unless deactivation is directed by ATC or unless the installed aircraft equipment has not been tested and calibrated as required by FAR 91.217. If deactivation is required by ATC, turn off the altitude reporting feature of your transponder. An instruction by ATC to "stop altitude sqawk, altitude differs (number of feet) feet," may be an indication that your transponder is transmitting incorrect altitude information or that you have an incorrect altimeter setting. While an incorrect altimeter setting has no effect on the Mode C altitude information transmitted by your transponder (transponders are preset at 29.92), it would cause you to fly at an actual altitude different from your assigned altitude. When a controller indicates that an altitude readout is invalid, the pilot should initiate a check to verify that the aircraft altimeter is set correctly.

3. Pilots of aircraft with operating Mode C altitude reporting transponders should report exact altitude or flight level to the nearest hundred-foot increment when establishing initial contact with an ATC facility. Exact altitude or flight level reports on initial contact provide ATC with information that is required prior to using Mode C altitude information for separation purposes. This will significantly reduce altitude verification requests.

d. Transponder Ident Feature.

1. The transponder shall be operated only as specified by ATC. Activate the "IDENT" feature only upon request of the ATC controller.

e. Code Changes.

1. When making routine code changes, pilots should avoid inadvertent selection of codes 7500, 7600, or 7700, thereby causing momentary false alarms at automated ground facilities. For example, when switching from code 2700 to code 7200, switch first to 2200, then to 7200, NOT to 7700 and then 7200. This procedure applies to nondiscrete code 7500 and all discrete codes in the 7600 and 7700 series (i.e., 7600-7677, 7700-7777) which will trigger special indicators in automated facilities. Only nondiscrete code 7500 will be decoded as the hijack code.

2. Under no circumstances should a pilot of a civil aircraft operate the transponder on Code 7777. This code is reserved for military interceptor operations.

3. Military pilots operating VFR or IFR within restricted/warning areas should adjust their transponders to code 4000 unless another code has been assigned by ATC.

f. Mode C Transponder Requirements.

1. Specific details concerning requirements to carry and operate Mode C transponders, as well as exceptions and ATC authorized deviations from the requirements, are found in FAR 91.215 and FAR 99. 12.

2. In general, the FAR requires aircraft to be equipped with Mode C transponders when operating:

(a) at or above 10,000 feet MSL over the 48 contiguous states or the District of Columbia, excluding that airspace below 2,500 feet AGL;

(b) within 30 miles of a TCA primary airport, below 10,000 feet MSL. Balloons, gliders, and aircraft not equipped with an engine-driven electrical system are excepted from the above requirements when operating below the floor of Positive Control Area and/or, outside of a TCA and below the ceiling of the TCA (or 10,000 feet MSL, whichever is lower);

(c) within and above all ARSAs, up to 10,000 feet MSL;

(d) within 10 miles of certain designated airports, excluding that airspace which is both outside the airport traffic area and below 1,200 feet AGL. Balloons, gliders, and aircraft not equipped with an engine-driven electrical system are excepted from this requirement.

3. FAR 99.12 requires an aircraft flying into, within, or across the contiguous U.S. ADIZ be equipped with a Mode C or Mode S transponder. Balloons, gliders, and aircraft not equipped with an engine-driven electrical system are excepted from this requirement.

181

4. Pilots shall ensure that their aircraft transponder is operating on an appropriate ATC assigned VFR/IFR code and Mode C when operating in such airspace. If in doubt about the operational status of either feature of your transponder while airborne, contact the nearest ATC facility or FSS and they will advise you what facility you should contact for determining the status of your equipment.

5. In-flight requests for "immediate" deviation from the transponder requirement may be approved by controllers only when the flight will continue IFR or when weather conditions prevent VFR descent and continued VFR flight in airspace not affected by the FAR. All other requests for deviation should be made by contacting the nearest Flight Service or Air Traffic facility in person or by telephone. The nearest ARTCC will normally be the controlling agency and is responsible for coordinating requests involving deviations in other ARTCC areas.

g. Transponder operations under visual flight rules (VFR).

1. Unless otherwise instructed by an Air Traffic Control Facility, adjust transponder to reply on Mode 3/A code 1200 regardless of altitude.

2. Adjust transponder to reply on Mode C, with altitude reporting capability activated if the aircraft is so equipped, unless deactivation is directed by ATC or unless the installed equipment has not been tested and calibrated as required by FAR 91.217. If deactivation is required and your transponder is so designed, turn off the altitude reporting switch and continue to transmit Mode C framing pulses. If this capability does not exist, turn off Mode C.

h. Radar Beacon Phraseology.

Air traffic controllers, both civil and military, will use the following phraseology when referring to operation of the Air Traffic Control Radar Beacon System (ATCRBS). Instructions by ATC refer only to Mode A/3 or Mode C operation and do not affect the operation of the transponder on other Modes.

1. SQUAWK (number) - Operate radar beacon transponder on designated code in Mode A/3.

2. IDENT - Engage the "IDENT" feature (military UP) of the transponder.

3. SQUAWK (number) and IDENT - Operate transponder on specified code in Mode A/3 and engage the "IDENT'' (military I/P) feature.

4. SQUAWK STANDBY - Switch transponder to standby position.

5. SQUAWK LOW/NORMAL - Operate transponder on low or normal sensitivity as specified. Transponder is operated in "NORMAL" position unless ATC specifies "LOW," ("ON" is used instead of "NORMAL" as a master control label on some types of transponders.)

6. SQUAWK ALTITUDE - Activate Mode C with automatic altitude reporting.

7. STOP ALTITUDE SQUAWK - Turn off altitude reporting switch and continue transmitting Mode C framing pulses. If your equipment does not have this capability, turn off Mode C.

8. STOP SQUAWK (mode in use) - Switch off specified mode. (Used for military aircraft when the controller is unaware of military service requirements for the aircraft to continue operation on another Mode.)

9. STOP SQUAWK - Switch off transponder.

10. SQUAWK MAYDAY - Operate transponder in the emergency position (Mode A Code 7700 for civil transponder. Mode 3 Code 7700 and emergency feature for military transponder.)

11. SQUAWK VFR - Operate radar beacon transponder on code 1200 in the Mode A/3, or other appropriate VFR code.

1-15 Special Traffic Management Programs.

a. Special procedures may be established when a location requires special traffic handling to accommodate above normal traffic demand (e.g., the Indianapolis 500, the Super Bowl) or reduced airport capacity (e.g., airport runway/taxiway closures for airport construction). The special procedures may remain in effect until the problem has been resolved or until local traffic management procedures can handle the situation and a need for special handling no longer exists.

b. The Airport Reservations Office (ARO) has been established to monitor the operation of the high-density rule required by FAR 93, Subpart K. The ARO receives and processes all IFR requests for operations at designated high-density traffic airports and allots reservations on a "first come, first serve" basis determined at the time the request is received at the office. Standby lists are not maintained. The toll free number to obtain a slot is 1-800-322-1212. For telephones without TouchTone service, the number is (202) 426-9347.

c. The high-density airports are: John F. Kennedy International Airport, La Guardia Airport, Chicago O'Hare International Airport, and Washington National Airport.

1. Reservations for John F. Kennedy International Airport are required between 3 p.m. and 7:59 p.m. local time.

2. Reservations at Chicago O'Hare International Airport are required between 6:45 a.m. and 9:15 p.m. local time.

3. Reservations for La Guardia Airport and Washington National Airport are required between 6 a.m. and 11:59 p.m. local time.

d. Requests for IFR reservations will be accepted 48 hours prior to the proposed time of operation at the affected airport. An exception to the 48 hour limitation is made for holidays.

SECTION 2. RADIO COMMUNICATIONS PHRASEOLOGY AND TECHNIQUES

2-1 General.

a. Radio communications are a critical link in the ATC system. The link can be a strong bond between pilot and controller or it can be broken with surprising speed and disastrous results. Discussion herein provides basic procedures for new pilots and also highlights safe operating concepts for all pilots.

b. The single, most important thought in pilot-controller communications is understanding. It is essential, therefore, that pilots acknowledge each radio communication with ATC by using the appropriate aircraft call sign. Brevity is important, and contacts should be kept as brief as possible, but the controller must know what you want to do before he can properly carry out his control duties. And you, the pilot, must know exactly what he wants you to do. Since concise phraseology may not always be adequate, use whatever words are necessary to get your message across.

c. All pilots will find the Pilot/Controller Glossary very helpful in learning what certain words or phrases mean. Good phraseology enhances safety and is the mark of a professional pilot. Jargon, chatter, and "CB" slang have no place in ATC communications. The Pilot/Controller Glossary is the same glossary used in the ATC controller's handbook. We recommend that it be studied and reviewed from time to time to sharpen your communication skills.

2-2 Radio Technique.

a. Listen before you transmit. Many times you can get the information you want through ATIS or by monitoring the frequency. Except for a few situations where some frequency overlap occurs, if you hear someone else talking, the keying of your transmitter will be futile and you will probably jam their receivers, causing them to repeat their call. If you have just changed frequencies, pause, listen, and make sure the frequency is clear.

b. Think before keying your transmitter. Know what you want to say, and if it is lengthy (e.g., a flight plan or IFR position report), jot it down.

c. The microphone should be very close to your lips, and after pressing the mike button, a slight pause may be necessary to be sure the first word is transmitted. Speak in a normal, conversational tone.

d. When you release the button, wait a few seconds before calling again. The controller or FSS specialist may be jotting down your number, looking for your flight plan, transmitting on a different frequency, or selecting his transmitter to your frequency.

e. Be alert to the sounds or the lack of sounds in your receiver. Check your volume, recheck your frequency, and make sure that your microphone is not stuck in the transmit position. Frequency blockage can, and has, occurred for extended periods of time due to unintentional transmitter operation. This type of interference is commonly referred to as a "stuck mike," and controllers may refer to it in this manner when attempting to assign an alternate frequency. If the assigned frequency is completely blocked by this type of interference, use the procedures described for en route IFR radio frequency outage to establish or reestablish communications with ATC.

f. Be sure that you are within the performance range of your radio equipment and the ground station equipment. Remote radio sites do not always transmit and receive on all of a facility's available frequencies, particularly with regard to VOR sites where you can hear but not reach a ground station's receiver. Remember that higher altitudes increase the range of VHF "line of sight" communications.

2-3 Contact Procedures.

a. Initial Contact -
        1. The terms initial contact or initial callup means the first radio call you make to a given facility or the first call to a different controller or FSS specialist within a facility. Use the following format:
        (a) Name of the facility being called;
        (b) Your full aircraft identification as filed in the flight plan or as discussed under Aircraft Call Signs below;
        (c) The type of message to follow or your request if it is short, and
        (d) The word "over" if required.

EXAMPLE:
        "NEW YORK RADIO, MOONEY THREE ONE ONE ECHO."

EXAMPLE:

>"COLUMBIA GROUND, CESSNA THREE ONE SIX ZERO FOXTROT, I-F-R MEMPHIS."

EXAMPLE:

>"MIAMI CENTER, BARON FIVE SIX THREE HOTEL REQUEST VFR TRAFFIC ADVISORIES."

2. Many FSSs are equipped with RCOs and can transmit on the same frequency at more than one location. The frequencies available at specific locations are indicated on charts above FSS communications boxes. To enable the specialist to utilize the correct transmitter, advise the location and the frequency on which you expect a reply.

EXAMPLE:

>St. Louis FSS can transmit on frequency 122.3 at either Farmington, MO, or Decatur, IL. If you are in the vicinity of Decatur, your callup should be "SAINT LOUIS RADIO, PIPER SIX NINER SIX YANKEE, RECEIVING DECATUR ONE TWO TWO POINT THREE."

3. If radio reception is reasonably assured, inclusion of your request, your position or altitude, and the phrase "have numbers" or "information Charlie received" (for ATIS) in the initial contact helps decrease radio frequency congestion. Use discretion, and do not overload the controller with information he does not need. If you do not get a response from the ground station, recheck your radios or use another transmitter, but keep the next contact short.

EXAMPLE:

>"ATLANTA CENTER, DUKE FOUR ONE ROMEO, REQUEST V-F-R TRAFFIC ADVISORIES, TWENTY NORTHWEST ROME, SEVEN THOUSAND FIVE HUNDRED, OVER."

b. Initial Contact When your Transmitting and Receiving Frequencies are Different.

1. If you are attempting to establish contact with a ground station and you are receiving on a different frequency than that transmitted, indicate the VOR name or the frequency on which you expect a reply. Most FSSs and control facilities can transmit on several VOR stations in the area. Use the appropriate FSS call-sign as

indicated on charts. EXAMPLE: New York FSS transmits on the Kennedy, the Hampton, and the Calverton VORTACs. If you are in the Calverton area, your callup should be "NEW YORK RADIO, CESSNA THREE ONE SIX ZERO FOXTROT, RECEIVING CALVERTON V-O-R, OVER."

 2. If the chart indicates FSS frequencies above the VORTAC or in the FSS communications boxes, transmit or receive on those frequencies nearest your location.

 3. When unable to establish contact and you wish to call any ground station, use the phrase "ANY RADIO (tower or station), GIVE CESSNA THREE ONE SIX ZERO FOXTROT A CALL ON (frequency) OR (V-O-R)." If an emergency exists or you need assistance, so state.

 c. Subsequent Contacts and Responses to Callup from a Ground Facility -Use the same format as used for the initial contact, except you should state your message or request with the callup in one transmission. The ground station name and the word "over" may be omitted if the message requires an obvious reply and there is no possibility for misunderstandings. You should acknowledge all callups or clearances unless the controller or FSS specialist advises otherwise. There are some occasions when the controller must issue time-critical instructions to other aircraft, and he may be in a position to observe your response, either visually or on radar. If the situation demands your response, take appropriate action or immediately advise the facility of any problem. Acknowledge with your aircraft identification and one of the words "wilco," "roger," " affirmative," " negative," or other appropriate remarks; e.g., "PIPER TWO ONE FOUR LIMA, ROGER." If you have been receiving services (e.g., VFR traffic advisories) and you are leaving the area or changing frequencies, advise the ATC facility and terminate contact.

 d. Acknowledgment of Frequency Changes -

 1. When advised by ATC to change frequencies, acknowledge the instruction. If you select the new frequency without an acknowledgment, the controller's workload is increased because he has no way of knowing whether you received the instruction or have had radio communications failure.

 2. At times, a controller/specialist may be working a sector with multiple frequency assignments. In order to eliminate unnecessary verbiage and to free the controller/specialist for higher priority transmissions, the controller/specialist may request the pilot "(Identification), change to my frequency 123.4." This phrase should alert the pilot that he is only changing frequencies, not controller/specialist, and that initial callup phraseology may be abbreviated.

EXAMPLE:
"UNITED TWO TWENTY-TWO ON ONE TWO THREE POINT
FOUR."

e. Compliance with Frequency Changes - When instructed by ATC to change
frequencies, select the new frequency as soon as possible unless instructed to make
the change at a specific time, fix, or altitude. A delay in making the change could
result in an untimely receipt of important information. If you are instructed to make
the frequency change at a specific time, fix, or altitude, monitor the frequency you
are on until reaching the specified time, fix, or altitudes unless instructed otherwise
by ATC. (Reference: ARTCC Communications, chapter 11).

2-4 Aircraft Call Signs.

a. Precautions in the Use of Call Signs -
1. Improper use of call signs can result in pilots executing a clearance
intended for another aircraft. Call signs should never be abbreviated on an initial
contact or at any time when other aircraft call signs have similar numbers/sounds
or identical letters/number; e.g., Cessna 6132F, Cessna 1622F, Baron 123F,
Cherokee 7732F, etc.

EXAMPLE: Assume that a controller issues an approach clearance to an
aircraft at the bottom of a holding stack, and an aircraft with a similar call sign (at
the top of the stack) acknowledges the clearance with the last two or three numbers
of his call sign. If the aircraft at the bottom of the stack did not hear the clearance
and intervene, flight safety would be affected, and there would be no reason for
either the controller or pilot to suspect that anything is wrong. This kind of "human
factors" error can strike swiftly and is extremely difficult to rectify.

2. Pilots, therefore, must be certain that aircraft identification is complete
and clearly identified before taking action on an ATC clearance. ATC specialists
will not abbreviate call signs of air carrier or other civil aircraft having authorized
call signs. ATC specialists may initiate abbreviated call signs of other aircraft by
using the prefix and the last three digits/letters of the aircraft identification after
communications are established. The pilot may use the abbreviated call sign in
subsequent contacts with the ATC specialist. When aware of similar/identical call
signs, ATC specialists will take action to minimize errors by emphasizing certain
numbers/letters, by repeating the entire call sign, by repeating the prefix, or by

asking pilots to use a different call sign temporarily. Pilots should use the phrase "VERIFY CLEARANCE FOR (your complete call sign)" if doubt exists concerning proper identity.

3. Civil aircraft pilots should state the aircraft type, model or manufacturer's name, followed by the digits/letters of the registration number. When the aircraft manufacturer's name or model is stated, the prefix "N" is dropped; e.g., Aztec Two Four Six Four Alpha.

EXAMPLE:
BONANZA SIX FIVE FIVE GOLF.

EXAMPLE:
BREEZY SIX ONE THREE ROMEO EXPERIMENTAL (omit "Experimental" after initial contact).

4. Air Taxi or other commercial operators not having FAA authorized call signs should prefix their normal identification with the phonetic word "Tango."

EXAMPLE:
TANGO AZTEC TWO FOUR SIX FOUR ALPHA.

5. Air carriers and commuter air carriers having FAA authorized call signs should identify themselves by stating the complete call sign (using group form for the numbers) and the word "heavy" if appropriate.

EXAMPLE:
UNITED TWENTY-FIVE HEAVY.

EXAMPLE:
MIDWEST COMMUTER SEVEN ELEVEN.

6. Military aircraft use a variety of systems including serial numbers, word call signs, and combinations of letters/numbers. Examples include Army Copter 48931, Air Force 61782, MAC 31792, Pat 157, Air Evac 17652, Navy Golf Alfa Kilo 21, Marine 4 Charlie 36, etc.

b. Air Ambulance Flights - Because of the priority afforded air ambulance flights in the ATC system, extreme discretion is necessary when using the term "LIFE-

GUARD." It is only intended for those missions of an urgent medical nature and to be utilized only for that portion of the flight requiring expeditious handling. When requested by the pilot, necessary notification to expedite ground handling of patients, etc., is provided by ATC; however, when possible, this information should be passed in advance through non-ATC communications systems.

    1. Civilian air ambulance flights responding to medical emergencies (first call to an accident scene, carrying patients, organ donors, organs, or other urgently needed lifesaving medical material) will be expedited by ATC when necessary. When expeditious handling is necessary, add the word "lifeguard" in the remarks section of the flight plan. In radio communications, use the call sign LIFEGUARD followed by the aircraft registration letters/numbers.

    2. Similar provisions have been made for the use of AIR EVAC and MED EVAC by military air ambulance flights, except that these military flights will receive priority handling only when specifically requested.

EXAMPLE:
    LIFEGUARD TWO SIX FOUR SIX.

    3. Air carrier and air taxi flights responding to medical emergencies will also be expedited by ATC when necessary. The nature of these medical emergency flights usually concerns the transportation of urgently needed life saving medical materials or vital organs. IT IS IMPERATIVE THAT THE COMPANY/PILOT DETERMINE, BY THE NATURE/URGENCY OF THE SPECIFIC MEDICAL CARGO, IF PRIORITY ATC ASSISTANCE IS REQUIRED. Pilots shall ensure that the word "lifeguard" is included in the remarks section of the flight plan and use the call sign LIFEGUARD followed by the company name and flight number for all transmissions when expeditious handling is required. It is important for ATC to be aware of "lifeguard" status, and it is the pilot's responsibility to ensure that this information is provided to ATC.

EXAMPLE:
    LIFEGUARD DELTA THIRTY-SEVEN.

  c. Student Pilots Radio Identification -
    1. The FAA desires to help the student pilot in acquiring sufficient practical experience in the environment in which he will be required to operate. To receive additional assistance while operating in areas of concentrated air traffic, a student pilot need only identify himself as a student pilot during his initial call to an FAA

radio facility.

EXAMPLE:
>DAYTON TOWER, THIS IS FLEETWING ONE TWO THREE FOUR, STUDENT PILOT.

2. This special identification will alert FAA ATC personnel and enable them to provide the student pilot with such extra assistance and consideration as he may need. This procedure is not mandatory.

2-5 Description of Interchange or Leased Aircraft.

a. Controllers issue traffic information based on familiarity with airline equipment and color/markings. When an air carrier dispatches a flight using another company's equipment and the pilot does not advise the terminal ATC facility, the possible confusion in aircraft identification can compromise safety.

b. Pilots flying an "interchange" or "leased" aircraft not bearing the colors/ markings of the company operating the aircraft should inform the terminal ATC facility on first contact the name of the operating company and trip number, followed by the company name as displayed on the aircraft, and aircraft type.

EXAMPLE:
>AIR CAL THREE ELEVEN, UNITED (INTERCHANGE/LEASE), BOEING SEVEN TWO SEVEN.

2-6 Ground Station Call Signs.

Pilots, when calling a ground station, should begin with the name of the facility being called followed by the type of the facility being called as indicated in the following examples:

2-7 Phonetic Alphabet.

The International Civil Aviation Organization (ICAO) phonetic alphabet is used by FAA personnel when communications conditions are such that the information cannot be readily received without their use. ATC facilities may also request pilots to use phonetic letter equivalents when aircraft with similar sounding identifications are receiving communications on the same frequency. Pilots should use the phonetic alphabet when identifying their aircraft during initial contact with Air Traffic Control facilities. Additionally, use the phonetic equivalents for single letters and to spell out groups of letters or difficult words during adverse communications conditions.

2-8 Figures.

a. Figures indicating hundreds and thousands in round numbers, as for ceiling heights, and upper wind levels up to 9,900 shall be spoken in accordance with the following:

EXAMPLE:
> 500........FIVE HUNDRED

EXAMPLE:
> 4,500.........FOUR THOUSAND FIVE HUNDRED

b. Numbers above 9,900 shall be spoken by separating the digits preceding the word "thousand."

EXAMPLE:
> 10,000.....ONE ZERO THOUSAND

EXAMPLE:
> 13,500.....ONE THREE THOUSAND FIVE HUNDRED

c. Transmit airway or jet route numbers as follows:

EXAMPLE:
> V12...... VICTOR TWELVE

EXAMPLE:

      J533......J FIVE THIRTY-THREE

d. All other numbers shall be transmitted by pronouncing each digit.

EXAMPLE:

      10.......ONE ZERO

e. When a radio frequency contains a decimal point, the decimal point is spoken as "POINT."

EXAMPLE:

      122.1......ONE TWO TWO POINT ONE

NOTE - ICAO Procedures require the decimal point be spoken as "DECIMAL," and FAA will honor such usage by military aircraft and all other aircraft required to use ICAO Procedures.

2-9 Altitudes and Flight Levels.

a. Up to but not including 18,000 feet MSL, state the separate digits of the thousands plus the hundreds if appropriate.

EXAMPLE:

      12,000......ONE TWO THOUSAND

EXAMPLE:

      12,500......ONE TWO THOUSAND FIVE HUNDRED

b. At and above 18,000 feet MSL (FL 180), state the words "flight level" followed by the separate digits of the flight level.

EXAMPLE:

      190......FLIGHT LEVEL ONE NINER ZERO

2-10 Directions.

The three digits of bearing, course, heading, or wind direction should always be magnetic. The word "true" must be added when it applies.

EXAMPLE:

(Magnetic course) 005......ZERO ZERO FIVE

EXAMPLE:

(True course) 050......ZERO FIVE ZERO TRUE

EXAMPLE:

(Magnetic bearing) 360......THREE SIX ZERO

EXAMPLE:

(Magnetic heading) 100......ONE ZERO ZERO

EXAMPLE:

(Wind direction) 220......TWO TWO ZERO

2-11 Speeds.

The separate digits of the speed followed by the word KNOTS. Except, controllers may omit the word KNOTS when using speed adjustment procedures; e.g., REDUCE/INCREASE SPEED TO TWO FIVE ZERO.

EXAMPLES:

(Speed) 250......TWO FIVE ZERO KNOTS
(Speed) 190......ONE NINER ZERO KNOTS

The separate digits of the Mach number preceded by MACH.

EXAMPLES:

(Mach number) 1.5......MACH ONE POINT FIVE
(Mach number) 0.64.....MACH POINT SIX FOUR
(Mach number) 0.7......MACH POINT SEVEN

2-12 Time.

a. FAA uses Coordinated Universal Time (UTC) for all operations. The term "Zulu" is used when ATC procedures require a reference to UTC.

194

EXAMPLE:
        0920......ZERO NINER TWO ZERO

b. To Convert from Standard Time to Coordinated Universal Time:

        Eastern Standard Time.........Add 5 hours
        Central Standard Time.........Add 6 hours
        Mountain Standard Time.....Add 7 hours
        Pacific Standard Time..........Add 8 hours
        Alaska Standard Time..........Add 9 hours
        Hawaii Standard Time.........Add 10 hours

NOTE - For Daylight Time, subtract 1 hour from each.

c. The 24-hour clock system is used in radio-telephone transmissions. The hour is indicated by the first two figures and the minutes by the last two figures.

EXAMPLE:
        0000......ZERO ZERO ZERO ZERO

EXAMPLE:
        0920......ZERO NINER TWO ZERO

d. Time may be stated in minutes only (two figures) in radio-telephone communications when no misunderstanding is likely to occur.

e. Current time in use at a station is stated in the nearest quarter minute in order that pilots may use this information for time checks. Fractions of a quarter minute less than 8 seconds are stated as the preceding quarter minute; fractions of a quarter minute of 8 seconds or more are stated as the succeeding quarter minute.

EXAMPLE:
        0929:05......TIME, ZERO NINER TWO NINER

EXAMPLE:
        0929:10......TIME, ZERO NINER TWO NINER AND ONE-QUARTER

195

2-13 Communications With Tower When Aircraft Transmitter or Receiver or Both Are Inoperative.

a. Arriving Aircraft -

1. Receiver inoperative - If you have reason to believe your receiver is inoperative, remain outside or above the airport traffic area until the direction and flow of traffic have been determined; then, advise the tower of your type aircraft, position, altitude, intention to land, and request that you be controlled with light signals. (Reference-Traffic Control Light Signals, Chapter 10). When you are approximately 3 to 5 miles from the airport, advise the tower of your position and join the airport traffic pattern. From this point on, watch the tower for light signals. There after, if a complete pattern is made, transmit your position downwind and/or turning base leg.

2. Transmitter inoperative - Remain outside or above the airport traffic area until the direction and flow of traffic have been determined; then, join the airport traffic pattern. Monitor the primary local control frequency as depicted on Sectional Charts for landing or traffic information, and look for a light signal which may be addressed to your aircraft. During hours of daylight, acknowledge tower transmissions or light signals by rocking your wings. At night, acknowledge by blinking the landing or navigation lights. To acknowledge tower transmissions during daylight hours, hovering helicopters will turn in the direction of the controlling facility and flash the landing light. While in flight, helicopters should show their acknowledgment of receiving a transmission by making shallow banks in opposite directions. At night, helicopters will acknowledge receipt of transmissions by flashing either the landing or the search light.

3. Transmitter and receiver inoperative - Remain outside or above the airport traffic area until the direction and flow of traffic have been determined; then, join the airport traffic pattern and maintain visual contact with the tower to receive light signals. Acknowledge light signals as noted above.

b. Departing Aircraft - If you experience radio failure prior to leaving the parking area, make every effort to have the equipment repaired. If you are unable to have the malfunction repaired, call the tower by telephone and request authorization to depart without two-way radio communications. If tower authorization is granted, you will be given departure information and requested to monitor the tower frequency or watch for light signals as appropriate. During daylight hours, acknowledge tower transmissions or light signals by moving the ailerons or rudder. At night, acknowledge by blinking the landing or navigation lights. If radio malfunction occurs after departing the parking area, watch the tower for light signals or monitor tower frequency.

NOTE - Refer to FAR 91.129 and FAR 91.125.

2-14 Communications For VFR Flights.

a. FSSs are allocated frequencies for different functions; for example, 122.0 MHz is assigned as the En Route Flight Advisory Service frequency at selected FSSs. In addition, certain FSSs provide Airport Advisory Service on 123.6 MHz. Other FSS frequencies are listed in the Airport/Facility Directory. If you are in doubt as to what frequency to use, 122.2 MHz is assigned to the majority of FSSs as a common en route simplex frequency.

NOTE - In order to expedite communications, state the frequency being used and the aircraft location during initial callup.

EXAMPLE:

DAYTON RADIO, THIS IS NOVEMBER ONE TWO THREE FOUR FIVE ON ONE TWO TWO POINT TWO, OVER SPRINGFIELD V-O-R, OVER.

b. Certain VOR voice channels are being utilized for recorded broadcasts; e.g., ATIS, HIWAS, etc. These services and appropriate frequencies are listed in the Airport/Facility Directory. On VFR flights, pilots are urged to monitor these frequencies. When in contact with a control facility, notify the controller if you plan to leave the frequency to monitor these broadcasts.

SECTION 3. AIRPORT OPERATIONS

3-1 General.

Increased traffic congestion, aircraft in climb and descent attitudes, and pilots' preoccupation with cockpit duties are some factors that increase the hazardous accident potential near the airport. The situation is further compounded when the weather is marginal, that is, just meeting VFR requirements. Pilots must be particularly alert when operating in the vicinity of an airport. This section defines some rules, practices, and procedures that pilots should be familiar with and adhere to for safe airport operations.

197

3-2 Tower Controlled Airports.

a. When operating at an airport where traffic control is being exercised by a control tower, pilots are required to maintain two-way radio contact with the tower while operating within the airport traffic area unless the tower authorizes otherwise. Initial callup should be made about 15 miles from the airport. Unless there is a good reason to leave the tower frequency before exiting the airport traffic area, it is a good operating practice to remain on the tower frequency for the purpose of receiving traffic information. In the interest of reducing tower frequency congestion, pilots are reminded that it is not necessary to request permission to leave the tower frequency once outside of the airport traffic area.

b. When necessary, the tower controller will issue clearances or other information for aircraft to generally follow the desired flight path (traffic patterns) when flying in the airport traffic area/control zone and the proper taxi routes when operating on the ground. If not otherwise authorized or directed by the tower, pilots of fixed-wing aircraft approaching to land must circle the airport to the left. Pilots approaching to land in a helicopter must avoid the flow of fixed-wing traffic. However, in all instances, an appropriate clearance must be received from the tower before landing.

c. The following terminology for the various components of a traffic pattern has been adopted as standard for use by control towers and pilots.

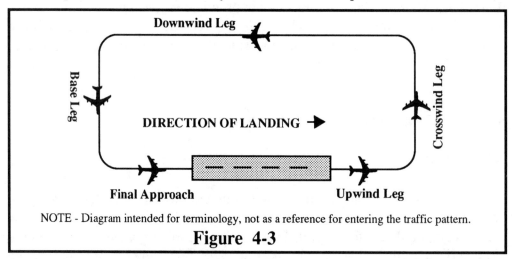

Downwind Leg

Base Leg

Crosswind Leg

DIRECTION OF LANDING →

Final Approach   **Upwind Leg**

NOTE - Diagram intended for terminology, not as a reference for entering the traffic pattern.

Figure 4-3

1. Upwind leg - A flight path parallel to the landing runway in the direction of landing.

2. Crosswind leg - A flight path at right angles to the landing runway off its takeoff end.

3. Downwind leg - A flight path parallel to the landing runway in the opposite direction of landing.

4. Base leg - A flight path at right angles to the landing runway off its approach end and extending from the downwind leg to the intersection of the extended runway centerline.

5. Final approach - A flight path in the direction of landing along the extended runway centerline from the base leg to the runway.

d. Many towers are equipped with a tower radar display. The radar uses are intended to enhance the effectiveness and efficiency of the local control, or tower, position. They are not intended to provide radar services or benefits to pilots except as they may accrue through a more efficient tower operation. The four basic uses are:

1. To determine an aircraft's exact location - This is accomplished by radar identifying the VFR aircraft through any of the techniques available to a radar position, such as having the aircraft squawk ident. Once identified, the aircraft's position and spatial relationship to other aircraft can be quickly determined, and standard instructions regarding VFR operation in the airport traffic area will be issued. Once initial radar identification of a VFR aircraft has been established and the appropriate instructions have been issued, radar monitoring may be discontinued; the reason being that the local controller's primary means of surveillance in VFR conditions is visually scanning the airport and local area.

2. To provide radar traffic advisories - Radar traffic advisories may be provided to the extent that the local controller is able to monitor the radar display. Local control has primary control responsibilities to the aircraft operating on the runways, which will normally supersede radar monitoring duties.

3. To provide a direction or suggested heading - The local controller may provide pilots flying VFR with generalized instructions which will facilitate operations; e.g., PROCEED SOUTHWEST BOUND, ENTER A RIGHT DOWN-WIND RUNWAY THREE ZERO, or provide a suggested heading to establish radar identification or as an advisory aid to navigation; e.g., SUGGESTED HEADING TWO TWO ZERO, FOR RADAR IDENTIFICATION. In both cases, the instructions are advisory aids to the pilot flying VFR and are not radar vectors. PILOTS HAVE COMPLETE DISCRETION REGARDING ACCEPTANCE OF THE SUGGESTED HEADINGS OR DIRECTIONS AND HAVE SOLE RE-SPONSIBILITY FOR SEEING AND AVOIDING OTHER AIRCRAFT.

4. To provide information and instructions to aircraft operating within the airport traffic area - In an example of this situation, the local controller would use the radar to advise a pilot on an extended downwind when to turn base leg.

NOTE - The above tower radar applications are intended to augment the standard functions of the local control position. There is no controller requirement to maintain constant radar identification. In fact, such a requirement could compromise the local controller's ability to visually scan the airport and local area to meet FAA responsibilities to the aircraft operating on the runways and within the airport traffic area. Normally, pilots will not be advised of being in radar contact since that continued status cannot be guaranteed and since the purpose of the radar identification is not to establish a link for the provision of radar services.

e. A few of the radar-equipped towers are authorized to use the radar to ensure separation between aircraft in specific situations, while still others may function as limited radar approach controls. The various radar uses are strictly a function of FAA operational need. The facilities may be indistinguishable to pilots since they are all referred to as tower and no publication lists the degree of radar use. Therefore, WHEN IN COMMUNICATION WITH A TOWER CONTROLLER WHO MAY HAVE RADAR AVAILABLE, DO NOT ASSUME THAT CONSTANT RADAR MONITORING AND COMPLETE ATC RADAR SERVICES ARE BEING PROVIDED.

3-3 Visual Indicators At Controlled Airports.

a. At those airports without an operating control tower, a segmented circle visual indicator system, if installed, is designed to provide traffic pattern information. (Reference-Traffic Advisory Practices at Airports Without Operating Control Tower, Section 1-7 this chapter). The segmented circle system consists of the following components:

1. The segmented circle - Located in a position affording maximum visibility to pilots in the air and on the ground and providing a centralized location for other elements of the system.

2. The wind direction indicator - A wind cone, wind sock, or wind tee installed near the operational runway to indicate wind direction. The large end of the wind cone/wind sock points into the wind as does the large end (cross bar) of the wind tee. In lieu of a tetrahedron and where a wind sock or wind cone is collocated with a wind tee, the wind tee may be manually aligned with the runway in use to indicate landing direction. These signaling devices may be located in the center of the segmented circle and may be lighted for night use. Pilots are cautioned against using a tetrahedron to indicate wind direction.

3. The landing direction indicator - A tetrahedron is installed when conditions at the airport warrant its use. It may be used to indicate the direction of landings and takeoffs. A tetrahedron may be located at the center of a segmented circle and may be lighted for night operations. The small end of the tetrahedron points in the

direction of landing. Pilots are cautioned against using a tetrahedron for any purpose other than as an indicator of landing direction. Further, pilots should use extreme caution when making runway selection by use of a tetrahedron in very light or calm wind conditions as the tetrahedron may not be aligned with the designated calm-wind runway. At airports with control towers, the tetrahedron should only be referenced when the control tower is not in operation. Tower instructions supersede tetrahedron indications.

      4. Landing strip indicators - Installed in pairs as shown in the segmented circle diagram and used to show the alignment of landing strips.

      5. Traffic pattern indicators - Arranged in pairs in conjunction with landing strip indicators and used to indicate the direction of turns when there is a variation from the normal left traffic pattern. (If there is no segmented circle installed at the airport, traffic pattern indicators may be installed on or near the end of the runway.)

  b. Preparatory to landing at an airport without a control tower, or when the control tower is not in operation, the pilot should concern himself with the indicator for the approach end of the runway to be used. When approaching for landing, all turns must be made to the left unless a traffic pattern indicator indicates that turns should be made to the right. If the pilot will mentally enlarge the indicator for the runway to be used, the base and final approach legs of the traffic pattern to be flown immediately become apparent. Similar treatment of the indicator at the departure end of the runway will clearly indicate the direction of turn after takeoff.

  c. When two or more aircraft are approaching an airport for the purpose of landing, the aircraft at the lower altitude has the right of way, but it shall not take advantage of this rule to cut in front of another which is on final approach to land, or to overtake that aircraft (FAR 91.113(f)).

3-4 Traffic Patterns.

At most airports and military air bases, traffic pattern altitudes for propeller-driven aircraft generally extend from 600 feet to as high as 1,500 feet above the ground. Also, traffic pattern altitudes for military turbojet aircraft sometimes extend up to 2,500 feet above the ground. Therefore, pilots of en route aircraft should be constantly on the alert for other aircraft in traffic patterns and avoid these areas whenever possible. Traffic pattern altitudes should be maintained unless otherwise required by the applicable distance from cloud criteria (FAR 91.155). (See Figure 4-4, page 202).

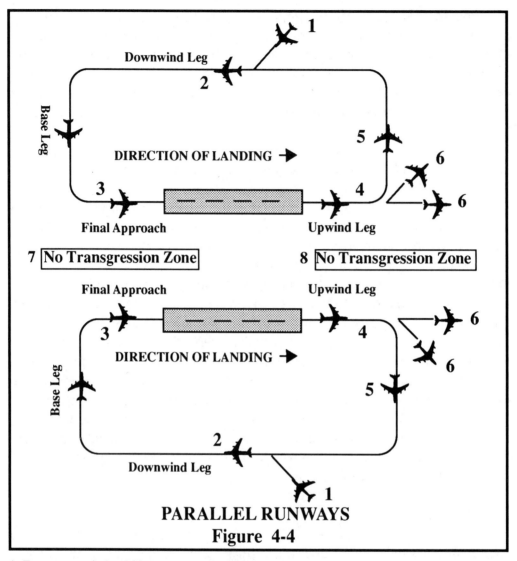

PARALLEL RUNWAYS
Figure 4-4

1. Enter pattern in level flight, abeam the midpoint of the runway, at pattern altitude (1,000 ft. AGL is recommended pattern altitude unless established otherwise).
2. Maintain pattern altitude until abeam approach end of the landing runway, or downwind leg.
3. Complete turn to final at least 1/4 mile from the runway.
4. Continue straight ahead until beyond departure end of runway.
5. If remaining in the traffic pattern, commence turn to crosswind leg beyond the departure end of the runway, within 300 feet of pattern altitude.
6. If departing the traffic pattern, continue straight out, or exit with a 45 degree turn beyond the departure end of the runway, after reaching pattern altitude.
7. Do not overshoot final or continue on a track which will penetrate the final approach of the parallel runway.
8. Do not continue on a track which will penetrate the departure path of the parallel runway.

3-5 Unexpected Maneuvers In The Airport Traffic Pattern.

There have been several incidents in the vicinity of controlled airports that were caused primarily by aircraft executing unexpected maneuvers. ATC service is based upon observed or known traffic and airport conditions. Controllers establish the sequence of arriving and departing aircraft by requiring them to adjust flight as necessary to achieve proper spacing. These adjustments can only be based on observed traffic, accurate pilot reports, and anticipated aircraft maneuvers. Pilots are expected to cooperate so as to preclude disrupting traffic flows or creating conflicting patterns. The pilot in command of an aircraft is directly responsible for and is the final authority as to the operation of his aircraft. On occasion it may be necessary for a pilot to maneuver his aircraft to maintain spacing with the traffic he has been sequenced to follow. The controller can anticipate minor maneuvering such as shallow "S" turns. The controller cannot, however, anticipate a major maneuver such as a 360 degree turn. If a pilot makes a 360 degree turn after he has obtained a landing sequence, the result is usually a gap in the landing interval and, more importantly, it causes a chain reaction which may result in a conflict with following traffic and an interruption of the sequence established by the tower or approach controller. Should a pilot decide he needs to make maneuvering turns to maintain spacing behind a preceding aircraft, he should always advise the controller if at all possible. Except when requested by the controller or in emergency situations, a 360 degree turn should never be executed in the traffic pattern or when receiving radar service without first advising the controller.

3-6 Use of Runways.

   a. Runways are identified by numbers which indicate the nearest 10-degree increment of the azimuth of the runway centerline. For example, where the magnetic azimuth is 183 degrees, the runway designation would be 18; for a magnetic azimuth of 87 degrees, the runway designation would be 9. For a magnetic azimuth ending in the number 5, such as 185, the runway designation could be either 18 or 19. Wind direction issued by the tower is also magnetic and wind velocity is in knots.
   b. Airport proprietors are responsible for taking the lead in local aviation noise control. Accordingly, they may propose specific noise abatement plans to the FAA. If approved, these plans are applied in the form of Formal or Informal Runway Use

Programs for noise abatement purposes.

     1. At airports where no runway use program is established, ATC clearances may specify:

          (a) The runway most nearly aligned with the wind when it is 5 knots or more;

          (b) The "calm wind" runway when wind is less than 5 knots, or

          (c) Another runway if operationally advantageous.

NOTE - It is not necessary for a controller to specifically inquire if the pilot will use a specific runway or to offer him a choice of runways. If a pilot prefers to use a different runway from that specified or the one most nearly aligned with the wind, he is expected to inform ATC accordingly.

     2. At airports where a runway use program is established, ATC will assign runways deemed to have the least noise impact. If in the interest of safety a runway different from that specified is preferred, the pilot is expected to advise ATC accordingly. ATC will honor such requests and advise pilots when the requested runway is noise sensitive. When use of a runway other than the one assigned is requested, pilot cooperation is encouraged to preclude disruption of traffic flows or the creation of conflicting patterns.

3-7 Low Level Wind Shear Alert System (LLWAS).

  a. This computerized system detects the presence of a possible hazardous low-level wind shear by continuously comparing the winds measured by sensors installed around the periphery of an airport with the wind measured at the center field location. If the difference between the center field wind sensor and a peripheral wind sensor becomes excessive, a thunderstorm or thunderstorm gust front wind shear is probable. When this condition exists, the tower controller will provide arrival and departure aircraft with an advisory of the situation, which includes the center field wind plus the remote site location and wind.

  b. Since the sensors are not all associated with specific runways, descriptions of the remote sites will be based on an eight-point compass system.

EXAMPLE:

     DELTA ONE TWENTY FOUR CENTER FIELD WIND TWO SEVEN ZERO AT ONE ZERO. SOUTH BOUNDARY WIND ONE FOUR ZERO AT THREE ZERO.

  c. An airport equipped with the Low Level Wind Shear Alert System is so indicated in the Airport/Facility Directory under Weather Data Sources for that particular airport.

3-8 Braking Action Reports.

a. ATC furnishes pilots the quality of braking action received from pilots or the airport management. The quality of braking action is described by the terms "good," "fair," "poor," and "nil" or a combination of these terms. Where available from airport management and when airports are covered with compacted snow and/ or ice, numerical readings from friction measurement devices including the Mu-Meter, Saab Friction Tester, Runway Friction Tester, Bowmonk, Skiddometer, and Tapley Meter will be issued at pilot's request. These numbers will be below 0.4 and reflect the slipperiness of the pavement surface. This information should be used with other knowledge including previous experience, aircraft type and weight, wind conditions, and tire type to determine the runway suitability.

b. Pilots should describe the quality of braking action by using the terms noted above. In describing braking action for a portion of a runway, pilots should use descriptive terms that are easily understood, such as, "braking action poor the first/ last half of the runway." Report references to local landmarks, buildings, etc., should be avoided.

3-9 Braking Action Advisories.

a. When tower controllers have received runway braking action reports which include the terms poor or nil, or whenever weather conditions are conducive to deteriorating or rapidly changing runway braking conditions, the tower will include on the ATIS broadcast the statement, "BRAKING ACTION ADVISORIES ARE IN EFFECT."

b. During the time that Braking Action Advisories are in effect, ATC will issue the latest braking action report for the runway in use to each arriving and departing aircraft. Pilots should be prepared for deteriorating braking conditions and should request current runway condition information if not volunteered by controllers. Pilots should also be prepared to provide a descriptive runway condition report to controllers after landing.

3-10 Intersection Takeoffs.

a. In order to enhance airport capacities, reduce taxiing distances, minimize departure delays, and provide for more efficient movement of air traffic, controllers may initiate intersection takeoffs as well as approve them when the pilot requests. If for ANY reason a pilot prefers to use a different intersection or the full length of the runway or desires to obtain the distance between the intersection and the runway end, HE IS EXPECTED TO INFORM ATC ACCORDINGLY.

b. An aircraft is expected to taxi to (but not onto) the end of the assigned runway unless prior approval for an intersection departure is received from ground control.

c. Pilots should state their position on the airport when calling the tower for takeoff from a runway intersection.

d. Controllers are required to separate small aircraft (12,500 pounds or less, maximum certificated takeoff weight) departing (same or opposite direction) from an intersection behind a large nonheavy aircraft on the same runway, by ensuring that at least a 3-minute interval exists between the time the preceding large aircraft has taken off and the succeeding small aircraft begins takeoff roll. To inform the pilot of the required 3-minute hold, the controller will state, HOLD FOR WAKE TURBULENCE. If after considering wake turbulence hazards, the pilot feels that a lesser time interval is appropriate, he may request a waiver to the 3-minute interval. Pilots must initiate such a request by stating, REQUEST WAIVER TO 3-MINUTE INTERVAL, or by making a similar statement. Controllers may then issue a takeoff clearance if other traffic permits, since the pilot has accepted responsibility for his own wake turbulence separation.

e. The 3-minute interval is not required when the intersection is 500 feet or less from the departure point of the preceding aircraft and both aircraft are taking off in the same direction. Controllers may permit the small aircraft to alter course after takeoff to avoid the flight path of the preceding departure.

f. The 3-minute interval is mandatory behind a heavy aircraft in all cases.

3-11 Simultaneous Operations On Intersecting Runways.

a. Despite the many new and lengthened runways which have been added to the nation's airports in recent years, limited runway availability remains a major contributing factor to operational delays. Many high-density airports have gained operational experience with intersecting runways which clearly indicates that simultaneous operations are safe and feasible. Tower controllers may authorize simultaneous landings or a simultaneous landing and takeoff on intersecting runways when the following conditions are met:

1. The runways are dry and the controller has received no reports that braking action is less than good.

2. A simultaneous takeoff and landing operation may be conducted only in VFR conditions.

3. Instructions are issued to restrict one aircraft from entering the intersecting runway being used by another aircraft.

4. Traffic information issued is acknowledged by the pilots of both aircraft.

5. The measured distance from runway threshold to intersection is issued if the pilot requests it.

6. The conditions specified in 3, 4, and 5 are met at or before issuance of the landing clearance

7. The distance from landing threshold to the intersection is adequate for the category of aircraft being held short. Controllers are provided a general table of aircraft category/minimum runway length requirements as a guide. Operators of STOL aircraft should identify their aircraft as such on initial contact with the tower, unless a Letter of Agreement concerning this fact, is in effect. WHENEVER A HOLD SHORT CLEARANCE IS RECEIVED, IT IS INCUMBENT ON THE PILOT TO DETERMINE HIS/HER ABILITY TO HOLD SHORT OF AN INTERSECTION AFTER LANDING WHEN INSTRUCTED TO DO SO. ADDITIONALLY, PILOTS SHOULD INCLUDE THE WORDS "HOLD SHORT OF (POINT)" IN THE ACKNOWLEDGMENT OF SUCH CLEARANCES.

8. There is no tailwind for the landing aircraft restricted to hold short of the intersection.

b. THE SAFETY AND OPERATION OF AN AIRCRAFT REMAIN THE RESPONSIBILITY OF THE PILOT. IF FOR ANY REASON; e.g. DIFFICULTY IN DISCERNING LOCATION OF AN INTERSECTION AT NIGHT, INABILITY TO HOLD SHORT OF AN INTERSECTION, WIND FACTORS, ETC., A PILOT ELECTS TO USE THE FULL LENGTH OF THE RUNWAY, A DIFFERENT RUNWAY, OR DESIRES TO OBTAIN THE DISTANCE FROM THE LANDING THRESHOLD TO THE INTERSECTION, HE IS EXPECTED TO PROMPTLY INFORM ATC ACCORDINGLY.

3-12 Low Approach.

a. A low approach (sometimes referred to as a low pass) is the go-around maneuver following an approach. Instead of landing or making a touch-and-go, a pilot may wish to go around (low approach) in order to expedite a particular operation (a series of practice instrument approaches is an example of such an operation). Unless otherwise authorized by ATC, the low approach should be made straight ahead, with no turns or climb made until the pilot has made a thorough visual check for other aircraft in the area.

b. When operating within an airport traffic area, a pilot intending to make a low approach should contact the tower for approval. This request should be made prior to starting the final approach.

c. When operating to an airport, not within an airport traffic area, a pilot intending to make a low approach should, prior to leaving the final approach fix inbound (nonprecision approach) or the outer marker or fix used in lieu of the outer marker inbound (precision approach), so advise the FSS, UNICOM, or make a broadcast as appropriate. (Reference-Traffic Advisory Practices at Airports Without Operating Control Towers, Section 1-7 this chapter).

3-13 Traffic Control Light Signals.

a. The following procedures are used by ATCTs in the control of aircraft, ground vehicles, equipment, and personnel not equipped with radio. These same procedures will be used to control aircraft, ground vehicles, equipment, and personnel equipped with radio if radio contact cannot be established. ATC personnel use a directive traffic control signal which emits an intense narrow light beam of a selected color (either red, white, or green) when controlling traffic by light signals.

b. Although the traffic signal light offers the advantage that some control may be exercised over nonradio-equipped aircraft, pilots should be cognizant of the disadvantages which are:

    1. The pilot may not be looking at the control tower at the time a signal is directed toward him.

    2. The directions transmitted by a light signal are very limited since only approval or disapproval of a pilot's anticipated actions may be transmitted. No supplement or explanatory information may be transmitted except by the use of the "General Warning Signal" which advises the pilot to be on the alert.

c. Between sunset and sunrise, a pilot wishing to attract the attention of the control tower should turn on a landing light and taxi the aircraft into a position, clear of the active runway, so that light is visible to the tower. The landing light should remain on until appropriate signals are received from the tower.

d. Air Traffic Control Light Gun Signals (See figure 4-5, page 209.).

e. During daylight hours, acknowledge tower transmissions or light signals by moving the ailerons or rudder. At night, acknowledge by blinking the landing or navigation lights. If radio malfunction occurs after departing the parking area, watch the tower for light signals or monitor tower frequency.

COLOR & TYPE	AIRCRAFT ON GROUND	AIRCRAFT IN FLIGHT
Steady Green	Cleared for takeoff	Cleared to land
Flashing Green	Cleared for taxi	Return for landing (followed by steady green
Steady Red	STOP	Give way to other aircraft and continue circling
Flashing Red	Clear the taxiway/runway	Airport unsafe, do not land
Flashing White	Return to starting point	Not applicable
Alternating Red and Green	Exercise extreme caution	Exercise extreme caution

LIGHT GUN SIGNALS
Figure 4-5

3-14 Communications.

a. Pilots of departing aircraft should communicate with the control tower on the appropriate ground control/clearance delivery frequency prior to starting engines to receive engine start time, taxi and/or clearance information. Unless otherwise advised by the tower, remain on that frequency during taxiing and runup, then change to local control frequency when ready to request takeoff clearance. (Reference-Automatic Terminal Information Service (ATIS) for continuous broadcast of terminal information, Section 1-8 this chapter).

b. The majority of ground control frequencies are in the 121.6-121.9 MHz band width. Ground control frequencies are provided to eliminate frequency congestion on the tower (local control) frequency and are limited to communications between the tower and aircraft on the ground and between the tower and utility vehicles on the airport, and provide a clear VHF channel for arriving and departing aircraft. They are used for issuance of taxi information, clearances, and other necessary contacts between the tower and aircraft or other vehicles operated on the airport. A pilot who has just landed should not change from the tower frequency to the ground control frequency until he is directed to do so by the controller. Normally, only one ground control frequency is assigned at an airport; however, at locations where the amount of traffic so warrants, a second ground control frequency and/or another frequency designated as a clearance delivery frequency, may be assigned.

c. A controller may omit the ground or local control frequency if the controller believes the pilot knows which frequency is in use. If the ground control frequency is in the 121 MHz band width the controller may omit the numbers preceding the decimal point; e.g., 121.7, CONTACT GROUND POINT SEVEN. However, if any doubt exists as to what frequency is in use, the pilot should promptly request the controller to provide that information.

d. Controllers will normally avoid issuing a radio frequency change to helicopters, known to be single-piloted, which are hovering, air taxiing, or flying near the ground. At times, it may be necessary for pilots to alert ATC regarding single-pilot operations to minimize delay of essential ATC communications. Whenever possible, ATC instructions will be relayed through the frequency being monitored until a frequency change can be accomplished. You must promptly advise ATC if you are unable to comply with a frequency change. Also, you should advise ATC if you must land to accomplish the frequency change unless it is clear the landing; e.g., on a taxiway or in a helicopter operating area, will have no impact on other air traffic.

3-15 Gate Holding Due To Departure Delays.

a. Pilots should contact ground control or clearance delivery prior to starting engines as gate hold procedures will be in effect whenever departure delays exceed or are anticipated to exceed 15 minutes. The sequence for departure will be maintained in accordance with initial callup unless modified by flow control restrictions. Pilots should monitor the ground control or clearance delivery frequency for engine start-up advisories or new proposed start time if the delay changes.

b. The tower controller will consider that pilots of turbine powered aircraft are ready for takeoff when they reach the runway or warm-up block unless advised otherwise.

3-16 VFR Flights In Terminal Areas.

Use reasonable restraint in exercising the prerogative of VFR flight, especially in terminal areas. The weather minimums and distances from clouds are minimums. Giving yourself a greater margin in specific instances is just good judgment.

a. Approach Area - Conducting a VFR operation in a control zone when the official visibility is 3 or 4 miles is not prohibited, but good judgment would dictate that you keep out of the approach area.

b. Reduced Visibility - It has always been recognized that precipitation reduces forward visibility. Consequently, although again it may be perfectly legal to cancel your IFR flight plan at any time you can proceed VFR, it is good practice, when precipitation is occurring, to continue IFR operation into a terminal area until you are reasonably close to your destination.

c. Simulated Instrument Flights -In conducting simulated instrument flights, be sure that the weather is good enough to compensate for the restricted visibility of the safety pilot and your greater concentration on your flight instruments. Give yourself a little greater margin when your flight plan lies in or near a busy airway or close to an airport.

3-17 Taxiing.

a. General: Approval must be obtained prior to moving an aircraft or vehicle onto the movement area during the hours an airport traffic control tower is in operation.

1. Always state your position on the airport when calling the tower for taxi instructions.

2. The movement area is normally described in local bulletins issued by the airport manager or control tower. These bulletins may be found in FSSs, fixed base operators offices, air carrier offices, and operations offices.

3. The control tower also issues bulletins describing areas where they cannot provide ATC service due to nonvisibility or other reasons.

4. A clearance must be obtained prior to taxiing on a runway, taking off, or landing during the hours an airport traffic control tower is in operation.

5. When ATC clears an aircraft to "taxi to" an assigned takeoff runway, the absence of holding instructions authorizes the aircraft to "cross" all runways which the taxi route intersects except the assigned takeoff runway. It does not include authorization to "taxi onto" or "cross" the assigned takeoff runway at any point. In order to preclude any misunderstandings in radio communications, ATC will not use the word "cleared" in conjunction with authorization for aircraft to taxi.

6. In absence of holding instructions, a clearance to "taxi to" any point other than an assigned takeoff runway is a clearance to cross all runways that intersect the taxi route to that point.

7. When ATC authorizes an aircraft to taxi to an assigned departure runway and hold short instructions will be issued, they will first specify the runway, issue

taxi instructions, and then state the hold short instructions. This does not authorize the aircraft to "enter" or "cross" the assigned departure runway at any point.

b. ATC clearances or instructions pertaining to taxiing are predicated on known traffic and known physical airport conditions. Therefore, it is important that pilots clearly understand the clearance or instructions. Although an ATC clearance is issued for taxiing purposes, when operating in accordance with the FARs, it is the responsibility of the pilot to avoid collision with other aircraft. Since "the pilot in command of an aircraft is directly responsible for, and is the final authority as to, the operation of that aircraft" the pilot should obtain clarification of any clearance or instruction which is not understood.

1. Good operating practice dictates that pilots acknowledge all runway crossing, hold short, or takeoff clearances unless there is some misunderstanding at which time the pilot should query the controller until the clearance is understood. When cleared onto the active runway for departure, pilots operating single-pilot airplanes should monitor only assigned ATC communication frequencies until flight from the airport traffic area is complete. After receipt of clearance for landing, they should monitor only assigned ATC communications frequencies until the landing and taxi activities are completed. In all cases, proper effective scanning for other aircraft, surface vehicles, or other objects should be continuously exercised.

2. If the pilot is unfamiliar with the airport or for any reason confusion exists as to the correct taxi routing, a request may be made for progressive taxi instructions which include step-by-step routing directions. Progressive instructions may also be issued if the controller deems it necessary due to traffic or field conditions; e.g., construction or closed taxiways.

c. At those airports where the U.S. Government operates the control tower and ATC has authorized noncompliance with the requirement for two-way radio communications while operating within the airport traffic area, or at those airports where the U.S. Government does not operate the control tower and radio communications cannot be established, pilots will obtain a clearance by visual light signal prior to taxiing on a runway and prior to takeoff and landing.

d. The following phraseologies and procedures are used in radio-telephone communications with aeronautical ground stations.

1. Request for taxi instructions prior to departure: State your aircraft identification, location, type of operation planned (VFR or IFR), and the point of first intended landing.

EXAMPLE:

> Aircraft: OHIO STATE GROUND, CESSNA FOUR ZERO SIERRA UNIFORM AT HANGAR EIGHT, READY TO TAXI VFR TO PORTSMOUTH.

> Tower: CESSNA FOUR ZERO SIERRA UNIFORM, TAXI TO RUNWAY TWO SEVEN LEFT, WIND TWO FIVE ZERO AT TEN, ALTIMETER THREE ZERO ZERO ZERO. or

> Tower: CESSNA FOUR ZERO SIERRA UNIFORM, RUNWAY TWO THREE, TAXI VIA TAXIWAY ALPHA AND CHARLIE, HOLD SHORT OF RUNWAY TWO SEVEN LEFT.

2. Request for taxi instructions after landing: State your aircraft identification, location and that you request taxi instructions.

EXAMPLE:

> Aircraft: OHIO STATE GROUND, CESSNA SEVEN ZERO SIERRA UNIFORM CLEAR OF RUNWAY TWO THREE, REQUEST CLEARANCE TO THE STUDENT RAMP.
> Tower: CESSNA SEVEN ZERO SIERRA UNIFORM, TAXI TO THE STUDENT RAMP VIA TAXIWAY HOTEL AND TAXIWAY CHARLIE.

3-18 Taxi During Low Visibility.

a. Pilots and aircraft operators should be constantly aware that during certain low visibility conditions the movement of aircraft and vehicles on airports may not be visible to the tower controller. This may prevent visual confirmation of an aircraft's adherence to taxi instructions. Pilots should, therefore exercise extreme vigilance and proceed cautiously under such conditions.

b. Of vital importance is the need for pilots to notify the controller when difficulties are encountered or at the first indication of becoming disoriented. Pilots should proceed with extreme caution when taxiing toward the sun. When vision difficulties are encountered pilots should immediately notify the controller.

3-19 Exiting The Runway After Landing.

After landing, unless otherwise instructed by the control tower, continue to taxi in the landing direction, proceed to the nearest suitable taxiway and exit the runway without delay. Do not turn on to another runway or make a 180 degree turn to taxi back on an active runway or change to ground control frequency while on an active runway without authorization from the tower. The pilot is expected to expeditiously change to the ground control frequency after the tower advises to make the frequency change. Do not enter any taxiway, other than the taxiway entered after exiting the runway, without ATC clearance.

3-20 Use of Aircraft Lighting.

  a. Aircraft position and anticollision lights are required to be lighted on aircraft operated from sunset to sunrise. Anticollision lights, however, need not be lighted when the pilot in command determines that, because of operating conditions, it would be in the interest of safety to turn off the lights (FAR 91.209). For example, strobe lights should be turned off on the ground when they adversely affect ground personnel or other pilots, and in flight when there is adverse reflection from clouds.
  b. An aircraft anticollision light system can use one or more rotating beacons and/ or strobe lights, be colored either red or white, and have different (higher than minimum) intensities when compared to other aircraft. Many aircraft have both a rotating beacon and a strobe light system.
  c. The FAA has a voluntary pilot safety program, OPERATION LIGHTS ON, to enhance the see-and-avoid concept. Pilots are encouraged to turn on their anticollision lights any time the engine(s) are running, day or night. Use of these lights is especially encouraged when operating on airport surfaces during periods of reduced visibility and when snow or ice control vehicles are or may be operating. Pilots are also encouraged to turn on their landing lights during takeoff; i.e., either after takeoff clearance has been received or when beginning takeoff roll. Pilots are further encouraged to turn on their landing lights when operating below 10,000 feet, day or night, especially when operating within 10 miles of any airport, or in conditions of reduced visibility and in areas where flocks of birds may be expected, i.e., coastal areas, lake areas, around refuse dumps, etc. Although turning on aircraft lights does enhance the see-and-avoid concept, pilots should not become complacent about keeping a sharp lookout for other aircraft. Not all aircraft are equipped with lights and some pilots may not have their lights on. Aircraft manufacturers' recommendations for operation of landing lights and electrical systems should be

observed.

d. Prop and jet blast forces generated by large aircraft have overturned or damaged several smaller aircraft taxiing behind them. To avoid similar results, and in the interest of preventing upsets and injuries to ground personnel from such forces, the FAA recommends that air carriers and commercial operators turn on their rotating beacons anytime their aircraft engines are in operation. General aviation pilots using rotating beacon equipped aircraft are also encouraged to participate in this program which is designed to alert others to the potential hazard. Since this is a voluntary program, exercise caution and do not rely solely on the rotating beacon as an indication that the aircraft engines are in operation.

3-21 Flight Inspection/"Flight Check" Aircraft In Terminal Areas.

a. FLIGHT CHECK is a call sign used to alert pilots and air traffic controllers when an FAA aircraft is engaged in flight inspection/certification of NAVAIDs and flight procedures. Flight Check aircraft fly preplanned high/low altitude flight patterns such as grids, orbits, DME arcs, and tracks, including low passes along the full length of the runway to verify NAVAID performance. In most instances, these flight checks are being automatically recorded and/or flown in an automated mode.

b. Pilots should be especially watchful and avoid the flight paths of any aircraft using the call sign FLIGHT CHECK or FLIGHT CHECK RECORDED. The latter call sign, e.g., FLIGHT CHECK 47 RECORDED indicates that automated flight inspections are in progress in terminal areas. These flights will normally receive special handling from ATC. Pilot patience and cooperation in allowing uninter-rupted recordings can significantly help expedite flight inspections, minimize costly, repetitive runs, and reduce the burden on the U.S. taxpayer.

TEST QUESTIONS

1. Which of the following is a continuous broadcast of recorded noncontrol information in selected high activity terminal areas?

A. UNICOM.
B. MULTICOM.
C. ATIS.

2. Which of the following will be issued to pilots being controlled by ATC if the controller is aware the aircraft is at an altitude which, in the controller's judgment, places the aircraft in unsafe proximity to terrain, obstructions or other aircraft?

A. Safety alert.
B. Terminal alert.
C. Traffic advisory.

3. Pilot participation within a Terminal Radar Service Area (TRSA) is

A. mandatory.
B. urged but is not mandatory.
C. decided by the controller.

4. Some transponders are equipped with automatic altitude reporting capability refered to as

A. Mode C.
B. Mode T.
C. 4096.

5. Under no circumstances should a pilot of a civil aircraft operate the transponder on Code

A. 7700.
B. 7777.
C. 7600.

6. When advised by ATC to change frequencies, the pilot should

A. change immediately.
B. wait 5 seconds, then change.
C. acknowledge the instruction before changing.

7. The following altitude (10,000 feet) should be read as

A. Ten thousand feet.
B. Ten point zero feet.
C. One zero thousand feet.

8. A time of 10:00 am (Eastern Standard Time) would convert to which of the following using Coordinated Universal Time (UTC)?

A. 1500 (UTC).
B. 1000 (UTC).
C. 500 (UTC).

9. If, while approaching an airport traffic area (ATA), you determine that your transmitter and receiver are inoperative the pilot should

A. remain outside and above the ATA until the direction and flow of traffic have been determined.
B. leave the area immediately.
C. flash landing light and proceed to land.

10. When approaching an airport served by an airport traffic area (ATA), the pilot should make initial callup at about

A. 3 miles from the airport.
B. 5 miles from the airport.
C. 15 miles from the airport.

11. At most airports and military bases, traffic pattern altitudes for propeller-driven aircraft generally extend from

A. 1,000 to 2,000 feet.
B. 600 to 1,500 feet.
C. 500 to 1,000 feet.

12. Runways are identified by numbers which indicate the nearest 10 degree increment of azimuth based on

A. true north.
B. magnetic deviation.
C. magnetic north.

13. A flashing red light gun signal received from the tower by an aircraft in flight indicates

A. airport unsafe, do not land.
B. return for landing immediately.
C. continue circling.

ANSWERS

1. C 2. A 3. B 4. A 5. B 6.C 7. C 8. A 9. A 10. C 11. B 12. C 13. A

AIR TRAFFIC PROCEDURES

SECTION 1. PREFLIGHT

1-1. Preflight Preparation.

a. Certain preflight actions are required by part 91 of the FARs. This part requires that pilots make themselves aware of ALL available information concerning their flight. For flights outside the vicinity of an airport preflight regulations require:

1. Weather Reports and Forecasts.
2. Fuel Requirements.
3. Alternatives available if planned flight cannot be completed.
4. Any known traffic delays.

For any flight:
1. Runway lengths at airports of intended use.
2. Takeoff and landing distance data pertinent to aircraft being flown.

Every pilot is urged to receive a preflight briefing and to file a flight plan. This briefing should consist of the latest or most current weather, airport, and en route NAVAID information. Briefing service may be obtained from an FSS either by telephone or interphone, by radio when airborne, or by a personal visit to the station. Pilots with a current medical certificate in the 48 contiguous states may access toll-free the Direct User Access Terminal System (DUATS) through a personal computer. DUATS will provide alpha-numeric preflight weather data and allow pilots to file domestic VFR or IFR flight plans.

NOTE. Pilots filing flight plans via "fast file" who desire to have their briefing recorded, should include a statement at the end of the recording as to the source of their weather briefing.

b. The information required by the FAA to process flight plans is contained on FAA Form 7233-1, Flight Plan. (Reference-Flight Plan - VFR Flights, this chapter Section 1-3). The forms are available at all flight service stations. Additional copies will be provided on request.

c. Consult an FSS or a Weather Service Office (WSO) for preflight weather briefing.

d. FSSs are required to advise pilots of pertinent NOTAMs if a standard briefing is requested, but if they are overlooked, don't hesitate to remind the specialist that you have not received NOTAM information.

NOTE. NOTAMs which are known in sufficient time for publication and are of 7 days duration or longer are normally incorporated into the Notices to Airmen publication and carried there until cancellation time. FDC NOTAMs, which apply to instrument flight procedures, are also included in the Notices to Airmen publication up to and including the number indicated in the FDC NOTAM legend. Printed NOTAMs are not provided during a briefing unless specifically requested by the pilot since the FSS specialist has no way of knowing whether the pilot has already checked the Notices to Airmen publication prior to calling. Remember to ask for NOTAMs in the Notices to Airmen publication. This information is not normally furnished during your briefing. (Reference-Notice to Airmen (NOTAM) System, this chapter).

e. Pilots are urged to use only the latest issue of aeronautical charts in planning and conducting flight operations. Aeronautical charts are revised and reissued on a regular scheduled basis to ensure that depicted data are current and reliable. In the conterminous U.S., Sectional Charts are updated each 6 months. Charts that have been superseded by those of a more recent date may contain obsolete or incomplete flight information. The proposed date of obsolescence is listed on the front of each chart. (Reference-General Description of each VFR Chart Series, Chapter 15).

f. When requesting a preflight briefing, identify yourself as a pilot and provide the following:

1. Type of flight planned; e.g., VFR or IFR.
2. Aircraft's number or pilot's name.
3. Aircraft type.
4. Departure airport.
5. Route of flight.
6. Destination.
7. Flight altitude(s).
8. Estimated Time of Departure (ETD).
9. Estimated Time En Route (ETE).

g. Prior to conducting a briefing, briefers are required to have the background information listed above so that they may tailor the briefing to the needs of the proposed flight. The objective is to communicate a "picture" of meteorological and aeronautical information necessary for the conduct of a safe and efficient flight. Briefers use all available weather and aeronautical information to summarize data applicable to the proposed flight. They do not read weather reports and forecasts verbatim unless specifically requested by the pilot. Refer to chapter 13 PRE-FLIGHT BRIEFINGS for those items of a weather briefing that should be expected or requested.

h. The Federal Aviation Administration (FAA) by Federal Aviation Regulation, Part 93, Subpart K, has designated High Density Traffic Airports (HDTAs) and has prescribed air traffic rules and requirements for operating aircraft (excluding helicopter operations) to and from these airports (Reference-Airport/Facility Directory, Special Notices Section, for details).

i. In addition to the filing of a flight plan, if the flight will traverse or land in one or more foreign countries, it is particularly important that pilots leave a complete itinerary with someone directly concerned, keep that person advised of the flight's progress, and inform him that, if serious doubt arises as to the safety of the flight, he should first contact the FSS.

j. Pilots operating under provisions of FAR 135 and not having an FAA assigned 3-letter designator, are urged to prefix the normal registration (N) number with the letter "T" on flight plan filing; e.g., TN1234B. (Reference-Aircraft Call Signs, Chapter 10).

1-2. Notice to Airmen (NOTAM) System.

a. Time-critical aeronautical information which is of either a temporary nature or not sufficiently known in advance to permit publication on aeronautical charts or in other operational publications receives immediate dissemination via the National Notice to Airmen (NOTAM) System.

NOTE. NOTAM information is that aeronautical information that could affect a pilot's decision to make a flight. It includes such information as airport or primary runway closures, changes in the status of navigational aids, ILSs, radar service availability, and other information essential to planned en route, terminal, or landing operations.

b. NOTAM information is classified into three categories. They are NOTAM (D) Distant, NOTAM (L) Local, Flight Data Center NOTAMs (FDC).

1. NOTAM (L) - Local

(a) NOTAM (L) information is disseminated locally to the FSS responsible for the airport concerned. They are not attached to the hourly weather reports. A separate file of local NOTAMs is maintained at each FSS for facilities in their area only. NOTAM (L) information for other FSS areas must be specifically requested directly from the FSS that has responsibility for the airport concerned.

(b) NOTAM (L) information includes such data as taxiway closures, men and equipment near or crossing runways, airport rotating beacon outages, and airport lighting aids that do not affect instrument approach criteria, such as VASI.

NOTE - DUATS vendors are not required to provide NOTAM (L) information.

2. NOTAM (D) - Distant

(a) NOTAM (D) information provides for both distant and local dissemination. The information is transferred to all FSSs within 200 nautical miles of the affected area. The complete file of all NOTAM (D) information is maintained in a computer data base at the National Communications Center (NATCOM), located in Kansas City. This category of information is distributed automatically, appended to the hourly weather reports, via the Service A telecommunications system. Air traffic facilities, primarily FSSs, with Service A capability have access to the entire NATCOM data base of NOTAMs. These NOTAMs remain available via Service A for the duration of their validity or until published.

(b) NOTAM (D) information includes runway closures, navigation aid frequency changes, approach lighting outages, change in tower operating hours, and enroute navigational facilities. Airports providing NOTAM (D) services will be so marked in the Airport/Facility Directory (A/FD).

3. FDC NOTAMs

(a) On those occasions when it becomes necessary to disseminate information which is REGULATORY in nature, the National Flight Data Center (NFDC), in Washington, DC, will issue an FDC NOTAM. FDC NOTAMs contain such things as amendments to published instrument approach procedures and other current aeronautical charts. They are also used to advertise temporary flight restrictions caused by such things as natural disasters or large-scale public events that may generate a congestion of air traffic over a site.

(b) FDC NOTAMs are transmitted via Service A only once and are kept on file at the FSS until published or canceled. FSSs are responsible for maintaining a file of current, unpublished FDC NOTAMs concerning conditions within 400 miles of their facilities. FDC information concerning conditions that are more than 400 miles from the FSS, or that is already published, is given to a pilot only on request.

NOTE 1. DUATS vendors will provide FDC NOTAMs only upon site-specific requests using a location identifier.

NOTE 2. NOTAM data may not always be current due to the changeable nature of National Airspace System components, delays inherent in processing information, and occasional temporary outages of the United States NOTAM System. While en route, pilots should contact FSSs and obtain updated information for their route of flight and destination.

c. An integral part of the NOTAM System is the biweekly Notice to Airmen publication. Data is included in this publication to reduce congestion on the telecommunications circuits and, therefore, is not available via Service A. Once published, the information is not provided during pilot weather briefings unless specifically requested by the pilot. This publication contains two sections.

1. The first section consists of notices that meet the criteria for NOTAM (D) and are expected to remain in effect for an extended period and FDC NOTAMs that are current at the time of publication. Occasionally, some NOTAM (L) and other unique information is included in this section when it will contribute to flight safety.

2. The second section contains special notices that are either too long or concern a wide or unspecified geographic area and are not suitable for inclusion in the first section. The content of these notices vary widely and there are no specific criteria for their inclusion, other than their enhancement of flight safety.

3. The number of the last FDC NOTAM included in the publication is noted on the first page to aid the user in updating the listing with any FDC NOTAMs which may have been issued between the cut-off date and the date the publication is received. All information contained will be carried until the information expires, is cancelled, or in the case of permanent conditions, is published in other publications, such as the A/FD.

4. All new notices entered, excluding FDC NOTAMs, will be published only if the information is expected to remain in effect for at least 7 days after the effective date of the publication.

1-3. Flight Plan - VFR Flights.

a. Except for operations in or penetrating a Coastal or Domestic ADIZ or DEWIZ a flight plan is not required for VFR flight. However, it is strongly recommended that one be filed with an FAA FSS. This will ensure that you receive VFR Search and Rescue Protection. (Reference-Search and Rescue, Chapter 12 for the proper method of filing).

b. To obtain maximum benefits from the flight plan program, flight plans should be filed directly with the nearest FSS. For your convenience, FSSs provide aeronautical and meteorological briefings while accepting flight plans. Radio may be used to file if no other means are available.

NOTE. Some states operate aeronautical communications facilities which will accept and forward flight plans to the FSS for further handling.

c. When a "stopover" flight is anticipated, it is recommended that a separate flight plan be filed for each "leg" when the stop is expected to be more than 1 hour duration.

d. Pilots are encouraged to give their departure times directly to the FSS serving the departure airport or as otherwise indicated by the FSS when the flight plan is filed. This will ensure more efficient flight plan service and permit the FSS to advise you of significant changes in aeronautical facilities or meteorological conditions. When a VFR flight plan is filed, it will be held by the FSS until 1 hour after the proposed departure time unless:

1. The actual departure time is received.

2. A revised proposed departure time is received.

3. At a time of filing, the FSS is informed that the proposed departure time will be met, but actual time cannot be given because of inadequate communications (assumed departures).

e. On pilot's request, at a location having an active tower, the aircraft identification will be forwarded by the FSS to the tower for reporting the actual departure time. This procedure should be avoided at busy airports.

f. Although position reports are not required for VFR flight plans, periodic reports to FAA FSSs along the route are good practice. Such contacts permit significant information to be passed to the transiting aircraft and also serve to check the progress of the flight should it be necessary for any reason to locate the aircraft.

EXAMPLE:

> BONANZA 314K, OVER KINGFISHER AT (time), VFR FLIGHT PLAN, TULSA TO AMARILLO.

EXAMPLE:

> CHEROKEE 5133J, OVER OKLAHOMA CITY AT (time), SHREVE-PORT TO DENVER, NO FLIGHT PLAN.

g. Pilots not operating on an IFR flight plan and when in level cruising flight, are cautioned to conform with VFR cruising altitudes appropriate to the direction of flight.

h. When filing VFR flight plans, indicate aircraft equipment capabilities by appending the appropriate suffix to aircraft type. Under some circumstances, ATC computer tapes can be useful in constructing the radar history of a downed or crashed aircraft. In each case, knowledge of the aircraft's transponder equipment is necessary in determining whether or not such computer tapes might prove effective. The appropriate codes are as follows:

> X - No transponder.
> T - Transponder no altitude encoding capability.
> U - Transponder with altitude encoding capability.
> B - DME and transponder, no altitude encoding capability.
> A - DME and transponder with altitude encoding capability.
> M - TACAN only, no transponder.

(Equipment Codes Cont.)

N - TACAN only, transponder, no altitude encoding capability.
P - TACAN only, transponder with altitude encoding capability.
C - RNAV and transponder, no altitude encoding capability.
R - RNAV and transponder with altitude encoding capability.
W - RNAV but no transponder.

i. Flight Plan Form - (See Figure 11-1).

U.S. DEPARTMENT OF TRANSPORTATION FEDERAL AVIATION ADMINISTRATION **FLIGHT PLAN**	CIVIL AIRCRAFT PILOTS. FAR Part 91 requires you file an IFR flight plan to operate under instrument flight rules in controlled airspace. Failure to file could result in a civil penalty not to exceed $1,000 for each violation (Section 901 of the Federal Aviation Act of 1958, as amended). Filing of a VFR flight plan is recommended as a good operating practice. See also Part 99 for requirements concerning DVFR flight plans.

1. TYPE: VFR / IFR / DVFR	2. AIRCRAFT IDENTIFICATION	3. AIRCRAFT TYPE/ SPECIAL EQUIPMENT	4. TRUE AIRSPEED KTS	5. DEPARTURE POINT	6. DEPARTURE TIME — PROPOSED (Z) / ACTUAL (Z)	7. CRUISING ALTITUDE

8. ROUTE OF FLIGHT

9. DESTINATION (Name of airport and city)	10. EST. TIME ENROUTE — HOURS / MINUTES	11. REMARKS

12. FUEL ON BOARD — HOURS / MINUTES	13. ALTERNATE AIRPORT(S)	14. PILOT'S NAME, ADDRESS & TELEPHONE NUMBER & AIRCRAFT HOME BASE — 17. DESTINATION CONTACT/TELEPHONE (OPTIONAL)	15. NUMBER ABOARD

16. COLOR OF AIRCRAFT	**CLOSE VFR FLIGHT PLAN WITH _____ FSS ON ARRIVAL**

Figure 11-1

j. Explanation of VFR Flight Plan Items -
Block 1. Check the flight plan type. Check both the VFR and IFR blocks if composite VFR/IFR.
Block 2. Enter your complete aircraft identification including the prefix "N" if applicable.
Block 3. Enter the designator for the aircraft, or if unknown, the aircraft manufacturer's name.

225

Block 4. Enter your true airspeed (TAS).

Block 5. Enter the departure airport identifier code, or if unknown, the name of the airport.

Block 6. Enter the proposed departure time in Coordinated Universal Time (UTC). If airborne, specify the actual or proposed departure time as appropriate.

Block 7. Enter the appropriate VFR altitude (to assist the briefer in providing weather and wind information). If the flight requires more than one altitude, enter the first altitude to be flown.

Block 8. Define the route of flight by using NAVAID identifier codes and airways.

Block 9. Enter the destination airport identifier code, or if unknown, the airport name.

NOTE - Include the city name (or even the state name) if needed for clarity.

Block 10. Enter your estimated time en route in hours and minutes.

Block 11. Enter only those remarks pertinent to ATC or to the clarification of other flight plan information, such as the appropriate radio-telephone (call sign) associated with the designator filed in Block 2. Items of a personal nature are not accepted.

Block 12. Specify the fuel on board in hours and minutes.

Block 13. Specify an alternate airport if desired.

Block 14. Enter your complete name, address, and telephone number. Enter sufficient information to identify home base, airport, or operator.

NOTE - This information is essential in the event of search and rescue operations.

Block 15. Enter total number of persons on board (POB) including crew.

Block 16. Enter the predominant colors.

Block 17. Record the FSS name for closing the flight plan. If the flight plan is closed with a different FSS or facility, state the recorded FSS name that would normally have closed your flight plan. (Optional) - Record a destination telephone number to assist search and rescue contact should you fail to report or cancel your flight plan within one hour after your estimated time of arrival (ETA).

NOTE. The information transmitted to the destination FSS will consist only of flight plan Blocks 2, 3, 9, and 10. Estimated time en route (ETE) will be converted to the correct estimated time of arrival (ETA).

1-4. Flight Plan - Defense VFR (DVFR) Flights.

VFR flights into a Coastal or Domestic ADIZ/DEWIZ are required to file VFR flight plans for security purposes. (See FAR 99.)

1-5. Composite Flight Plan (VFR/IFR) Flights.

a. Flight plans which specify VFR operation for one portion of a flight, and IFR for another portion, will be accepted by the FSS at the point of departure. If VFR flight is conducted for the first portion of the flight, the pilot should report this departure time to the FSS with which he filed his VFR/IFR flight plan; and, subsequently, close the VFR portion and request ATC clearance from the FSS nearest the point at which change from VFR to IFR is proposed. Regardless of the type facility you are communicating with (FSS, center, or tower), it is the pilot's responsibility to request that facility to CLOSE VFR FLIGHT PLAN. The pilot must remain in VFR weather conditions until operating in accordance with the IFR clearance.

b. When a flight plan indicates IFR for the first portion of flight and VFR for the latter portion, the pilot will normally be cleared to the point at which the change is proposed. Once the pilot has reported over the clearance limit and does not desire further IFR clearance, he should advise ATC to cancel the IFR portion of his flight plan. Then, he should contact the nearest FSS to activate the VFR portion of his flight plan. If the pilot desires to continue his IFR flight plan beyond the clearance limit, he should contact ATC at least 5 minutes prior to the clearance limit and request further IFR clearance. If the requested clearance is not received prior to reaching the clearance limit fix, the pilot will be expected to established himself in a standard holding pattern on the radial or course to the fix unless a holding pattern for the clearance limit fix is depicted on a U.S. Government or commercially produced (meeting FAA requirements) Low or High Altitude En Route, Area or STAR Chart. In this case the pilot will hold according to the depicted pattern.

1-6. Flights Outside The United States and U.S. Territories.

a. When conducting flights, particularly extended flights, outside the U.S. and its territories, full account should be taken of the amount and quality of air navigation services available in the airspace to be traversed. Every effort should be made to secure information on the location and range of navigational aids, availability of communications and meteorological services, the provision of air traffic services, including alerting service, and the existence of search and rescue services.

b. Pilots should remember that there is a need to continuously guard the VHF emergency frequency 121.5 MHz when on long over-water flights, except when communications on other VHF channels, equipment limitations, or cockpit duties prevent simultaneous guarding of two channels. Guarding of 121.5 MHz is particularly critical when operating in proximity to flight information region (FIR) boundaries, for example, operations on Route R220 between Anchorage and Tokyo, since it serves to facilitate communications with regard to aircraft which may experience in-flight emergencies, communications, or navigational difficulties. (Reference ICAO Annex 10, Vol II Paras 5.2.2.1.1.1 and 5.2.2. 1.1.2.)

c. The filing of a flight plan, always good practice, takes on added significance for extended flights outside U.S. airspace and is, in fact, usually required by the laws of the countries being visited/overflown. It is also particularly important in the case of such flights that pilots leave a complete itinerary and schedule of the flight with someone directly concerned, keep that person advised of the flight's progress and inform him that if serious doubt arises as to the safety of the flight he should first contact the appropriate FSS. Round Robin Flight Plans to Mexico are not accepted.

d. All pilots should review the foreign airspace and entry restrictions published in the IFIM during the flight planning process. Foreign airspace penetration without official authorization can involve both danger to the aircraft and the imposition of severe penalties and inconvenience to both passengers and crew. A flight plan on file with ATC authorities does not necessarily constitute the prior permission required by certain other authorities. The possibility of fatal consequences cannot be ignored in some areas of the world.

e. Current NOTAMs for foreign locations must also be reviewed. The publication International Notices to Airmen, published biweekly, contains considerable information pertinent to foreign flight. Current foreign NOTAMs are also available from the U.S. International NOTAM Office in Washington, D.C., through any local FSS.

f. When customs notification is required, it is the responsibility of the pilot to arrange for customs notification in a timely manner. The following guidelines are applicable:

1. When customs notification is required on flights to Canada and Mexico and a predeparture flight plan cannot be filed or an advise customs message (ADCUS) cannot be included in a predeparture flight plan, call the nearest en route domestic or International FSS as soon as radio communication can be established and file a VFR or DVFR flight plan, as required, and include as the last item the advise customs information. The station with which such a flight plan is filed will forward it to the appropriate FSS who will notify the customs office responsible for the destination airport.

2. If the pilot fails to include ADCUS in the radioed flight plan, it will be assumed that other arrangements have been made and FAA will not advise customs.

3. The FAA assumes no responsibility for any delays in advising customs

228

if the flight plan is given too late for delivery to customs before arrival of the aircraft. It is still the pilot's responsibility to give timely notice even though a flight plan is given to the FAA.

1-7. Change In Flight Plan.

In addition to altitude or flight level, destination and/or route changes, increasing or decreasing the speed of an aircraft constitutes a change in a flight plan. Therefore, at any time the average true airspeed at cruising altitude between reporting points varies or is expected to vary from that given in the flight plan by plus or minus 5 percent, or 10 knots, whichever is greater, ATC should be advised.

1-8. Change In Proposed Departure Time.

a. To prevent computer saturation in the en route environment, parameters have been established to delete proposed departure flight plans which have not been activated. Most centers have this parameter set so as to delete these flight plans a minimum of 1 hour after the proposed departure time. To ensure that a flight plan remains active, pilots whose actual departure time will be delayed 1 hour or more beyond their filed departure time are requested to notify ATC of their departure time.

b. Due to traffic saturation, control personnel frequently will be unable to accept these revisions via radio. It is recommended that you forward these revisions to the nearest FSS.

1-9. Closing VFR/DVFR Flight Plans.

A pilot is responsible for ensuring that his VFR or DVFR flight plan is cancelled (FAR 91.153 and FAR 91.169). You should close your flight plan with the nearest FSS, or if one is not available, you may request any ATC facility to relay your cancellation to the FSS. Control towers do not automatically close VFR or DVFR flight plans since they do not know if a particular VFR aircraft is on a flight plan. If you fail to report or cancel your flight plan within 1/2 hour after your ETA, search and rescue procedures are started.

TEST QUESTIONS

1. If more than one cruising altitude is planned for a particular flight, which should be entered in block 7 (CRUISING ALTITUDE) of the flight plan?

A. Initial cruising altitude.
B. Highest cruising altitude.
C. Lowest cruising altitude.

2. What information should be entered in block 9 (DESTINATION) for a VFR day flight?

A. The name of the airport of first intended landing.
B. The name of destination airport if no stopover for more than 1 hour is intended.
C. The name of the airport where the airplane is based.

3. What information should be entered in block 12 (FUEL ON BOARD) for a day VFR flight?

A. The estimated time en route plus 30 minutes.
B. The estimated time en route plus 45 minutes.
C. The amount of usable fuel on board expressed in time.

4. How should a VFR flight plan be closed at the completion of the flight at a controlled airport?

A. The tower will automatically close the flight plan when the aircraft turns off the runway.
B. The pilot must close the flight plan with the nearest FSS or other FAA facility upon landing.
C. The tower will relay the instructions to the nearest FSS when the aircraft contacts the tower for landing.

5. Which preflight action is required by law for all flights?

A. All weather reports and forecasts.
B. Runway lengths of intended use.
C. Fuel requirements.

6. Which of the following NOTAMs deals with information which is regulatory in nature?

A. (FDC) NOTAM.
B. NOTAM (L).
C. NOTAM (D).

7. When telephoning a weather briefing facility for preflight weather information, pilots should state

A. the full name and address of the pilot in command.
B. the intended route, destination, and type of aircraft.
C. the radio frequencies to be used.

8. Which equipment code should be entered in the flight plan for an aircraft having an altitude encoding transponder?

A. T.
B. U.
C. A.

9. How long after the proposed time of departure will the FAA facility delete your flight plan from the computer?

A. 30 minutes.
B. 1 hour.
C. 2 hours.

ANSWERS

1. A 2. B 3. C 4. B 5. B 6. A 7. B 8. B 9. B

12

EMERGENCY PROCEDURES

SECTION 1. GENERAL

1-1. Pilot Responsibility and Authority.

a. The pilot in command of an aircraft is directly responsible for and is the final authority as to the operation of that aircraft. In an emergency requiring immediate action, the pilot in command may deviate from any rule in the FAR, Subpart A, General, and Subpart B, Flight Rules, to the extent required to meet that emergency. (FAR 91.3(b).)

b. If the emergency authority of FAR 91.3.(b) is used to deviate from the provisions of an ATC clearance, the pilot in command must notify ATC as soon as possible and obtain an amended clearance.

c. Unless deviation is necessary under the emergency authority of FAR 91.3, pilots of IFR flights experiencing two-way radio communications failure are expected to adhere to the procedures prescribed under "IFR operations, two-way radio communications failure." (FAR 91.185)

1-2. Emergency Condition - Request Assistance Immediately.

a. An emergency can be either a distress or urgency condition as defined in the Pilot/Controller Glossary. Pilots do not hesitate to declare an emergency when they are faced with distress conditions such as fire, mechanical failure, or structural damage. However, some are reluctant to report an urgency condition when they encounter situations which may not be immediately perilous, but are potentially catastrophic. An aircraft is in at least an urgency condition the moment the pilot becomes doubtful about position, fuel endurance, weather, or any other condition that could adversely affect flight safety. This is the time to ask for help, not after the situation has developed into a distress condition.

b. Pilots who become apprehensive for their safety for any reason should request assistance immediately. Ready and willing help is available in the form of radio, radar, direction finding stations and other aircraft. Delay has caused accidents and cost lives. Safety is not a luxury! Take action!

SECTION 2. EMERGENCY SERVICES AVAILABLE TO PILOTS

2-1. Radar Service For VFR Aircraft In Difficulty.

a. Radar-equipped ATC facilities can provide radar assistance and navigation service (vectors) to VFR aircraft in difficulty when the pilot can talk with the controller, and the aircraft is within radar coverage. Pilots should clearly understand that authorization to proceed in accordance with such radar navigational assistance does not constitute authorization for the pilot to violate FARs. In effect, assistance is provided on the basis that navigational guidance information is advisory in nature, and the responsibility for flying the aircraft safely remains with the pilot.

b. Experience has shown that many pilots who are not qualified for instrument flight cannot maintain control of their aircraft when they encounter clouds or other reduced visibility conditions. In many cases, the controller will not know whether flight into instrument conditions will result from his instructions. To avoid possible hazards resulting from being vectored into IFR conditions, a pilot in difficulty should keep the controller advised of the weather conditions in which he is operating and the weather along the course ahead and observe the following:

      1. If a course of action is available which will permit flight and a safe landing in VFR weather conditions, noninstrument rated pilots should choose the VFR condition rather than requesting a vector or approach that will take them into IFR weather conditions; or

      2. If continued flight in VFR conditions is not possible, the noninstrument rated pilot should so advise the controller and indicating the lack of an instrument rating, declare a distress condition, or

      3. If the pilot is instrument rated and current, and the aircraft is instrument equipped, the pilot should so indicate by requesting an IFR flight clearance. Assistance will then be provided on the basis that the aircraft can operate safely in IFR weather conditions.

2-2. Transponder Emergency Operation.

a. When a distress or urgency condition is encountered, the pilot of an aircraft with a coded radar beacon transponder, who desires to alert a ground radar facility, should squawk MODE 3/A, Code 7700/Emergency and MODE C altitude reporting and then immediately establish communications with the ATC facility.

b. Radar facilities are equipped so that Code 7700 normally triggers an alarm or special indicator at all control positions. Pilots should understand that they might not be within a radar coverage area. Therefore, they should continue squawking Code 7700 and establish radio communications as soon as possible.

2.3. Intercept and Escort.

a. The concept of airborne intercept and escort is based on the Search and Rescue (SAR) aircraft establishing visual and/or electronic contact with an aircraft in difficulty, providing in-flight assistance, and escorting it to a safe landing. If bailout, crash landing or ditching becomes necessary, SAR operations can be conducted without delay. For most incidents, particularly those occurring at night and/or during instrument flight conditions, the availability of intercept and escort services will depend on the proximity of SAR units with suitable aircraft on alert for immediate dispatch. In limited circumstances, other aircraft flying in the vicinity of an aircraft in difficulty can provide these services.

b. If specifically requested by a pilot in difficulty or if a distress condition is declared, SAR coordinators will take steps to intercept and escort an aircraft. Steps may be initiated for intercept and escort if an urgency condition is declared and unusual circumstances make such action advisable.

c. It is the pilot's prerogative to refuse intercept and escort services. Escort services will normally be provided to the nearest adequate airport. Should the pilot receiving escort services continue onto another location after reaching a safe airport, or decide not to divert to the nearest safe airport, the escort aircraft is not obligated to continue and further escort is discretionary. The decision will depend on the circumstances of the individual incident.

2-4. Emergency Locator Transmitters.

a. GENERAL. Emergency Locator Transmitters (ELTs) are required for most general aviation airplanes (FAR 91.207). ELTs of various types have been developed as a means of locating downed aircraft. These electronic, battery operated transmitters emit a distinctive downward swept audio tone on 121.5 MHz and 243.0 MHz. If "armed" and when subject to crash generated forces they are designed to automatically activate and continuously emit these signals. The transmitters will operate continuously for at least 48 hours over a wide temperature range. A properly installed and maintained ELT can expedite search and rescue operations and save lives.

b. TESTING. ELTs should be tested in accordance with the manufacturer's instructions, preferably in a shielded or screened room to prevent the broadcast of signals which could trigger a false alert. When this cannot be done, aircraft operational testing is authorized on 121.5 MHz and 243.0 MHz as follows:

1. Tests should be conducted only during the first 5 minutes after any hour. If operational tests must be made outside of this time-frame, they should be coordinated with the nearest FAA Control Tower or FSS.

2. Tests should be no longer than three audible sweeps.

3. If the antenna is removable, a dummy load should be substituted during test procedures.

4. Airborne tests are not authorized.

c. FALSE ALARMS. Caution should be exercised to prevent the inadvertent activation of ELTs in the air or while they are being handled on the ground. Accidental or unauthorized activation will generate an emergency signal that cannot be distinguished from the real thing, leading to expensive and frustrating searches. A false ELT signal could also interfere with genuine emergency transmissions and hinder or prevent the timely location of crash sites. Frequent false alarms could also result in complacency and decrease the vigorous reaction that must be attached to an ELT signal. Numerous cases of inadvertent activation have occurred as a result of aerobatics, hard landings, movement by ground crews and aircraft maintenance. These false alarms can be minimized by monitoring 121.5 MHz and/or 243.0 MHz as follows:

1. In flight when a receiver is available.

2. Prior to engine shut down at the end of each flight.

3. When the ELT is handled during installation or maintenance.

4. When maintenance is being performed in the vicinity of the ELT.

5. When the aircraft is moved by a ground crew.

6. If an ELT signal is heard, turn off the ELT to determine if it is transmitting. If it has been activated, maintenance might be required before the unit is returned to the "ARMED" position.

d. IN-FLIGHT MONITORING AND REPORTING. Pilots are encouraged to monitor 121.5 MHz and/or 243.0 MHz while in flight to assist in identifying possible emergency ELT transmissions. On receiving a signal, report the following information to the nearest air traffic facility:

1. Your position at the time the signal was first heard.

2. Your position at the time the signal was last heard.

3. Your position at maximum signal strength.

4. Your flight altitudes and frequency on which the emergency signal was heard - 121.5 MHz or 243.0 MHz. If possible, positions should be given relative to a navigation aid. If the aircraft has homing equipment, provide the bearing to the

236

emergency signal with each reported position.

2-5. FAA Sponsored Explosive Detection (Dog/Handler Team) Locations.

a. At many of our major airports a program has been established by the FAA to make available explosives detection dog/handler teams. The dogs are trained by the Air Force and the overall program is run by FAA's Office of Civil Aviation Security. Local police departments are the caretakers of the dogs and are allowed to use the dogs in their normal police patrol functions. The local airport, however, has first call on the teams' services. The explosives detection teams were established so that no aircraft in flight is more than 1 hour from an airport at which it can be searched if a bomb threat is received. The following list contains those locations that presently have a team in existence. This list will be updated as more teams are established. If you desire this service, notify your company or an FAA facility.

TEAM LOCATIONS			
Airport Symbol	Location	Airport Symbol	Location
ATL	Atlanta, Georgia	MIA	Miami, Florida
BWI	Baltimore, Maryland	MSY	New Orleans, Louisiana
BHM	Birmingham, Alabama	PHX	Phoenix, Arizona
BIS	Bismarck, North Dakota	PIT	Pittsburgh, Pennsylvania
BOS	Boston, Massachusetts	PDX	Portland, Oregon
BUF	Buffalo, New York	SLC	Salt Lake City, Utah
ORD	Chicago, Illinois	SAN	San Diego, California
CLE	Cleveland, Ohio	SFO	San Francisco, California
DFW	Dallas, Texas	SJU	San Juan, Puerto Rico
IAH	Houston, Texas	SEA	Seattle, Washington
JAX	Jacksonville, Florida	GEG	Spokane, Washington
MCI	Kansas City, Missouri	STL	St. Louis, Missouri
LAX	Los Angeles, California	TUS	Tucson, Arizona
MEM	Memphis, Tennessee	TUL	Tulsa, Oklahoma

b. If due to weather or other considerations an aircraft with a suspected hidden explosive problem were to land or intended to land at an airport other than those listed, it is recommended that they call the FAA's Washington Operations Center

(Phone 202-426-3333) or have an air traffic facility with which you can communicate contact the above center requesting assistance.

2-6. Search and Rescue.

a. GENERAL. Search and Rescue (SAR) is a lifesaving service provided through the combined efforts of the federal agencies signatory to the National SAR Plan, and the agencies responsible for SAR within each state. Operational resources are provided by the U.S. Coast Guard, DOD components, the Civil Air Patrol, the Coast Guard Auxiliary, state, county and local law enforcement and other public safety agencies, and private volunteer organizations. Services include search for missing aircraft, survival aid, rescue, and emergency medical help for the occupants after an accident site is located.

b. NATIONAL SEARCH AND RESCUE PLAN. By federal interagency agreement, the National Search and Rescue Plan provides for an effective use of all available facilities in all types of SAR missions. These facilities include aircraft, vessels, pararescue and ground rescue teams, and emergency radio fixing. Under the plan, the U.S. Coast Guard is responsible for the coordination for SAR in the Maritime Region, and the USAF is responsible in the Inland Region. To carry out these responsibilities, the Coast Guard and the Air Force have established Rescue Coordination Centers (RCCs) to direct SAR activities within their Regions. For aircraft emergencies, distress and urgency information normally will be passed to the appropriate RCC through an ARTCC or FSS.

c. OVERDUE AIRCRAFT.

1. ARTCCs and FSSs will alert the SAR system when information is received from any source that an aircraft is in difficulty, overdue, or missing. A filed flight plan is the most timely and effective indicator that an aircraft is overdue. Flight plan information is invaluable to SAR forces for search planning and executing search efforts.

2. Prior to departure on every flight, local or otherwise, someone at the departure point should be advised of your destination and route of flight if other than direct. Search efforts are often wasted and rescue is often delayed because of pilots who thoughtlessly takeoff without telling anyone where they are going. File a flight plan for your safety.

3. According to the National Search and Rescue Plan, "The life expectancy of an injured survivor decreases as much as 80 percent during the first 24 hours, while the chances of survival of uninjured survivors rapidly diminishes after the first 3 days."

238

4. An Air Force Review of 325 SAR missions conducted during a 23-month period revealed that "Time works against people who experience a distress but are not on a flight plan, since 36 hours normally pass before family concern initiates an (alert)."

d. VFR SEARCH AND RESCUE PROTECTION.

1. To receive this valuable protection file a VFR Flight Plan with an FAA FSS. For maximum protection, file only to the point of first intended landing, and refile for each leg to final destination. When a lengthy flight plan is filed, with several stops en route and an ETE to final destination, a mishap could occur on any leg, and unless other information is received, it is probably that no one would start looking for you until 30 minutes after your ETA at your final destination.

2. If you land at a location other than the intended destination, report the landing to the nearest FAA FSS and advise them of your original destination.

3. If you land en route and are delayed more than 30 minutes, report this information to the nearest FSS and give them your original destination.

4. If your ETE changes by 30 minutes or more, report a new ETA to the nearest FSS and give them your original destination. Remember that if you fail to respond within one-half hour after your ETA at final destination, a search will be started to locate you.

5. It is important that you close your flight plan IMMEDIATELY AFTER ARRIVAL AT YOUR FINAL DESTINATION WITH THE FSS DESIGNATED WHEN YOUR FLIGHT PLAN WAS FILED. The pilot is responsible for closure of a VFR flight plan; they are not closed automatically. This will prevent needless search efforts.

6. The rapidity of rescue on land or water will depend on how accurately your position may be determined. If a flight plan has been followed and your position is on course, rescue will be expedited.

e. SURVIVAL EQUIPMENT.

1. For flight over uninhabited land areas, it is wise to take and know how to use survival equipment for the type of climate and terrain.

2. If a forced landing occurs at sea, chances for survival are governed by the degree of crew proficiency in emergency procedures and by the availability and effectiveness of water survival equipment.

f. OBSERVANCE OF DOWNED AIRCRAFT.

1. Determine if crash is marked with a yellow cross; if so, the crash has already been reported and identified.

2. If possible, determine type and number of aircraft and whether there is evidence of survivors.

3. Fix the position of the crash as accurately as possible with reference to a navigational aid. If possible provide geographic or physical description of the area to aid ground search parties.

4. Transmit the information to the nearest FAA or other appropriate radio facility.

5. If circumstances permit, orbit the scene to guide in other assisting units until their arrival or until you are relieved by another aircraft.

6. Immediately after landing, make a complete report to the nearest FAA facility, or Air Force or Coast Guard Rescue Coordination Center. The report can be made by long distance collect telephone.

GROUND-AIR VISUAL CODE FOR USE BY SURVIVORS	
Code Symbol	Message
V	Require assistance
X	Require medical assistance
N	No or Negative
Y	Yes or Affirmative
-->	Proceeding in this direction

SECTION 3. DISTRESS AND URGENCY PROCEDURES

3-1. Distress and Urgency Communications.

a. A pilot who encounters a distress or urgency condition can obtain assistance simply by contacting the air traffic facility or other agency in whose area of responsibility the aircraft is operating, stating the nature of the difficulty, pilot's intentions and assistance desires. Distress and urgency communications procedures are prescribed by the International Civil Aviation Organization (ICAO), however, and have decided advantages over the informal procedure described above.

b. Distress and urgency communications procedures discussed in the following

240

paragraphs relate to the use of air-ground voice communications.

c. The initial communication, and if considered necessary, any subsequent transmissions by an aircraft in distress should begin with the signal MAYDAY, preferably repeated three times. The signal PAN-PAN should be used in the same manner for an urgency condition.

d. Distress communications have absolute priority over all other communications, and the word MAYDAY commands radio silence on the frequency in use. Urgency communications have priority over all other communications except distress, and the word PAN-PAN warns other stations not to interfere with urgency transmissions.

e. Normally, the station addressed will be the air traffic facility or other agency providing air traffic services, on the frequency in use at the time. If the pilot is not communicating and receiving services, the station to be called will normally be the air traffic facility or other agency in whose area of responsibility the aircraft is operating, on the appropriate assigned frequency. If the station addressed does not respond, or if time or the situation dictates, the distress or urgency message may be broadcast, or a collect call may be used, addressing "Any Station (Tower) (Radio) (Radar)."

f. The station addressed should immediately acknowledge a distress or urgency message, provide assistance, coordinate and direct the activities of assisting facilities, and alert the appropriate search and rescue coordinator if warranted. Responsibility will be transferred to another station only if better handling will result.

g. All other stations, aircraft and ground, will continue to listen until it is evident that assistance is being provided. If any station becomes aware that the station being called either has not received a distress or urgency message, or cannot communicate with the aircraft in difficulty, it will attempt to contact the aircraft and provide assistance.

h. Although the frequency in use or other frequencies assigned by ATC are preferable, the following emergency frequencies can be used for distress or urgency communications, if necessary or desirable:

1. 121.5 MHz and 243.0 MHz - Both have a range generally limited to line of sight. 121.5 MHz is guarded by direction finding stations and some military and civil aircraft; 243.0 MHz is guarded by military aircraft. Both 121.5 MHz and 243.0 MHz are guarded by military towers, most civil towers, FSSs, and radar facilities. Normally ARTCC emergency frequency capability does not extend to radar coverage limits. If an ARTCC does not respond when called on 121.5 MHz or 243.0 MHz, call the nearest tower or FSS.

2. 2182 kHz - The range is generally less than 300 miles for the average aircraft installation. It can be used to request assistance from stations in the maritime service. 2182 kHz is guarded by major radio stations serving Coast Guard Rescue Coordination Centers, and Coast Guard units along the sea coasts of the U.S. and shores of the Great Lakes. The call "Coast Guard" will alert all Coast Guard Radio Stations within range. 2182 kHz is also guarded by most commercial coast stations and some ships and boats.

3-2. Obtaining Emergency Assistance.

a. A pilot in any distress or urgency condition should immediately take the following action, not necessarily in the order listed, to obtain assistance:

1. Climb, if possible, for improved communications, and better radar and direction finding detection. However, it must be understood that unauthorized climb or descent under IFR conditions within controlled airspace is prohibited, except as permitted by FAR 91.3(b).

2. If equipped with a radar beacon transponder (civil) or IFF/SIF (military):

(a) Continue squawking assigned Mode A/3 discrete code/VFR code and Mode C altitude encoding when in radio contact with an air traffic facility or other agency providing air traffic services, unless instructed to do otherwise.

(b) If unable to immediately establish communications with an air traffic facility/agency, squawk Mode A/3, Code 7700/Emergency and Mode C.

3. Transmit a distress or urgency message consisting of as many as necessary of the following elements, preferably in the order listed:

(a) If distress, MAYDAY, MAYDAY, MAYDAY; if urgency, PAN-PAN, PAN-PAN, PAN-PAN.

(b) Name of station addressed.

(c) Aircraft identification and type.

(d) Nature of distress or urgency.

(e) Weather.

(f) Pilots intentions and request.

(g) Present position, and heading; or if lost, last known position, time, and heading since that position.

(h) Altitude or flight level.

(i) Fuel remaining in minutes.

(j) Number of people on board.

(k) Any other useful information.

b. After establishing radio contact, comply with advice and instructions received.

Cooperate. Do not hesitate to ask questions or clarify instructions when you do not understand or if you cannot comply with clearance. Assist the ground station to control communications on the frequency in use. Silence interfering radio stations. Do not change frequency or change to another ground station unless absolutely necessary. If you do, advise the ground station of the new frequency and station name prior to the change, transmitting in the blind if necessary. If two-way communications cannot be established on the new frequency, return immediately to the frequency or station where two-way communications last existed.

c. When in a distress condition with bailout, crash landing or ditching imminent, take the following additional actions to assist search and rescue units:

1. Time and circumstances permitting, transmit as many as necessary of the message elements in subparagraph a(3) and any of the following that you think might be helpful

(a) ELT status.

(b) Visible landmarks.

(c) Aircraft color.

(d) Number of persons on board.

(e) Emergency equipment on board.

2. Actuate your ELT if the installation permits.

3. For bailout, and for crash landing or ditching if risk of fire is not a consideration, set your radio for continuous transmission.

4. If it becomes necessary to ditch, make every effort to ditch near a surface vessel. If time permits, an FAA facility should be able to get the position of the nearest commercial or Coast Guard vessel from a Coast Guard Rescue Coordination Center.

5. After a crash landing unless you have good reason to believe that you will not be located by search aircraft or ground teams, it is best to remain with your aircraft and prepare means for signalling search aircraft.

3-3. Ditching Procedures.

a. A successful aircraft ditching is dependent on three primary factors. In order of importance they are:

1. Sea conditions and wind.

2. Type of aircraft.

3. Skill and technique of pilot.

b. Common oceanographic terminology:

1. Sea. The condition of the surface that is the result of both waves and swells.

2. Wave (or Chop). The condition of the surface caused by the local winds.

3. Swell. The condition of the surface which has been caused by a distance disturbance.

4. Swell Face. The side of the swell toward the observer. The backside is the side away from the observer. These definitions apply regardless of the direction of swell movement.

5. Primary Swell. The swell system having the greatest height from trough to crest.

6. Secondary Swells. Those swell systems of less height than the primary swell.

7. Fetch. The distance the waves have been driven by a wind blowing in a constant direction, without obstruction.

8. Swell Period. The time interval between the passage of two successive crests at the same spot in the water, measured in seconds.

9. Swell Velocity. The speed and direction of the swell with relation to a fixed reference point, measured in knots. There is little movement of water in the horizontal direction. Swells move primarily in a vertical motion, similar to the motion observed when shaking out a carpet.

10. Swell Direction. The direction from which a swell is moving. This direction is not necessarily the result of the wind present at the scene. The swell may be moving into or across the local wind. Swells, once set in motion, tend to maintain their original direction for as long as they continue in deep water, regardless of changes in wind direction.

11 . Swell Height. The height between crest and trough, measured in feet. The vast majority of ocean swells are lower than 12 to 15 feet, and swells over 25 feet are not common at any spot on the oceans. Successive swells may differ considerably in height.

c. In order to select a good heading when ditching an aircraft, a basic evaluation of the sea is required. Selection of a good ditching heading may well minimize damage and could save your life. It can be extremely dangerous to land into the wind without regard to sea conditions; the swell system, or systems, must be taken into consideration. Remember one axiom - AVOID THE FACE OF A SWELL.

1. In ditching parallel to the swell, it makes little difference whether touchdown is on the top of the crest or in the trough. It is preferable, however, to land on the top or back side of the swell, if possible. After determining which

heading (and its reciprocal) will parallel the swell, select the heading with the most into the wind component.

2. If only one swell system exists, the problem is relatively simple - even with a high, fast system. Unfortunately, most cases involve two or more swell systems running in different directions. With more than one system present, the sea presents a confused appearance. One of the most difficult situations occurs when two swell systems are at right angles. For example, if one system is eight feet high, and the other three feet, plan to land parallel to the primary system, and on the down swell of the secondary system. If both systems are of equal height, a compromise may be advisable. Select an intermediate heading at 45 degrees down swell to both systems. When landing down a secondary swell, attempt to touch down on the back side, not on the face of the swell.

3. If the swell system is formidable, it is considered advisable, in land planes, to accept more cross wind in order to avoid landing directly into the swell.

4. The secondary swell system is often from the same direction as the wind. Here, the landing may be made parallel to the primary system, with the wind and secondary system at an angle. There is a choice of two directions paralleling the primary system. One direction is down wind and down the secondary swell, and the other is into the wind and into the secondary swell, the choice will depend on the velocity of the wind versus the velocity and height of the secondary swell.

d. The simplest method of estimating the wind direction and velocity is to examine the wind streaks on the water. These appear as long streaks up and down wind. Some persons may have difficulty determining wind direction after seeing the streaks on the water. Whitecaps fall forward with the wind but are overrun by the waves thus producing the illusion that the foam is sliding backward. Knowing this, and by observing the direction of the streaks, the wind direction is easily determined. Wind velocity can be estimated by noting the appearance of the whitecaps, foam and wind streaks.

1. The behavior of the aircraft on making contact with the water will vary within wide limits according to the state of the sea. If landed parallel to a single swell system, the behavior of the aircraft may approximate that to be expected on a smooth sea. If landed into a heavy swell or into a confused sea, the deceleration forces may be extremely great - resulting in breaking up of the aircraft. Within certain limits, the pilot is able to minimize these forces by proper sea evaluation and selection of ditching heading.

2. When on final approach the pilot should look ahead and observe the surface of the sea. There may be shadows and whitecaps - signs of large seas. Shadows and whitecaps close together indicate short and rough seas. Touchdown

in these areas is to be avoided. Select and touchdown in any area (only about 500 feet is needed) where the shadows and whitecaps are not so numerous.

3. Touchdown should be at the slowest speed and rate of descent which permit safe handling and optimum nose up attitude on impact. Once first impact has been made, there is often little the pilot can do to control a landplane.

e. Once preditching preparations are completed, the pilot should turn to the ditching heading and commence let-down. The aircraft should be flown low over the water, and slowed down until ten knots or so above stall. At this point, additional power should be used to overcome the increased drag caused by the nose up attitude. When a smooth stretch of water appears ahead, cut power, and touchdown at the best recommended speed as fully stalled as possible. By cutting power when approaching a relatively smooth area, the pilot will prevent over shooting and will touchdown with less chance of planing off into a second uncontrolled landing. Most experienced seaplane pilots prefer to make contact with the water in a semi-stalled attitude, cutting power as the tail makes contact. This technique eliminates the chance of misjudging altitude with a resultant heavy drop in a fully stalled condition. Care must be taken not to drop the aircraft from too high altitude or to balloon due to excessive speed. The altitude above water depends on the aircraft. Over glassy smooth water, or at night without sufficient light, it is very easy, for even the most experienced pilots to misjudge altitude by 50 feet or more. Under such conditions, carry enough power to maintain nine to twelve degrees nose up attitude, and 10 to 20 percent over stalling speed until contact is made with the water. The proper use of power on the approach is of great importance. If power is available on one side only, a little power should be used to flatten the approach; however, the engine should not be used to such an extent that the aircraft cannot be turned against the good engines right down to the stall with a margin of rudder movement available. When near the stall, sudden application of excessive unbalanced power may result in loss of directional control. If power is available on one side only, a slightly higher than normal glide approach speed should be used. This will insure good control and some margin of speed after leveling off without excessive use of power. The use of power in ditching is so important that when it is certain that the coast cannot be reached, the pilot should, if possible, ditch before fuel is exhausted. The use of power in a night or instrument ditching is far more essential than under daylight contact conditions.

1. If no power is available, a greater than normal approach speed should be used down to the flare-out. This speed margin will allow the glide to be broken early and more gradually, thereby giving the pilot time and distance to feel for the surface decreasing the possibility of stalling high or flying into the water. When landing

parallel to a swell system, little difference is noted between landing on top of a crest or in the trough. If the wings of aircraft are trimmed to the surface of the sea rather than the horizon, there is little need to worry about a wing hitting a swell crest. The actual slope of a swell is very gradual. If forced to land into a swell, touchdown should be made just after passage of the crest. If contact is made on the face of the swell, the aircraft may be swamped or thrown violently into the air, dropping heavily into the next swell. If control surfaces remain intact, the pilot should attempt to maintain the proper nose above the horizon attitude by rapid and positive use of the controls.

f. After Touchdown. In most cases drift, caused by crosswind can be ignored; the forces acting on the aircraft after touchdown are of such magnitude that drift will be only a secondary consideration. If the aircraft is under good control, the "crab" may be kicked out with rudder just prior to touchdown. This is more important with high wing aircraft, for they are laterally unstable on the water in a crosswind and may roll to the side in ditching.

NOTE: This information has been extracted from Appendix H of the "National Search And Rescue Manual."

3-4. Special Emergency (Air Piracy).

a. A special emergency is a condition of air piracy, or other hostile act by a person(s) aboard an aircraft, which threatens the safety of the aircraft or its passengers.

b. The pilot of an aircraft reporting a special emergency condition should:

1. If circumstances permit, apply distress or urgency radio-telephone procedures (Reference-Distress and Urgency Communications, section 3-1 this chapter). Include the details of the special emergency.

2. If circumstances do not permit the use of prescribed distress or urgency procedures, transmit:

(a) On the air/ground frequency in use at the time.

(b) As many as possible of the following elements spoken distinctly and in the following order:

(1) Name of the station addressed (time and circumstances permitting).

(2) The identification of the aircraft and present position.

(3) The nature of the special emergency condition and pilot intentions (circumstances permitting).

247

(4) If unable to provide this information, use code words and/or transponder as follows: state TRANSPONDER SEVEN FIVE ZERO ZERO . Meaning: "I am being hijacked/forced to a new destination"; and/or use Transponder Setting MODE 3/A, Code 7500.

NOTE. Code 7500 will never be assigned by ATC without prior notification from the pilot that his aircraft is being subjected to unlawful interference. The pilot should refuse the assignment of Code 7500 in any other situation and inform the controller accordingly. Code 7500 will trigger the special emergency indicator in all radar ATC facilities.

c. Air traffic controllers will acknowledge and confirm receipt of transponder Code 7500 by asking the pilot to verify it. If the aircraft is not being subjected to unlawful interference, the pilot should respond to the query by broadcasting in the clear that he is not being subjected to unlawful interference. Upon receipt of this information, the controller will request the pilot to verify the code selection depicted in the code selector windows in the transponder control panel and change the code to the appropriate setting. If the pilot replies in the affirmative or does not reply, the controller will not ask further questions but will flight follow, respond to pilot requests and notify appropriate authorities.

d. If it is possible to do so without jeopardizing the safety of the flight, the pilot of a hijacked passenger aircraft, after departing from the cleared routing over which the aircraft was operating, will attempt to do one or more of the following things, insofar as circumstances may permit:

1. Maintain a true airspeed of no more than 400 knots, and preferably an altitude of between 10,000 and 25,000 feet.

2. Fly a course toward the destination which the hijacker has announced.

e. If these procedures result in either radio contact or air intercept, the pilot will attempt to comply with any instructions received which may direct him to an appropriate landing field.

3-5. Fuel Dumping.

a. Should it become necessary to dump fuel, the pilot should immediately advise ATC. Upon receipt of information that an aircraft will dump fuel, ATC will broadcast or cause to be broadcast immediately and every 3 minutes thereafter the following on appropriate ATC and FSS radio frequencies:

EXAMPLE:

ATTENTION ALL AIRCRAFT - FUEL DUMPING IN PROGRESS OVER-(location), AT-(altitude), BY-(type aircraft) (flight direction).

248

b. Upon receipt of such a broadcast, pilots of aircraft affected, which are not on IFR flight plans or special VFR clearances, should clear the area specified in the advisory. Aircraft on IFR flight plans or special VFR clearances will be provided specific separation by ATC. At the termination of the fuel dumping operation, pilots should advise ATC. Upon receipt of such information, ATC will issue, on the appropriate frequencies, the following:

EXAMPLE:
> ATTENTION ALL AIRCRAFT - FUEL DUMPING BY -(type aircraft) - TERMINATED.

SECTION 4. TWO-WAY RADIO COMMUNICATIONS FAILURE

4-1. Two-Way Radio Communications Failure.

  a. It is virtually impossible to provide regulations and procedures applicable to all possible situations associated with two-way radio communications failure. During two-way radio communications failure, when faced with a situation not covered in the regulations, pilots are expected to exercise good judgment in whatever action they elect to take. Should the situation so dictate they should not be reluctant to use the emergency action contained in FAR 91.3(b).

  b. Whether two-way radio communications failure constitutes an emergency depends on the circumstances, and in any event, it is a determination made by the pilot. FAR 91.3(b) authorizes a pilot to deviate from any rules in Subparts A and B to the extent required to meet the emergency.

  c. In the event of two-way radio communications failure, ATC service will be provided on the basis that the pilot is operating in accordance with FAR 91.185. A pilot experiencing two-way radio communications failure should (unless emergency authority is exercised) comply with FAR 91.185.

  d. VFR conditions. If the failure occurs in VFR conditions, or if VFR conditions are encountered after the failure, each pilot shall continue the flight under VFR and land as soon as practicable.

4-2. Transponder Operation During Two-Way Communications Failure.

  a. If a pilot of an aircraft with a coded radar beacon transponder experiences a loss of two-way radio capability he should:

1. Adjust his transponder to reply on Mode A/3, Code 7700 for a period of 1 minute.

2. Then change to Code 7600 and remain on 7600 for a period of 15 minutes or the remainder of the flight, whichever comes first.

3. Repeat steps (1) and (2) as practicable.

b. The pilot should understand that he may not be in an area of radar coverage.

4-3. Reestablishing Radio Contact

a. In addition to monitoring the NAVAID voice feature, the pilot should attempt to reestablish communications by attempting contact:

1. on the previously assigned frequency, or

2. with an FSS or *ARINC.

b. If communications are established with an FSS or ARINC, the pilot should advise that radio communications on the previously assigned frequency has been lost giving the aircraft's position, altitude, last assigned frequency and then request further clearance from the controlling facility. The preceding does not preclude the use of 121.5 MHz. There is no priority on which action should be attempted first. If the capability exists, do all at the same time.

NOTE -*AERONAUTICAL RADIO/INCORPORATED (ARINC) - is a commercial communications corporation which designs, constructs, operates, leases, or otherwise engages in radio activities serving the aviation community. *ARINC has the capability of relaying information to/from ATC facilities throughout the country.

TEST QUESTIONS

1. Who is directly responsible for and the final authority as to the operation of the aircraft?

A. Owner.
B. Pilot in command.
C. Operator.

2. When a distress or urgency condition is encountered, the pilot of an aircraft with a coded radar beacon transponder, who desires to alert a ground radar facility, should squawk

A. 7600.
B. 1200.
C. 7700.

3. Operational testing of an emergency locator transmitter (ELT) is permitted during

A. the last 5 minutes of any hour.
B. the first 5 minutes of any hour.
C. the first 15 minutes of any hour.

4. Accidental activation of an emergency locator transmitter (ELT) can be verified by monitoring

A. 121.5 MHz.
B. 125.1 MHz.
C. 119.5 MHz.

5. To receive the maximum protection of VFR search and rescue (SAR) the pilot should file a flight plan to the

A. final destination.
B. largest airport en route.
C. point of first intended landing.

6. During an urgency condition the initial communication, and if considered necessary, and any subsequent transmissions should begin with the signal

A. PAN-PAN.
B. MAYDAY.
C. BANG-BANG.

7. When ditching in open water, rember to

A. avoid the face of a swell.
B. always land into the wind.
C. always land down wind.

8. If a pilot of an aircraft with a coded radar beacon transponder experiences a loss of two-way radio capability they should

A. squawk 7700.
B. squawk 1200.
C. squawk 7700 for 1 minute, then 7600 for 15 minutes.

ANSWERS

1. B 2. C 3. B 4. A 5. C 6. A 7. A 8. C

13

SAFETY OF FLIGHT

SECTION 1. METEOROLOGY

1-1. National Weather Service Aviation Products.

a. Weather service to aviation is a joint effort of the National Weather Service (NWS), the Federal Aviation Administration (FAA), the military weather services, and other aviation oriented groups and individuals. The NWS maintains an extensive surface, upper air, and radar weather observing program; a nationwide aviation weather forecasting service; and also provides pilot briefing service. The majority of pilot weather briefings are provided by FAA personnel at flight service stations (FSSs). Surface weather observations are taken by NWS, by NWS-certified FAA, contract, and supplemental observers, and by automated observing systems. (Reference - Weather Observing Programs, Section 1-10 this chapter).

b. Aviation forecasts are prepared by 52 Weather Service Forecast Offices (WSFOs). These offices prepare and distribute approximately 500 terminal forecasts 3 times daily for specific airports in the 50 States and the Caribbean (4 times daily in Alaska and Hawaii). These forecasts, which are amended as required, are valid for 24 hours. The last 6 hours are given in categorical outlook terms as described in Categorical Outlooks. WSFOs also prepare a total of over 300 route forecasts and 39 synopses for Pilots Automatic Telephone Weather Answering Service (PATWAS), Transcribed Weather Broadcast (TWEB), and briefing purposes. The route forecasts that are issued during the morning and mid-day are valid for 12 hours while the evening issuance is valid for 18 hours. A centralized aviation forecast program originating from the National Aviation Weather Advisory Unit (NAWAU) in Kansas City was implemented in November 1982. In the conterminous U.S., all In-flight Advisories (SIGMETs, Convective SIGMETs, and AIRMETs) and all Area Forecasts (6 areas) are now issued by NAWAU. Area Forecasts are prepared 3 times a day in the conterminous states (4 times in Hawaii), and amended as required, while In-flight Advisories are issued only when conditions warrant. (Reference - In-Flight Weather Advisories Section 1-5 this chapter). Winds aloft forecasts are provided for 176 locations in the 48 contiguous states and 21 in Alaska for flight planning purposes. (Winds aloft forecasts for Hawaii are prepared locally.) All the aviation weather forecasts are given wide distribution through the Weather Message Switching Center in Kansas City (WMSC).

c. Weather element values may be expressed by using different measurement systems depending on several factors, such as whether the weather products will be used by the general public, aviation interests, international services, or a combination of these users.

1-2. FAA Weather Services.

a. The FAA maintains a nationwide network of Flight Service Stations (FSSs) to serve the weather needs of pilots. In addition, NWS meteorologists are assigned to most Air Route Traffic Control Centers (ARTCCs) as part of the Center Weather Service Unit (CWSU). They provide advisory service and short-term forecasts (nowcasts) to support the needs of the FAA and other users of the system.

b. The primary source of preflight weather briefings is an individual briefing obtained from a briefer at the FSS or NWS. These briefings, which are tailored to your specific flight, are available 24 hours a day through the local FSS or through the use of toll-free lines (INWATS). Numbers for these services can be found in the Airport/Facility Directory under the "FAA and NWS Telephone Numbers" section. They are also listed in the U.S. Government section of your local telephone directory under Department of Transportation, Federal Aviation Administration, or Department of Commerce, National Weather Service. (Reference - Preflight Briefing, Section 1-3 of this chapter explains the types of preflight briefings available and the information contained in each). NWS pilot briefers do not provide aeronautical information (NOTAMs, flow control advisories, etc.) nor do they accept flight plans.

c. Other sources of weather information are as follows:

1. The A.M. Weather telecast on the PBS television network is a jointly sponsored 15-minute weather program designed for pilots. It is broadcast Monday through Friday mornings. Check TV listings in your area for station and exact times.

2. The Transcribed Weather Broadcast (TWEB), telephone access to the TWEB (TEL-TWEB), Telephone Information Briefing Service (TIBS) (AFSS) and Pilots Automatic Telephone Weather Answering Service (PATWAS) (FSS) provide continuously updated recorded weather information for short or local flights. Separate paragraphs in this section give additional information regarding these services.

3. Weather and aeronautical information is also available from numerous private industry sources on an individual or contract pay basis. Information on how to obtain this service should be available from local pilot organizations.

4. The Direct User Access System (DUATS) can be accessed by pilots with

a current medical certificate toll-free in the 48 contiguous States via personal computer. Pilots can receive alphanumeric preflight weather data and file domestic VFR and IFR flight plans. The following are the contract DUATS vendors:

CONTEL Federal Systems
15000 Conference Center Drive
Chantilly, VA 22021-3808
Telephone - For filing flight plans and obtaining weather briefings: (800) 767-9989
For customer service: (800) 345-3828
Data Transformation Corporation
559 Greentree Road
Turnerville, NJ 08012
Telephone - For filing flight plans and obtaining weather briefings: (800) 245-3828
For customer service: (800) 243-3828

d. In-flight weather information is available from any FSS within radio range. (Reference - Pilots Automatic Telephone Weather Answering Service (PATWAS) and Telephone Information Briefing Service (TIBS), section 1-7, Transcribed Weather Broadcast (TWEB), section 1-8, and In-Flight Weather Broadcasts, section 1-9 this chapter for information on broadcasts.) En route Flight Advisory Service (EFAS) is provided to serve the nonroutine weather needs of pilots in flight. (Reference - En Route Flight Advisory Service (EFAS), section 1-4 this chapter gives details on this service).

1-3. Preflight Briefing.

a. Flight Service Stations (FSSs) are the primary source for obtaining preflight briefings and in-flight weather information. In some locations, the Weather Service Office (WSO) provides preflight briefings on a limited basis. Flight Service Specialists are qualified and certificated by the NWS as Pilot Weather Briefers. They are not authorized to make original forecasts, but are authorized to translate and interpret available forecasts and reports directly into terms describing the weather conditions which you can expect along your flight route and at your destination. Available aviation weather reports and forecasts are displayed at each FSS and WSO. Some of the larger FSSs provide a separate display for pilot use. Pilots should feel free to use these self briefing displays where available, or to ask for a briefing or assistance from the specialist on duty. Three basic types of preflight briefings are available to serve your specific needs. These are: Standard Briefing,

Abbreviated Briefing, and Outlook Briefing. You should specify to the briefer the type of briefing you want, along with appropriate background information. (Reference - Preflight Preparation, chapter 11 for items that are required). This will enable the briefer to tailor the information to your intended flight. The following paragraphs describe the types of briefings available and the information provided in each.

b. Standard Briefing - You should request a Standard Briefing any time you are planning a flight and you have not received a previous briefing or have not received preliminary information through mass dissemination media; e.g., TWEB, PATWAS, VRS, etc. The briefer will automatically provide the following information in the sequence listed, except as noted, when it is applicable to your proposed flight.

1. Adverse Conditions - Significant meteorological and aeronautical information that might influence the pilot to alter the proposed flight; e.g., hazardous weather conditions, runway closures, NAVAID outages, etc.

2. VFR Flight Not Recommended - When VFR flight is proposed and sky conditions or visibilities are present or forecast, surface or aloft, that in the briefer's judgment would make flight under visual flight rules doubtful, the briefer will describe the conditions, affected locations, and use the phrase "VFR flight is not recommended." This recommendation is advisory in nature. The final decision as to whether the flight can be conducted safely rests solely with the pilot.

3. Synopsis - A brief statement describing the type, location and movement of weather systems and/or air masses which might affect the proposed flight.
NOTE - These first 3 elements of a briefing may be combined in any order when the briefer believes it will help to more clearly describe conditions.

4. Current Conditions - Reported weather conditions applicable to the flight will be summarized from all available sources; e.g., SAs, PIREPs, RAREPs. This element will be omitted if the proposed time of departure is beyond 2 hours unless the information is specifically requested by the pilot.

5. En Route Forecast - Forecast en route conditions for the proposed route are summarized in logical order; i.e., departure/climbout, en route, and descent.

6. Destination Forecast - The destination forecast for the planned ETA. Any significant changes within 1 hour before and after the planned arrival are included.

7. Winds Aloft - Forecast winds aloft will be summarized for the proposed route. The briefer will interpolate wind directions and speeds between levels and stations as necessary to provide expected conditions at planned altitudes.

8. Notices to Airmen (NOTAMs) -
    (a) Available NOTAM (D) information pertinent to the proposed flight.
    (b) NOTAM (L) information pertinent to the departure and/or local area,

if available, and pertinent FDC NOTAMs within approximately 400 miles of the FSS providing the briefing.

NOTE 1 - NOTAM information may be combined with current conditions when the briefer believes it is logical to do so.

NOTE 2 - NOTAM (D) information and FDC NOTAMs which have been published in the Notices to Airmen publication are not included in pilot briefings unless a review of this publication is specifically requested by the pilot. For complete flight information you are urged to review Class II NOTAMs and the Airport/Facility Directory in addition to obtaining a briefing.

9. ATC Delays - Any known ATC delays and flow control advisories which might affect the proposed flight.

10. Pilots may obtain the following from FSS briefers upon request:

(a) Information on military training routes (MTR) and military operations area (MOA) activity within the flight plan area and a 100 NM extension around the flight plan area.

NOTE - Pilots are encouraged to request updated information from en route FSSs.

(b) A review of the Notices to Airmen publication for pertinent NOTAMs and Special Notices.

(c) Approximate density altitude data.

(d) Information regarding such items as air traffic services and rules, customs/immigration procedures, ADIZ rules, search and rescue, etc.

(e) LORAN-C NOTAMs.

(f) Other assistance as required.

c. Abbreviated Briefing - Request an Abbreviated Briefing when you need information to supplement mass disseminated data, update a previous briefing, or when you need only one or two specific items. Provide the briefer with appropriate background information, the time you received the previous information, and/or the specific items needed. You should indicate the source of the information already received so that the briefer can limit the briefing to the information that you have not received, and/or appreciable changes in meteorological conditions since your previous briefing. To the extent possible, the briefer will provide the information in the sequence shown for a Standard Briefing. If you request only one or two specific items, the briefer will advise you if adverse conditions are present or forecast. Details on these conditions will be provided at your request.

d. Outlook Briefing - You should request an Outlook Briefing whenever your proposed time of departure is six or more hours from the time of the briefing. The briefer will provide available forecast data applicable to the proposed flight. This type of briefing is provided for planning purposes only. You should obtain a Standard or Abbreviated Briefing prior to departure in order to obtain such items as current conditions, updated forecasts, winds aloft and NOTAMs.

e. In-Flight Briefing - You are encouraged to obtain your preflight briefing by telephone or in person before departure. In those cases where you need to obtain a preflight briefing or an update to a previous briefing by radio, you should contact the nearest FSS to obtain this information. After communications have been established, advise the specialist of the type briefing you require and provide appropriate background information. You will be provided information as specified in the above paragraphs, depending on the type briefing requested. In addition, the specialist will recommend shifting to the flight watch frequency when conditions along the intended route indicate that it would be advantageous to do so.

f. Following any briefing, feel free to ask for any information that you or the briefer may have missed. It helps to save your questions until the briefing has been completed. This way, the briefer is able to present the information in a logical sequence, and lessens the chance of important items being overlooked.

1-4. En Route Flight Advisory Service (EFAS).

a. EFAS is a service specifically designed to provide en route aircraft with timely and meaningful weather advisories pertinent to the type of flight intended, route of flight, and altitude. In conjunction with this service, EFAS is also a central collection and distribution point for pilot reported weather information. EFAS is provided by specially trained specialists in selected AFSSs/FSSs controlling multiple remote communications outlets covering a large geographical area and is normally available throughout the conterminous U.S. and Puerto Rico from 6 a.m. to 10 p.m. EFAS provides communications capabilities for aircraft flying at 5,000 feet above ground level to 17,500 feet MSL on a common frequency of 122.0 MHz. Discrete EFAS frequencies have been established to ensure communications coverage from 18,000 through 45,000 MSL serving in each specific ARTCC area. These discrete frequencies may be used below 18,000 feet when coverage permits reliable communication.

NOTE - When an EFAS outlet is located in a time zone different from the zone in which the flight watch control station is located, the availability of service may be plus or minus one hour from the normal operating hours.

b. Contact flight watch by using the name of the Air Route Traffic Control Center facility identification serving the area of your location, followed by your aircraft identification, and the name of the nearest VOR to your position. The specialist needs to know this approximate location to select the most appropriate transmitter/receiver outlet for communications coverage.

EXAMPLE:

> CLEVELAND FLIGHT WATCH, CESSNA ONE TWO THREE FOUR KILO, MANSFIELD V-O-R, OVER.

c. Charts depicting the location of the flight watch control stations (parent facility) and the outlets they use are contained in the Airport Facility Directories (A/FD). If you do not know in which flight watch area you are flying, initiate contact by using the words "FLIGHT WATCH," your aircraft identification, and the name of the nearest VOR. The facility will respond using the name of the flight watch facility.

EXAMPLE:

> FLIGHT WATCH, CESSNA ONE TWO THREE FOUR KILO, MANSFIELD V-O-R, OVER.

d. FSSs that provide En route Flight Advisory Service are listed regionally in the Airport/Facilities Directories.

e. EFAS is not intended to be used for filing or closing flight plans, position reporting, getting complete preflight briefings, or obtaining random weather reports and forecasts. En route flight advisories are tailored to the phase of flight that begins after climb-out and ends with descent to land. Immediate destination weather and terminal forecast will be provided on request. Pilots requesting information not within the scope of flight watch will be advised of the appropriate FSS frequency to contact to obtain the information. Pilot participation is essential to the success of EFAS by providing a continuous exchange of information on weather, winds, turbulence, flight visibility, icing, etc., between pilots and flight watch specialists. Pilots are encouraged to report good weather as well as bad, and to confirm expected conditions as well as unexpected to EFAS facilities.

1-5. In-Flight Weather Advisories.

a. The NWS issues in-flight weather advisories designated as Severe Weather Forecasts Alerts (AWW), Convective SIGMETs (WST), SIGMETs (WS), Center Weather Advisories (CWA), or AIRMETs (WA). These advisories are issued individually; however, the information contained in them is also included in relevant portions of the Area Forecast (FA). When these advisories are issued subsequent to the FA, they automatically amend appropriate portions of the FA until the FA itself has been amended. In-flight advisories serve to notify en route pilots of the possibility of encountering hazardous flying conditions which may not have been forecast at the time of the preflight briefing. Whether or not the condition described is potentially hazardous to a particular flight is for the pilot to evaluate on the basis of experience and the operational limits of the aircraft.

b. Severe Weather Forecast Alerts (AWW) are preliminary messages issued in order to alert users that a Severe Weather Bulletin (WW) is being issued. These messages define areas of possible severe thunderstorms or tornado activity. The messages are unscheduled and issued as required by the National Severe Storm Forecast Center at Kansas City, Missouri.

c. Convective SIGMETs are issued for the following phenomena:

    1. Tornadoes.

    2. Lines of thunderstorms.

    3. Embedded thunderstorms.

    4. Thunderstorm areas greater than or equal to thunderstorm intensity level 4 with an area coverage of 4/10 (40 percent) or more.

    5. Hail greater than or equal to 3/4 inch diameter.

NOTE - Since thunderstorms are the reason for issuing the Convective SIGMET, severe or greater turbulence, severe icing, and low-level wind shear (gust fronts, etc.) are implied and will not be specified in the advisory.

d. Convective Sigmet Bulletins -

    1. Three Convective SIGMET bulletins, each covering a specified geographic area, are issued. These areas are the Eastern (E), Central (C), and Western (W) U.S. The boundaries that separate the Eastern from the Central and the Central from the Western U.S. are 87 and 107 degrees West, respectively. These bulletins are issued on a scheduled basis, hourly at 55 minutes past the hour (H+55), and as special bulletins on an unscheduled basis.

    2. Each of the Convective SIGMET bulletins will be:

    (a) Made up of one or more individually numbered Convective SIGMETs,

    (b) Valid for 1 hour, and

    (c) Removed from system automatically at 40 minutes past the hour (H + 40).

    3. On an hourly basis, an outlook is made for each of the three Convective SIGMET regions. The outlook for a particular region is appended to the Convective SIGMET bulletin for the same region. However, it is not appended to special Convective SIGMETs. The outlook is reviewed each hour and revised when necessary. The outlook is a forecast and meteorological discussion for thunderstorm systems that are expected to require Convective SIGMET issuances during a time period 2-6 hours into the future. Furthermore, an outlook will always be made for each of the three regions, even if it is a negative statement.

e. SIGMETs within the conterminous U.S. are issued by the National Aviation Weather Advisory Unit (NAWAU) for the following hazardous weather phenomena:

    1. Severe and extreme turbulence.

    2. Severe icing.

    3. Widespread duststorms, sandstorms, or volcanic ash lowering visibilities to below three miles.

f. Center Weather Advisory: The CWA is an unscheduled in-flight, flow control, air traffic, and air crew advisory. By nature of its short lead time, the CWA is not a flight planning product. It is generally a nowcast for conditions beginning within the next 2 hours. CWAs will be issued:

    1. As a supplement to an existing SIGMET, Convective SIGMET, AIRMET, or Area Forecast (FA).

    2. When an In-flight Advisory has not been issued but observed or expected weather conditions meet SIGMET/AIRMET criteria based on current pilot reports and reinforced by other sources of information about existing meteorological conditions.

    3. When observed or developing weather conditions do not meet SIGMET, Convective SIGMET, or AIRMET criteria; e.g., in terms of intensity or area coverage, but current pilot reports or other weather information sources indicate that existing or anticipated meteorological phenomena will adversely affect the safe flow of air traffic within the air route traffic control center (ARTCC) area of responsibility.

g. AIRMETs within the conterminous U.S. are issued by the NAWAU for the following weather phenomena which are potentially hazardous to aircraft:

    1. Moderate icing.

    2. Moderate turbulence.

    3. Sustained winds of 30 knots or more at the surface.

    4. Widespread area of ceilings less than 1,000 feet and/or visibility less than three miles

    5. Extensive mountain obscurement.

NOTE - If the above phenomena are adequately forecast in the FA, an AIRMET will not be issued.

h. SIGMETs and AIRMETs are identified by an alphanumeric designator which consists of an alphabetic identifier and issuance number. The first time an advisory is issued for a phenomenon associated with a particular weather system, it will be given the next alphabetic designator in the series, and will be numbered as the first for that designator. Subsequent advisories will retain the same alphabetic designator until the phenomenon ends. In the conterminous U.S., this means that a phenomenon that is assigned an alphabetic designator in one area will retain that designator as it moves within the area or into one or more other areas. Issuances for the same phenomenon will be sequentially numbered, using the same alphabetic designator until the phenomenon no longer exist. Alphabetic designators NOVEMBER - YANKEE, except SIERRA, TANGO and ZULU are used only for SIGMETs, while designators SIERRA, TANGO, and ZULU are used for AIRMETs.

i. Each CWA will have a phenomenon number (1-6) immediately following the ARTCC identifier. This number will be assigned to each meteorologically distinct condition or conditions; e.g., jet stream clear air turbulence or low IFR and icing northwest of a low pressure center, meeting CWA issuance criteria. Following the product type (CWA) a two-digit issuance number will be entered starting at midnight local each day. In addition, those CWAs based on existing nonconvective SIGMETs/AIRMETs will include the associated alphanumeric designator, e.g., ALPHA 4.

EXAMPLE:
    ZKCl CWAO1/ALPHA 4

j. Each AWW is numbered sequentially beginning January 1 of each year.

EXAMPLE:
    MKC AWW 161755
    WW 279 SEVERE TSTM NY PA NJ 161830Z - 170000Z.
    AXIS..70 STATUTE MILES EITHER SIDE OF LINE..10W MSS TO
    20E ABE.
    HAIL SURFACE AND ALOFT..2 INCHES. SURFACE WIND GUSTS..65
    KNOTS.
    MAX TOPS TO 540. MEAN WIND VELOCITY 19020.
    REPLACES WW 278..OH PA NY

Status reports are issued as needed on Severe Weather Watch Bulletins to show progress of storms and to delineate areas no longer under the threat of severe storm activity. Cancellation bulletins are issued when it becomes evident that no severe weather will develop or that storms have subsided and are no longer severe.

1-6. Categorical Outlooks.

a. Categorical outlook terms, describing general ceiling and visibility conditions for advanced planning purposes, are defined as follows:

1. LIFR (Low IFR) - Ceiling less than 500 feet and/or visibility less than 1 mile.

2. IFR - Ceiling 500 to less than 1,000 feet and/or visibility 1 to less than 3 miles.

3. MVFR (Marginal VFR) - Ceiling 1,000 to 3,000 feet and/or visibility 3 to 5 miles inclusive

4. VFR - Ceiling greater than 3,000 feet and visibility greater than 5 miles; includes sky clear.

b. The cause of LIFR, IFR, or MVFR is indicated by either ceiling or visibility restrictions or both. The contraction "CIG" and/or weather and obstruction to vision symbols are used. If winds or gusts of 25 knots or greater are forecast for the outlook period, the word "WIND" is also included for all categories including VFR.

EXAMPLE:

LIFR CIG - Low IFR due to low ceiling.

EXAMPLE:

IFR F - IFR due to visibility restricted by fog.

EXAMPLE:

MVFR CIG HK - Marginal VFR due to both ceiling and visibility restricted by haze and smoke.

EXAMPLE:

IFR CIG R WIND - IFR due to both low ceiling and visibility restricted by rain; wind expected to be 25 knots or greater.

1-7. Pilots Automatic Telephone Weather Answering Service (PATWAS) and Telephone Information Briefing Service (TIBS).

a. PATWAS is provided by nonautomated flight service stations. PATWAS is a continuous recording of meteorological and aeronautical information, which is available at selected locations by telephone. Normally, the recording contains a summary of data for an area within 5ONM of the parent station; however, at some locations route information similar to that available on the Transcribed Weather Broadcast(TWEB) is included.

b. PATWAS is not intended to substitute for specialist-provided preflight briefings. It is, however, recommended for use as a preliminary briefing, and often will be valuable in helping you to make a "go or no go" decision.

c. TIBS is provided by Automated Flight Service Stations (AFSS) and provides continuous telephone recordings of meteorological and/or aeronautical information. Specifically, TIBS provides area and/or route briefings, airspace procedures, and special announcements (if applicable) concerning aviation interests.

d. Depending on user demand, other items may be provided; e.g., surface observations, terminal forecasts, winds/temperatures aloft forecasts, etc. A TOUCH-TONE telephone is necessary to fully utilize the TIBS program.

e. Pilots are encouraged to avail themselves of this service. PATWAS and TIBS locations are found in the Airport/Facility Directory under the FSS and National Weather Service Telephone Numbers section.

1-8. Transcribed Weather Broadcast (TWEB).

Equipment is provided at selected FSSs by which meteorological and aeronautical data are recorded on tapes and broadcast continuously over selected low-frequency (190-535 kHz) navigational aids (L/MF ranges or H facilities) and/or VORs. Broadcasts are made from a series of individual tape recordings, and changes, as they occur, are transcribed onto the tapes. The information provided varies depending on the type of equipment available. Generally, the broadcast contains route-oriented data with specially prepared NWS forecasts, In-flight Advisories, and winds aloft plus preselected current information, such as weather reports, NOTAMs, and special notices. In some locations, the information is broadcast over the local VOR only and is limited to such items as the hourly weather for the parent station and up to 5 immediately adjacent stations, local NOTAM information, terminal forecast (FT) for the parent station, adverse conditions extracted from In-flight Advisories, and other potentially hazardous conditions. At selected locations, telephone access to the TWEB has been provided (TEL-TWEB). Telephone numbers for this service are found in the FSS and National Weather Service Telephone Numbers section of the Airport/Facility Directory. These broadcasts are made available primarily for preflight and in-flight planning, and as such, should not be considered as a substitute for specialist-provided preflight briefings.

1-9. In-Flight Weather Broadcast.

a. Weather Advisory Broadcasts - FAA FSSs broadcast Severe Weather Forecast Alerts (AWW), Convective SIGMETs, SIGMETs, CWAs, and AIRMETs during their valid period when they pertain to the area within 150 NM of the FSS or a broadcast facility controlled by the FSS as follows:

1. Severe Weather Forecast Alerts (AWW) and Convective SIGMET - Upon receipt and at 15 minute intervals H+OO, H+15, H+30, and H+45 for the first hour after issuance.

EXAMPLE:

AVIATION BROADCAST, WEATHER ADVISORY (Severe Weather Forecast Alert or Convective SIGMET identification) (text of advisory).

2. SIGMETs, CWAs, and AIRMETs - Upon receipt and at 30-minute intervals at H+15 and H+45 for the first hour after issuance.

EXAMPLE:

AVIATION BROADCAST, WEATHER ADVISORY, (area or ARTCC identification) (SIGMET, CWA, or AIRMET identification) (text of ad - visory).

3. Thereafter, a summarized alert notice will be broadcast at H+15 and H+45 during the valid period of the advisories.

EXAMPLE:

AVIATION BROADCAST, WEATHER ADVISORY, A (Severe Weather Forecast Alert, Convective SIGMET, SIGMET, CWA, or AIRMET) IS CURRENT FOR (description of weather) (area affected).

4. Pilots, upon hearing the alert notice, if they have not received the advisory or are in doubt, should contact the nearest FSS and ascertain whether the advisory is pertinent to their flights.

b. ARTCCs broadcast a Severe Weather Forecast Alert (AWW), Convective SIGMET, SIGMET, or CWA alert once on all frequencies, except emergency, when any part of the area described is within 150 miles of the airspace under their jurisdiction. These broadcasts contain SIGMET or CWA (identification) and a brief description of the weather activity and general area affected.

EXAMPLE:

ATTENTION ALL AIRCRAFT, SIGMET DELTA THREE, FROM MYTON TO TUBA CITY TO MILFORD, SEVERE TURBULENCE AND SEVERE CLEAR ICING BELOW ONE ZERO THOUSAND FEET. EXPECTED TO CONTINUE BEYOND ZERO THREE ZERO ZERO ZULU.

EXAMPLE:

ATTENTION ALL AIRCRAFT, CONVECTIVE SIGMET TWO SEVEN EASTERN. FROM THE VICINITY OF ELMIRA TO PHILLIPSBURG. SCATTERED EMBEDDED THUNDERSTORMS MOVING EAST AT ONE ZERO KNOTS. A FEW INTENSE LEVEL FIVE CELLS, MAXI-MUM TOPS FOUR FIVE ZERO.

EXAMPLE:

ATTENTION ALL AIRCRAFT, KANSAS CITY CENTER WEATHER ADVISORY ONE ZERO THREE. NUMEROUS REPORTS OF MOD-ERATE TO SEVERE ICING FROM EIGHT TO NINER THOUSAND FEET IN A THREE ZERO MILE RADIUS OF ST. LOUIS. LIGHT OR NEGATIVE ICING REPORTED FROM FOUR TWO THOUSAND FEET REMAINDER OF KANSAS CITY CENTER AREA.

NOTE - Terminal control facilities have the option to limit the AWW, Convective SIGMET, SIGMET, or CWA broadcast as follows: local control and approach control positions may opt to broadcast SIGMET or CWA alerts only when any part of the area described is within 50 miles of the airspace under their jurisdiction.

c. Hazardous In-Flight Weather Advisory Service (HIWAS) - This is a continuous broadcast of in-flight weather advisories including summarized AWW, SIGMETs, Convective SIGMETs, CWAs, AIRMETs, and urgent PIREPs. HIWAS has been adopted as a national program and will be implemented throughout the conterminous U.S. as resources permit. In those areas where HIWAS is commissioned, ARTCC, Terminal ATC, and FSS facilities have discontinued the broadcast of in-flight advisories as described in the preceding paragraph. HIWAS is an additional source of hazardous weather information which makes these data available on a continu-ous basis. It is not, however, a replacement for preflight or in-flight briefings or real-time weather updates from Flight Watch (EFAS). As HIWAS is implemented in individual center areas, the commissioning will be advertised in the Notices to Airmen publication.

1. Where HIWAS has been implemented, a HIWAS alert will be broadcast

on all except emergency frequencies once, upon receipt by ARTCC and terminal facilities, which will include an alert announcement, frequency instruction, number, and type of advisory updated; e.g., AWW, SIGMET, Convective SIGMET, or CWA.

EXAMPLE:
 ATTENTION ALL AIRCRAFT, MONITOR HIWAS OR CONTACT A FLIGHT SERVICE STATION ON FREQUENCY ONE TWO TWO POINT ZERO OR ONE TWO TWO POINT TWO FOR NEW CONVECTIVE SIGMET (identification) INFORMATION.

2. In HIWAS ARTCC areas, FSSs will broadcast a HIWAS update announcement once on all except emergency frequencies upon completion of recording an update to the HIWAS broadcast. Included in the broadcast will be the type of advisory updated; e.g. AWW, SIGMET, Convective SIGMET, CWA, etc.

EXAMPLE:
 ATTENTION ALL AIRCRAFT, MONITOR HIWAS OR CONTACT FLIGHT WATCH OR FLIGHT SERVICE FOR NEW CONVECTIVE SIGMET INFORMATION.

d. Unscheduled Broadcasts - These broadcasts are made by FSSs on VOR and selected VHF frequencies upon receipt of special weather reports, PIREPs, NOTAMs and other information considered necessary to enhance safety and efficiency of flight. These broadcasts will be made at random times and will begin with the announcement "Aviation Broadcast" followed by identification of the data.

EXAMPLE:
 AVIATION BROADCAST, SPECIAL WEATHER REPORT, (Notice to Airmen, Pilot Report, etc.) (location name twice) THREE SEVEN (past the hour) OBSERVATION...(etc.).

e. Alaskan Scheduled Broadcasts - Selected FSSs in Alaska having voice capability on radio ranges (VOR) or radio beacons (NDB) broadcast weather reports and Notice to Airmen information at 15 minutes past each hour from reporting points within approximately 150 miles from the broadcast station.

1-10. Weather Observing Programs.

a. Manual Observations - Surface weather observations are taken at more than 600 locations in the United States. With only a few exceptions, these stations are located at airport sites and most are manned by FAA or NWS personnel who manually observe, perform calculations, and enter the observation into the distribution system.

b. Automatic Meteorological Observing Stations (AMOS) -

1. Full parameter AMOS facilities provide data for the basic weather program at remote, unstaffed, or part-time staffed locations at approximately 90 locations in the United States. They report temperature, dew point, wind, pressure, and precipitation (liquid) amount. At staffed AMOS locations, an observer may manually add visually observed and manually calculated elements to the automatic reports. The elements manually added are sky condition, visibility, weather, obstructions to vision, and sea level pressure. The content and format of AMOS reports is the same as the manually observed reports, except the acronym "AMOS" or "RAMOS" (for Remote Automatic Meteorological Observing Station) will be the first item of the report.

2. Partial parameter AMOS stations only report some of the elements contained in the full parameter locations, normally wind. These observations are not normally disseminated through aviation weather circuits.

c. Automatic Observing Stations (AUTOB) - There are four AUTOBs in operation. They are located at Winslow, Arizona (INW); Sandberg, California (SDB); Del Rio, Texas (DRT); and Wendover, Utah (ENV). These stations report all normal surface aviation weather elements, but cloud height and visibility are reported in a manner different from the conventional weather report.

d. Automated Weather Observing System (AWOS) -

1. Automated weather reporting systems are increasingly being installed at airports. These systems consist of various sensors, a processor, a computer-generated voice subsystem, and a transmitter to broadcast local, minute-by-minute weather data directly to the pilot.

NOTE - When the barometric pressure exceeds 31.00 inches Hg., see Procedures, Section 2-2 this chapter for the altimeter setting procedures.

2. The AWOS observations will include the prefix "AWOS" to indicate that the data are derived from an automated system. Some AWOS locations will be augmented by certified observers who will provide weather and obstruction to vision information in the remarks of the report when the reported visibility is less than 3 miles. These sites, along with the hours of augmentation, are to be published

in the Airport/Facility Directory. Augmentation is identified in the observation as "observer weather." The AWOS wind speed, direction and gusts, temperature, dew point, and altimeter setting are exactly the same as for manual observations. The AWOS will also report density altitude when it exceeds the field elevation by more than 1,000 feet. The reported visibility is derived from a sensor near the touchdown of the primary instrument runway. The visibility sensor output is converted to a runway visibility value (RVV) equation, using a 10-minute harmonic average. The AWOS sensors have been calibrated against the FAA transmissometer standards used for runway visual range values. Since the AWOS visibility is an extrapolation of a measurement at the touchdown point of the runway, it may differ from the standard prevailing visibility. The reported sky condition/ceiling is derived from the ceilometer located next to the visibility sensor. The AWOS algorithm integrates the last 30 minutes of ceilometer data to derive cloud layers and heights. This output may also differ from the observer sky condition in that the AWOS is totally dependent upon the cloud advection over the sensor site.

3. These real-time systems are operationally classified into four basic levels: AWOS-A, AWOS-1, AWOS-2, and AWOS-3. AWOS-A only reports altimeter setting. AWOS-1 usually reports altimeter setting, wind data, temperature, dewpoint, and density altitude. AWOS-2 provides the information provided by AWOS-1 plus visibility. AWOS-3 provides the information provided by AWOS-2 plus cloud/ceiling data.

4. The information is transmitted over a discrete radio frequency or the voice portion of a local NAVAID. AWOS transmissions are receivable within 25 NM of the AWOS site, at or above 3,000 feet AGL. In many cases, AWOS signals may be received on the surface of the airport. The system transmits a 20 to 30 second weather message updated each minute. Pilots should monitor the designated frequency for the automated weather broadcast. A description of the broadcast is contained in subparagraph e. There is no two-way communication capability. Most AWOS sites also have a dial-up capability so that the minute-by-minute weather messages can be accessed via telephone.

5. AWOS information (system level, frequency, phone number, etc.) concerning specific locations is published, as the systems become operational, in the Airport/Facility Directory, and where applicable, on published Instrument Approach Procedures. Selected individual systems may be incorporated into nationwide data collection and dissemination networks in the future.

e. Automated Weather Observing System (AWOS) Broadcasts - Computer-generated voice is used in Automated Weather Observing Systems (AWOS) to automate the broadcast of the minute-by-minute weather observations. In addition, some systems are configured to permit the addition of an operator-generated voice message; e.g., weather remarks following the automated parameters. The phraseology used generally follows that used for other weather broadcasts. Following are explanations and examples of the exceptions.

    1. Location and Time - The location/name and the phrase AUTOMATED WEATHER OBSERVATION, followed by the time are announced.

        (a) If the airport's specific location is included in the airport's name, the airport's name is announced.

EXAMPLES:

    BREMERTON NATIONAL AIRPORT AUTOMATED WEATHER OBSERVATION, ONE FOUR FIVE SIX ZULU; RAVENSWOOD JACKSON COUNTY AIRPORT AUTOMATED WEATHER OBSERVATION, ONE FOUR FIVE SIX ZULU.

        (b) If the airport's specific location is not included in the airport's name, the location is announced followed by the airport's name.

EXAMPLES:

    SAULT ST MARIE, CHIPPEWA COUNTY INTERNATIONAL AIRPORT AUTOMATED WEATHER OBSERVATION; SANDUSKY, COWLEY FIELD AUTOMATED WEATHER OBSERVATION.

        (c) The word TEST is added following OBSERVATION when the system is not in commissioned status.

EXAMPLE:

    BREMERTON NATIONAL AIRPORT AUTOMATED WEATHER OBSERVATION TEST, ONE FOUR FIVE SIX ZULU.

        (d) The phrase TEMPORARILY INOPERATIVE is added when the system is inoperative.

EXAMPLE

    BREMERTON NATIONAL AIRPORT AUTOMATED WEATHER OBSERVING SYSTEM TEMPORARILY INOPERATIVE.

2. Ceiling and Sky Cover -

(a) Ceiling is announced as either CEILING or INDEFINITE CEILING. The phrases MEASURED CEILING and ESTIMATED CEILING are not used. With the exception of indefinite ceilings, all automated ceiling   heights are measured.

EXAMPLES:

BREMERTON NATIONAL AIRPORT AUTOMATED WEATHER OBSERVATION, ONE FOUR FIVE SIX ZULU. CEILING TWO THOUSAND OVERCAST;

BREMERTON NATIONAL AIRPORT AUTOMATED WEATHER OBSERVATION, ONE FOUR FIVE SIX ZULU. INDEFINITE CEIL-ING TWO HUNDRED, SKY OBSCURED.

(b) The word "Clear" is not used in AWOS due to limitations in the height ranges of the sensors. No clouds detected is announced as NO CLOUDS BELOW XXX or, in newer systems as CLEAR BELOW XXX (where XXX is the range limit of the sensor).

EXAMPLES:

NO CLOUDS BELOW ONE TWO THOUSAND.

CLEAR BELOW ONE TWO THOUSAND.

(c) A sensor for determining ceiling and sky cover is not included in some AWOS. In these systems, ceiling and sky cover are not announced. SKY CON-DITION MISSING is announced only if the system is configured with a ceilometer and the ceiling and sky cover information is not available.

3. Visibility -

(a) The lowest reportable visibility value in AWOS is less than 1/4. It is announced as VISIBILITY LESS THAN ONE QUARTER.

(b) A sensor for determining visibility is not included in some AWOS. In these systems, visibility is not announced. VISIBILITY MISSING is announced only if the system is configured with a visibility sensor and visibility information is not available.

4. Weather - In the future, some AWOSs are to be configured to determine the occurrence of precipitation. However, the type and intensity may not always be

determined. In these systems, the word PRECIPITATION will be announced if precipitation is occurring, but the type and intensity are not determined.

5. Remarks - If remarks are included in the observation, the word REMARKS is announced following the altimeter setting. Remarks are announced in the following order of priority:

(a) Automated "Remarks"

(l) Density Altitude.

(2) Variable Visibility.

(3) Variable Wind Direction.

(b) Manual Input Remarks. - Manual input remarks are prefaced with the phrase "observer." As a general rule the manual remarks are limited to:

(l) Type and intensity of precipitation.

(2) Thunderstorms, intensity (if applicable) and direction.

(3) Obstructions to vision when the visibility is 3 miles or less.

EXAMPLE:

REMARKS ... DENSITY ALTITUDE, TWO THOUSAND FIVE HUNDRED ...VISIBILITY VARIABLE BETWEEN ONE AND TWO ... WIND DIRECTION VARIABLE BETWEEN TWO FOUR ZERO AND THREE ONE ZERO...OBSERVED WEATHER ... THUNDERSTORM MODERATE RAIN SHOWERS AND FOG ...THUNDERSTORM OVERHEAD.

(c) If an automated parameter is "missing" and no manual input for that parameter is available, the parameter is announced as MISSING. For example, a report with the dew point "missing" and no manual input available, would be announced as follows:

EXAMPLE:

CEILING ONE THOUSAND OVERCAST ... VISIBILITY THREE ... PRECIPITATION ... TEMPERATURE THREE ZERO, DEW POINT MISSING ... WIND CALM ... ALTIMETER THREE ZERO ZERO ONE.

(d) "Remarks" are announced in the following order of priority:

(l) Automated "remarks."

I Density Altitude.

II Variable Visibility.

III Variable Wind Direction.

(2) Manual Input "Remarks." As a general rule, the remarks are announced in the same order as the parameters appear in the basic text of the observation; i.e., Sky Condition, Visibility, Weather and Obstructions to Vision, Temperature, Dew Point, Wind, and Altimeter Setting.

EXAMPLE:
REMARKS ... DENSITY ALTITUDE, TWO THOUSAND FIVE HUNDRED ... VISIBILITY VARIABLE BETWEEN ONE AND TWO ... WIND DIRECTION VARIABLE BETWEEN TWO FOUR ZERO AND THREE ONE ZERO ...OBSERVER CEILING ESTIMATED TWO THOUSAND BROKEN ... OBSERVER TEMPERATURE TWO, DEWPOINT MINUS FIVE.

1-11. Weather Radar Services.

a. The National Weather Service operates a network of 56 radar sites for detecting coverage, intensity, and movement of precipitation. The network is supplemented by FAA and DOD radar sites in the western sections of the country. Another 72 local warning radar sites augment the network by operating on an as needed basis to support warning and forecast programs.

b. Scheduled radar observations are taken hourly and transmitted in alpha-numeric format on weather telecommunications circuits for flight planning purposes. Under certain conditions, special radar reports are issued in addition to the hourly transmittals. Data contained in the reports are also collected by the National Meteorological Center and used to prepare hourly national radar summary charts for dissemination on facsimile circuits.

c. All En Route Flight Advisory Service facilities and many FSSs have equipment to directly access the radar displays from the individual weather radar sites. Specialists at these locations are trained to interpret the display for pilot briefing and in-flight advisory services. The Center Weather Service Units located in ARTCCs also have access to weather radar displays and provide support to all air traffic facilities within their center's area.

d. A clear radar display (no echoes) does not mean that there is no significant weather within the coverage of the radar site. Clouds and fog are not detected by the radar. However, when echoes are present, turbulence can be implied by the intensity of the precipitation, and icing is implied by the presence of the precipitation at temperatures at or below 0 degrees Celsius. Used in conjunction with other weather products, radar provides invaluable information for weather avoidance and flight planning.

e. Additional information on weather radar products and services can be found in Advisory Circular 00-45, AVIATION WEATHER SERVICES. (Reference - Section 1-25 this chapter.) (See A/FD charts, NWS Upper Air Observing Stations and Weather Network for the location of specific radar sites.)

1-12. ATC In-Flight Weather Avoidance Assistance.

  a. ATC Radar Weather Display -

    1. Areas of radar weather clutter result from rain or moisture. Radars cannot detect turbulence. The determination of the intensity of the weather displayed is based on its precipitation density. Generally, the turbulence associated with a very heavy rate of rainfall will normally be more severe than any associated with a very light rainfall rate.

    2. ARTCCs are phasing in computer generated digitized radar displays to replace broadband radar display. This new system, known as Narrowband Radar, provides the controller with two distinct levels of weather intensity by assigning radar display symbols for specific precipitation densities measured by the narrowband system.

  b. Weather Avoidance Assistance -

    1. To the extent possible, controllers will issue pertinent information on weather or chaff areas and assist pilots in avoiding such areas when requested. Pilots should respond to a weather advisory by either acknowledging the advisory or by acknowledging the advisory and requesting an alterative course of action as follows:

      (a) Request to deviate off course by stating the number of miles and the direction of the requested deviation. In this case, when the requested deviation is approved, the pilot is expected to provide his own navigation, maintain the altitude assigned by ATC and to remain within the specified mileage of his original course.

      (b) Request a new route to avoid the affected area.

      (c) Request a change of altitude.

      (d) Request radar vectors around the affected areas.

    2. For obvious reasons of safety, an IFR pilot must not deviate from the course or altitude or flight level without a proper ATC clearance. When weather conditions encountered are so severe that an immediate deviation is determined to be necessary and time will not permit approval by ATC, the pilot's emergency authority may be exercised.

    3. When the pilot requests clearance for a route deviation or for an ATC

radar vector, the controller must evaluate the air traffic picture in the affected area, and coordinate with other controllers (if ATC jurisdictional boundaries may be crossed) before replying to the request.

4. It should be remembered that the controller's primary function is to provide safe separation between aircraft. Any additional service, such as weather avoidance assistance, can only be provided to the extent that it does not derogate the primary function. It's also worth noting that the separation workload is generally greater than normal when weather disrupts the usual flow of traffic. ATC radar limitations and frequency congestion may also be a factor in limiting the controller's capability to provide additional service.

5. It is very important, therefore, that the request for deviation or radar vector be forwarded to ATC as far in advance as possible. Delay in submitting it may delay or even preclude ATC approval or require that additional restrictions be placed on the clearance. Insofar as possible the following information should be furnished to ATC when requesting clearance to detour around weather activity:

(a) Proposed point where detour will commence.

(b) Proposed route and extent of detour (direction and distance).

(c) Point where original route will be resumed.

(d) Flight conditions (IFR or VFR).

(e) Any further deviation that may become necessary as the flight progresses.

(f) Advise if the aircraft is equipped with functioning airborne radar.

6. To a large degree, the assistance that might be rendered by ATC will depend upon the weather information available to controllers. Due to the extremely transitory nature of severe weather situations, the controller's weather information may be of only limited value if based on weather observed on radar only. Frequent updates by pilots giving specific information as to the area affected, altitudes intensity and nature of the severe weather can be of considerable value. Such reports are relayed by radio or phone to other pilots and controllers and also receive widespread teletypewriter dissemination.

7. Obtaining IFR clearance or an ATC radar vector to circumnavigate severe weather can often be accommodated more readily in the en route areas away from terminals because there is usually less congestion and, therefore, offer greater freedom of action. In terminal areas, the problem is more acute because of traffic density, ATC coordination requirements, complex departure and arrival routes, adjacent airports, etc. As a consequence, controllers are less likely to be able to accommodate all requests for weather detours in a terminal area or be in a position to volunteer such routing to the pilot. Nevertheless, pilots should not hesitate to

advise controllers of any observed severe weather and should specifically advise controllers if they desire circumnavigation of observed weather.

1-13. Runway Visual Range (RVR).

a. RVR visibility values are measured by transmissometers mounted on towers along the runway. A full RVR system consists of:
  1. Transmissometer projector and related items.
  2. Transmissometer receiver (detector) and related items.
  3. Analogue recorder.
  4. Signal data converter and related items.
  5. Remote digital or remote display programmer.

b. The transmissometer projector and receiver are mounted on towers either 250 or 500 feet apart. A known intensity of light is emitted from the projector and is measured by the receiver. Any obscuring matter such as rain, snow, dust, fog, haze or smoke reduces the light intensity arriving at the receiver. The resultant intensity measurement is then converted to an RVR value by the signal data converter. These values are displayed by readout equipment in the associated air traffic facility and updated approximately once every minute for controller issuance to pilots.

c. The signal data converter receives information on the high intensity runway edge light setting in use (step 3, 4, or 5); transmission values from the transmissometer, and the sensing of day or night conditions. From the three data sources, the system will compute appropriate RVR values. Due to variable conditions, the reported RVR values may deviate somewhat from the true observed visual range due to the slant range consideration, brief time delays between the observed RVR conditions and the time they are transmitted to the pilot, and rapidly changing visibility conditions.

d. An RVR transmissometer established on a 500 foot baseline provides digital readouts to a minimum of 1,000 feet. A system established on a 250 foot baseline provides digital readouts to a minimum of 600 feet, which are displayed in 200 foot increments to 3,000 feet and in 500 foot increments from 3,000 feet to a maximum value of 6,000 feet.

e. RVR values for Category IIIa operations extend down to 700 feet RVR; however, only 600 and 800 feet are reportable RVR increments. The 800 RVR reportable value covers a range of 701 feet to 900 feet and is therefore a valid minimum indication of Category IIIa operations.

f. Ten minute maximum and minimum RVR values for the designated RVR runway are reported in the remarks section of the aviation weather report when the prevailing visibility is less than one mile and/or the RVR is 6,000 feet or less. ATCTs report RVR when the prevailing visibility is 1 mile or less and/or the RVR is 6,000 feet or less.

g. Details on the requirements for the operational use of RVR are contained in FAA ADVISORY CIRCULAR-97-1, "Runway Visual Range." Pilots are responsible for compliance with minimums prescribed for their class of operations in the appropriate FARs and/or operations specifications.

1-14. Reporting Cloud Heights.

a. Ceiling, by definition in the FARs and as used in Aviation Weather Reports and Forecasts, is the height above ground (or water) level of the lowest layer of clouds or obscuring phenomenon that is reported as "broken," "overcast," or "obscuration" and not classified as "thin" or "partial." For example, a forecast which reads "CIGS WILL BE GENLY 1 TO 2 THSD FEET" refers to heights above ground level (AGL). A forecast which reads "BRKN TO OVC LYRS AT 8 TO 12 THSD MSL" states that the height is above mean sea level (MSL).

b. Pilots usually report height values above MSL, since they determine heights by the altimeter. This is taken in account when disseminating and otherwise applying information received from pilots. ("Ceiling" heights are always above ground level.) In reports disseminated as PIREPs, height references are given the same as received from pilots, that is, above MSL. In the following example of an hourly observation, a pilot report of the heights of the bases and tops of an overcast layer in the terminal area is converted by the reporting station to reflect AGL to report the base of the overcast layer (E12). The pilot's reported top of the overcast layer (23) is not convened to AGL and is shown in the remarks section (last item) of the weather reporting (top ovc 23).

EXAMPLE:
    E12 OVC 2FK 132/49/47/0000/002/TOP OVC 23

c. In aviation forecasts (Terminal, Area, or In-flight Advisories) ceilings are denoted by the prefix "C" when used with sky cover symbols as in "LWRG to C5 OVC-1TRW," or by the contraction "CIG" before, or the contraction "AGL" after, the forecast cloud height value. When the cloud base is given in height above MSL, it is so indicated by the contraction "MSL" or "ASL" following the height value. The heights of cloud tops, freezing level, icing, and turbulence are always given in heights above ASL or MSL.

1-15. Reporting Prevailing Visibility.

a. Surface (horizontal) visibility is reported in weather observations in terms of statute miles and increments thereof; e.g., 1/16, 1/8, 1/4, 1/2, 3/4, 1, 1 1/4, etc. Visibility is determined through the ability to see and identify preselected and prominent objects at a known distance from the usual point of observation. Visibilities which are determined to be less than 7 miles, identify the obscuring atmospheric condition; e.g., fog, haze, smoke, etc., or combinations thereof.

b. Prevailing visibility is the greatest visibility equalled or exceeded throughout at least half of the horizon circle, which need not be continuous. Segments of the horizon circle which may have a significantly lower visibility may be reported in the remarks section of the weather report; e.g., the southeastern quadrant of the horizon circle may be determined to be 2 miles in fog while the remaining quadrants are determined to be 3 miles in fog.

c. When the prevailing visibility at the usual point of observation, or at the tower level, is less than 4 miles, certificated tower personnel will take visibility observations in addition to those taken at the usual point of observation. The lower of these two values will be used as the prevailing visibility for aircraft operations.

1-16. Estimating Intensity of Precipitation.

a. Light - Scattered drops or flakes that do not completely wet or cover an exposed surface, regardless of duration, to 0.10 inch per hour, maximum 0.01 inch in 6 minutes.

b. Moderate - 0.11 inch to 0.30 inch per hour, more than 0.01 inch to 0.03 inch in 6 minutes.

c. Heavy - More than 0.30 inch per hour, more than 0.03 inch in 6 minutes.

1-17. Estimating Intensity of Drizzle.

a. Light - Scattered drops that do not completely wet surface, regardless of duration, to 0.01 inch per hour.

b. Moderate - 0.01 inch to 0.02 inch per hour.

c. Heavy - More than 0.02 inch per hour.

1-18. Estimating Intensity of Snow.

a. Light - Visibility 5/8 statute mile or more.
b. Moderate - Visibility less than 5/8 statute mile but not less than 5/16 statute mile.
c. Heavy - Visibility less than 5/16 statute mile.

1-19. Pilot Weather Reports (PIREPs).

a. FAA air traffic facilities are required to solicit PIREPs when the following conditions are reported or forecast: Ceilings at or below 5,000 feet, Visibility at or below 5 miles; Thunderstorms and related phenomena, Icing of light degree or greater, Turbulence of moderate degree or greater, and Windshear.

b. Pilots are urged to cooperate and promptly volunteer reports of these conditions and other atmospheric data such as: Cloud bases, tops and layers; Flight visibility; Precipitation; Visibility restrictions such as haze, smoke and dust; Wind at altitude; and Temperature aloft.

c. PIREPs should be given to the ground facility with which communications are established; e.g., EFAS, FSS, ARTCC, or terminal ATC. One of the primary duties of EFAS facilities, radio call FLIGHT WATCH, is to serve as a collection point for the exchange of PIREPs with en route aircraft. If pilots are not able to make PIREPs by radio, reporting upon landing of the in-flight conditions encountered to the nearest FSS or Weather Service Office will be helpful. Some of the uses made of the reports are:

1. The ATCT uses the reports to expedite the flow of air traffic in the vicinity of the field and for hazardous weather avoidance procedures.

2. The FSS uses the reports to brief other pilots, to provide in-flight advisories, and weather avoidance information to en route aircraft.

3. The ARTCC uses the reports to expedite the flow of en route traffic, to determine most favorable altitudes and to issue information within the center's area.

4. The NWS uses the reports to verify or amend conditions contained in aviation forecasts and advisories. In some cases, pilot reports of hazardous conditions are the triggering mechanism for the issuance of advisories. They also use the reports for pilot weather briefings.

5. The NWS, other government organizations, the military, and private industry groups use PIREPs for research activities in the study of meteorological phenomena.

6. All air traffic facilities and the NWS forward the reports received from

pilots into the weather distribution system to assure the information is made available to all pilots and other interested parties.

d. The FAA, NWS, and other organizations that enter PIREPs into the weather reporting system use the six required elements.

1. Type of report.
2. Location.
3. Time.
4. Altitude.
5. Aircraft type.
6. Associated weather phenomenon.

Items 1 through 6 are included in all transmitted PIREPs. Although the PIREP should be as complete and concise as possible, pilots should not be overly concerned with strict format or phraseology. The important thing is that the information is relayed so other pilots may benefit from your observation. If a portion of the report needs clarification, the ground station will request the information. Completed PIREPs will be transmitted to weather circuits as in the following examples:

CMH UA /OV APE 23OO1O/TM 1516/FL085/TP BE80/SK BKN 065/WX FV03 H K/TA 20/TB LGT

Translation: One zero miles southwest of Appleton VOR; Time 1516 UTC; altitude eight thousand five hundred; aircraft type BE80; top of the broken cloud layer is six thousand five hundred; flight visibility 3 miles with haze and smoke; air Temperature 20 degrees Celsius; light turbulence.

CRW UV /OV BKW 360015-CRW/TM 1815/FL 120/TP BE99/SK OVC/WX R/ TA -08 /WV 290030/TB LGT-MDT/IC LGT RIME/RM MDT MXD ICG DURGC ROA NWBND FL 080-100 1750

Translation: From 15 miles north of Beckley VOR to Charleston VOR; time 1815 UTC; altitude 12,000 feet; type aircraft, BE-99; in clouds; rain; temperature -08 Celsius; wind 290 degrees magnetic at 30 knots; light to moderate turbulence; light rime icing; encountered moderate mixed icing during climb northwest bound from Roanoke, VA between 8,000 and 10,000 feet at 1750 UTC.

1-20. PIREPs Relating To Airframe Icing.

a. The effects of ice on aircraft are cumulative - thrust is reduced, drag increases, lift lessens, and weight increases. The results are an increase in stall speed and a deterioration of aircraft performance. In extreme cases, 2 to 3 inches of ice can form on the leading edge of the airfoil in less than 5 minutes. It takes but 1/2 inch of ice to reduce the lifting power of some aircraft by 50 percent and increases the frictional drag by an equal percentage.

b. A pilot can expect icing when flying in visible precipitation, such as rain or cloud droplets, and the temperature is 0 degrees Celsius or colder. When icing is detected, a pilot should do one of two things (particularly if the aircraft is not equipped with deicing equipment), he should get out of the area of precipitation or go to an altitude where the temperature is above freezing. This "warmer" altitude may not always be a lower altitude. Proper preflight action includes obtaining information on the freezing level and the above-freezing levels in precipitation areas. Report icing to ATC/FSS, and if operating IFR, request new routing or altitude if icing will be a hazard. Be sure to give the type of aircraft to ATC when reporting icing. The following describes how to report icing conditions.

1. Trace - Ice becomes perceptible. Rate of accumulation is slightly greater than the rate of sublimation. It is not hazardous even though deicing/anti-icing equipment is not utilized unless encountered for an extended period of time (over 1 hour).

2. Light - The rate of accumulation may create a problem if flight is prolonged in this environment (over 1 hour). Occasional use of deicing/anti-icing equipment removes/prevents accumulation. It does not present a problem if the deicing/anti-icing equipment is used.

3. Moderate - The rate of accumulation is such that even short encounters become potentially hazardous and use of deicing/anti-icing equipment or flight diversion is necessary.

4. Severe - The rate of accumulation is such that deicing/anti-icing equipment fails to reduce or control the hazard. Immediate flight diversion is necessary.

EXAMPLE:

Pilot Report: Give Aircraft Identification, Location, Time (UTC), Intensity of Type, Altitude/FL, Aircraft Type, IAS, and Outside Air Temperature.

NOTE 1 - Rime Ice: rough, milky, opaque ice formed by the instantaneous freezing of small supercooled water droplets.
NOTE 2 - Clear Ice: a glossy, clear, or translucent ice formed by the relatively slow freezing of large

281

supercooled water droplets.

NOTE 3 - The Outside Air Temperature (OAT) should be requested by the FSS/ATC if not included in the PIREP.

1-21. PIREPs Relating To Turbulence.

When encountering turbulence, pilots are urgently requested to report such conditions to ATC as soon as practicable. PIREPs relating to turbulence should state:
1. Aircraft location.
2. Time of occurrence in UTC.
3. Turbulence intensity.
4. Whether the turbulence occurred in or near clouds.
5. Aircraft altitude or flight level.
6. Type of aircraft.
7. Duration of turbulence.

EXAMPLE:

OVER OMAHA, 1232Z:, MODERATE TURBULENCE IN CLOUDS AT FLIGHT LEVEL THREE ONE ZERO, BOEING 707.

EXAMPLE:

FROM FIVE ZERO MILES SOUTH OF ALBUQUERQUE TO THREE ZERO MILES PHOENIX, 1250Z, OCCASIONAL MODERATE CHOP AT FLIGHT LEVEL THREE THREE ZERO, DC8.

1-22. Wind Shear PIREPs.

a. Because unexpected changes in wind speed and direction can be hazardous to aircraft operations at low altitudes on approach to and departing from airports, pilots are urged to promptly volunteer reports to controllers of wind shear conditions they encounter. An advance warning of this information will assist other pilots in avoiding or coping with a wind shear on approach or departure.

b. When describing conditions, use of the terms "negative" or "positive" wind shear should be avoided. PIREPs of "negative wind shear on final," intended to describe loss of airspeed and lift, have been interpreted to mean that no wind shear was encountered. The recommended method for wind shear reporting is to state the loss or gain of airspeed and the altitudes at which it was encountered.

EXAMPLE:

  DENVER TOWER, CESSNA 1234 ENCOUNTERED WIND SHEAR, LOSS OF 20 FEET.

EXAMPLE:

  TULSA TOWER, AMERICAN 721 ENCOUNTERED WIND SHEAR ON FINAL, GAINED 25 KNOTS BETWEEN 600 AND 400 FEET FOLLOWED BY LOSS OF 400 FEET AND SURFACE.

1. Pilots who are not able to report wind shear in these specific terms are encouraged to make reports in terms of the effect upon their aircraft.

EXAMPLE:

  MIAMI TOWER, GULFSTREAM 403 CHARLIE ENCOUNTERED AN ABRUPT WIND SHEAR AT 800 FEET ON FINAL, MAX THRUST REQUIRED.

2. Pilots using Inertial Navigation Systems (INS) should report the wind and altitude both above and below the shear level.

1-23. Clear Air Turbulence (CAT) PIREPs.

CAT has become a very serious operational factor to flight operations at all levels and especially to jet traffic flying in excess of 15,000 feet. The best available information on this phenomenon must come from pilots via the PIREP reporting procedures. All pilots encountering CAT conditions are urgently requested to report time, location, and intensity (light, moderate, severe, or extreme) of the element to the FAA facility with which they are maintaining radio contact. If time and conditions permit, elements should be reported according to the standards for other PIREPs and position reports. (See PIREPs Related to Turbulence, Section 1-21 this chapter).

1-24. Microbursts.

a. Relatively recent meteorological studies have confirmed the existence of microburst phenomenon. Microbursts are small-scale intense downdrafts which, on reaching the surface, spread outward in all directions from the downdraft center. This causes the presence of both vertical and horizontal wind shears that can be extremely hazardous to all types and categories of aircraft, especially at low altitudes. Due to their small size, short life-span, and the fact that they can occur over areas without surface precipitation, microbursts are not easily detectable using conventional weather radar or wind shear alert systems.

b. Parent clouds producing microburst activity can be any of the low or middle layer convective cloud types. Note, however, that microbursts commonly occur within the heavy rain portion of thunderstorms, and in much weaker, benign appearing convective cells that have little or no precipitation reaching the ground.

c. An important consideration for pilots is the fact that the microburst intensifies for about 5 minutes after it strikes the ground.

d. Characteristics of microbursts include:

    1. Size - The microburst downdraft is typically less than 1 mile in diameter as it descends from the cloud base to about 1,000-3,000 feet above the ground. In the transition zone near the ground, the downdraft changes to a horizontal outflow that can extend to approximately 2 1/2 miles in diameter.

    2. Intensity - The downdrafts can be as strong as 6,000 feet per minute. Horizontal winds near the surface can be as strong as 45 knots resulting in a 90 knot shear (headwind to tailwind change for a traversing aircraft) across the microburst. These strong horizontal winds occur within a few hundred feet of the ground.

    3. Visual Signs - Microbursts can be found almost anywhere that there is convective activity. They may be embedded in heavy rain associated with a thunderstorm or in light rain in benign appearing virga. When there is little or no precipitation at the surface accompanying the microburst, a ring of blowing dust may be the only visual clue of its existence.

    4. Duration - An individual microburst will seldom last longer than 15 minutes from the time it strikes the ground until dissipation. The horizontal winds continue to increase during the first 5 minutes with the maximum intensity winds lasting approximately 2-4 minutes. Sometimes microbursts are concentrated into a line structure, and under these conditions, activity may continue for as long as an hour. Once microburst activity starts, multiple microbursts in the same general area are not uncommon and should be expected.

e. Microburst wind shear may create a severe hazard for aircraft within 1,000 feet of the ground, particularly during the approach to landing and landing and takeoff phases. The impact of a microburst on aircraft which have the unfortunate experience of penetrating can be very dangerous. The aircraft may encounter a headwind (performance increasing) followed by a downdraft and tailwind (both performance decreasing), possibly resulting in terrain impact.

f. Pilots should heed wind shear PIREPs, as a previous pilot's encounter with a microburst may be the only indication received. However, since the wind shear intensifies rapidly in its early stages, a PIREP may not indicate the current severity of a microburst. Flight in the vicinity of suspected or reported microburst activity should always be avoided. Should a pilot encounter one, a wind shear PIREP should be made at once.

1-25. Thunderstorms.

  a. Turbulence, hail, rain, snow, lightning, sustained updrafts and downdrafts, icing conditions, all are present in thunderstorms. While there is some evidence that maximum turbulence exists at the middle level of a thunderstorm, recent studies show little variation of turbulence intensity with altitude.
  b. There is no useful correlation between the external visual appearance of thunderstorms and the severity or amount of turbulence or hail within them. The visible thunderstorm cloud is only a portion of a turbulent system whose updrafts and downdrafts often extend far beyond the visible storm cloud. Severe turbulence can be expected up to 20 miles from severe thunderstorms. This distance decreases to about 10 miles in less severe storms.
  c. Weather radar, airborne or ground based, will normally reflect the areas of moderate to heavy precipitation (radar does not detect turbulence). The frequency and severity of turbulence generally increases with the radar reflectivity which is closely associated with the areas of highest liquid water content of the storm. NO FLIGHT PATH THROUGH AN AREA OF STRONG OR VERY STRONG RADAR ECHOES SEPARATED BY 20-30 MILES OR LESS MAY BE CONSIDERED FREE OF SEVERE TURBULENCE.
  d. Turbulence beneath a thunderstorm should not be minimized. This is especially true when the relative humidity is low in any layer between the surface and 15,000 feet. Then the lower altitudes may be characterized by strong out-flowing winds and severe turbulence.
  e. The probability of lightning strikes occurring to aircraft is greatest when operating at altitudes where temperatures are between minus 5 degrees Celsius and plus 5 degrees Celsius. Lightning can strike aircraft flying in the clear in the vicinity of a thunderstorm.
  f. The NWS recognizes only two classes of intensities of thunderstorms as applied to aviation surface weather observations:
      1. T -Thunderstorm; and
      2. T+ - Severe thunderstorm.
  g. NWS radar systems are able to objectively determine radar weather echo

intensity levels by use of Video Integrator Processor (VIP) equipment. These thunderstorm intensity levels are on a scale of one to six.

EXAMPLE:

Alert provided by an ATC facility to an aircraft: (Aircraft identification) LEVEL FIVE INTENSE WEATHER ECHO BETWEEN TEN O'CLOCK AND TWO O'CLOCK, ONE ZERO MILES, MOVING EAST AT TWO ZERO, KNOTS TOPS FLIGHT LEVEL THREE NINE ZERO.

EXAMPLE:

Alert provided by an FSS: (Aircraft identification) LEVEL FIVE IN-TENSE WEATHER ECHO, TWO ZERO MILES WEST OF AT-LANTA V-O-R, TWO FIVE MILES WIDE, MOVING EAST AT TWO ZERO KNOTS, TOPS FLIGHT LEVEL THREE NINE ZERO.

1-26. Thunderstorm Flying.

a. Above all, remember this: never regard any thunderstorm "lightly" even when radar observers report the echoes are of light intensity. Avoiding thunderstorms is the best policy. Following are some Do's and Don'ts of thunderstorm avoidance:

1. Don't land or takeoff in the face of an approaching thunderstorm. A sudden gust front of low-level turbulence could cause loss of control.

2. Don't attempt to fly under a thunderstorm even if you can see through to the other side. Turbulence and wind shear under the storm could be disastrous.

3. Don't fly without airborne radar into a cloud mass containing scattered embedded thunderstorms. Scattered thunderstorms not embedded usually can be visually circumnavigated.

4. Don't trust the visual appearance to be a reliable indicator of the turbulence inside a thunderstorm.

5. Do avoid by at least 20 miles any thunderstorm identified as severe or giving an intense radar echo. This is especially true under the anvil of a large cumulonimbus.

6. Do clear the top of a known or suspected severe thunderstorm by at least 1,000 feet altitude for each 10 knots of wind speed at the cloud top. This should exceed the altitude capability of most aircraft.

7. Do circumnavigate the entire area if the area has 6/10 thunderstorm coverage.

8. Do remember that vivid and frequent lightning indicates the probability

of a severe thunderstorm.

      9. Do regard as extremely hazardous any thunderstorm with tops 35,000 feet or higher whether the top is visually sighted or determined by radar.

  b. If you cannot avoid penetrating a thunderstorm, following are some Do's before entering the storm:

      1. Tighten your safety belt, put on your shoulder harness if you have one and secure all loose objects.

      2. Plan and hold your course to take you through the storm in a minimum time.

      3. To avoid the most critical icing, establish a penetration altitude below the freezing level or above the level of minus 15 degrees Celsius.

      4. Verify that pitot heat is on and turn on carburetor heat or jet engine anti-ice. Icing can be rapid at any altitude and cause almost instantaneous power failure and/or loss of airspeed indication.

      5. Establish power settings for turbulence penetration airspeed recommended in your aircraft manual.

      6. Turn up cockpit lights to highest intensity to lessen temporary blindness from lightning.

      7. If using automatic pilot, disengage altitude hold mode and speed hold mode. The automatic altitude and speed controls will increase maneuvers of the aircraft thus increasing structural stress.

      8. If using airborne radar, tilt the antenna up and down occasionally. This will permit you to detect other thunderstorm activity at altitudes other than the one being flown.

  c. Following are some Do's and Don'ts during the thunderstorm penetration:

      1. Do keep your eyes on your instruments. Looking outside the cockpit can increase danger of temporary blindness from lightning.

      2. Don't change power settings; maintain settings for the recommended turbulence penetration airspeed.

      3. Do maintain constant attitude; let the aircraft "ride the waves." Maneuvers in trying to maintain constant altitude increases stress on the aircraft.

      4. Don't turn back once you are in the thunderstorm. A straight course through the storm most likely will get you out of the hazards most quickly. In addition, turning maneuvers increase stress on the aircraft.

SECTION 2. ALTIMETER SETTING PROCEDURES

2-1. General.

a. The accuracy of aircraft altimeters is subject to the following factors:

1. Nonstandard temperatures of the atmosphere.
2. Nonstandard atmospheric pressure.
3. Aircraft static pressure systems (position error).
4. Instrument error.

b. EXTREME CAUTION SHOULD BE EXERCISED WHEN FLYING IN PROXIMITY TO OBSTRUCTIONS OR TERRAIN IN LOW TEMPERATURES AND PRESSURES. This is especially true in extremely cold temperatures that cause a large differential between the Standard Day temperature and actual temperature. This circumstance can cause serious errors that result in the aircraft being significantly lower than the indicated altitude.

NOTE - Standard temperature at sea level is 15 degrees Celsius (59 degrees Fahrenheit). The temperature gradient from sea level is minus 2 degrees Celsius (3.6 degrees Fahrenheit) per 1,000 feet. Pilots should apply corrections for static pressure systems and/or instruments, if appreciable errors exist.

c. The adoption of a standard altimeter setting at the higher altitudes eliminates station barometer errors, some altimeter instrument errors, and errors caused by altimeter settings derived from different geographical sources.

2-2. Procedures.

The cruising altitude or flight level of aircraft shall be maintained by reference to an altimeter which shall be set, when operating:

a. Below 18,000 feet MSL-

1. When the barometric pressure is 31.00 inches Hg. or less - to the current reported altimeter setting of a station along the route and within 100 NM of the aircraft, or if there is no station within this area, the current reported altimeter setting of an appropriate available station. When an aircraft is en route on an instrument flight plan, air traffic controllers will furnish this information to the pilot at least once while the aircraft is in the controller's area of jurisdiction. In the case of an aircraft not equipped with a radio, set to the elevation of the departure airport or use an appropriate altimeter setting available prior to departure.

2. When the barometric pressure exceeds 31.00 inches Hg. - the following procedures will be placed in effect by NOTAM defining the geographic area affected:

(a) For all aircraft - Set 31.00 inches for en route operations below 18,000 feet MSL. Maintain this setting until beyond the affected area or until reaching final approach segment. At the beginning of the final approach segment, the current altimeter setting will be set, if possible. If not possible, 31.00 inches will remain set throughout the approach. Aircraft on departure or missed approach will set 31.00 inches prior to reaching any mandatory/crossing altitude or 1,500 feet AGL, whichever is lower. (Air Traffic Control will issue actual altimeter settings and advise pilots to set 31.00 inches in their altimeters for en route operations below 18,000 feet MSL in affected areas.)

(b) During preflight, barometric altimeters shall be checked for normal operation to the extent possible.

(c) For aircraft with the capability of setting the current altimeter setting and operating into airports with the capability of measuring the current altimeter setting, no additional restrictions apply.

(d) For aircraft operating VFR, there are no additional restrictions; however, extra diligence in flight planning and in operating in these conditions is essential.

(e) Airports unable to accurately measure barometric pressures above 31.00 inches of Hg. will report the barometric pressure as "missing" or "in excess of 31.00 inches of Hg." Flight operations to and from those airports are restricted to VFR weather conditions.

(f) The FAA Regional Flight Standards Division Manager of the Affected area is authorized to approve temporary waivers to permit emergency resupply or emergency medical service operation.

b. At or above 18,000 feet MSL - to 29.92 inches of mercury (standard setting). The lowest usable flight level is determined by the atmospheric pressure in the area of operation.

2-3. Altimeter Errors.

a. Most pressure altimeters are subject to mechanical, elastic, temperature, and installation errors. (Detailed information regarding the use of pressure altimeters is found in the Instrument Flying Handbook, Chapter IV.) Although manufacturing and installation specifications, as well as the periodic test and inspections required by regulations (FAR 43, Appendix E), act to reduce these errors, any scale error may be observed in the following manner:

1. Set the current reported altimeter setting on the altimeter setting scale.
2. Altimeter should now read field elevation if you are located on the same

289

reference level used to establish the altimeter setting.

3. Note the variation between the known field elevation and the altimeter indication. If this variation is in the order of plus or minus 75 feet, the accuracy of the altimeter is questionable and the problem should be referred to an appropriately rated repair station for evaluation and possible correction.

b. Once in flight, it is very important to frequently obtain current altimeter settings en route. If you do not reset your altimeter when flying from an area of high pressure or high temperatures into an area of low pressures or low temperature, your aircraft will be closer to the surface than the altimeter indicates. An inch error on the altimeter equals 1,000 feet of altitude. To quote an old saying: "Going from a high to a low, look out below."

c. A reverse situation, without resetting the altimeter when going from a low temperature or low pressure area into a high temperature or high pressure area, the aircraft will be higher than the altimeter indicates.

d. The possible results of the above situations is obvious, particularly if operating at the minimum altitude or when conducting an instrument approach. If the altimeter is in error, you may still be on instruments when reaching the minimum altitude (as indicated on the altimeter), whereas you might have been in the clear and able to complete the approach if the altimeter setting was correct.

2-4. High Barometric Pressure.

a. Cold, dry air masses may produce barometric pressures in excess of 31.00 inches of Mercury, and many altimeters do not have an accurate means of being adjusted for settings of these levels. When the altimeter cannot be set to the higher pressure setting, the aircraft actual altitude will be higher than the altimeter indicates. (Reference - Altimeter Errors, Section 2-3 this chapter).

b. When the barometric pressure exceeds 31.00 inches, air traffic controllers will issue the actual altimeter setting, and:

1. En Route/Arrivals - Advise pilots to remain set on 31.00 inches until reaching the final approach segment.

2. Departures - Advise pilots to set 31.00 inches prior to reaching any mandatory/crossing altitude or 1,500 feet, whichever is lower.

c. The altimeter error caused by the high pressure will be in the opposite direction to the error caused by the cold temperature.

2-5. Low Barometric Pressure.

When abnormally low barometric pressure conditions occur (below 28.00), flight operations by aircraft unable to set the actual altimeter setting are not recommended.

Note - The true altitude of the aircraft is lower than the indicated altitude if the pilot is unable to set the actual altimeter setting.

SECTION 3. WAKE TURBULENCE

3-1. General.

   a. Every aircraft generates a wake while in flight. Initially, when pilots encountered this wake in flight, the disturbance was attributed to "prop wash." It is known, however, that this disturbance is caused by a pair of counter rotating vortices trailing from the wing tips. The vortices from larger aircraft pose problems to encountering aircraft. For instance, the wake of these aircraft can impose rolling moments exceeding the roll control authority of the encountering aircraft. Further, turbulence generated within the vortices can damage aircraft components and equipment if encountered at close range. The pilot must learn to envision the location of the vortex wake generated by larger (transport category) aircraft and adjust the flight path accordingly.

   b. During ground operations and during takeoff, jet engine blast (thrust stream turbulence) can cause damage and upsets if encountered at close range. Exhaust velocity versus distance studies at various thrust levels have shown a need for light aircraft to maintain an adequate separation behind large turbojet aircraft. Pilots of larger aircraft should be particularly careful to consider the effects of their "jet blast" on other aircraft, vehicles, and maintenance equipment during ground operations. Lift is generated by the creation of a pressure differential over the wing surface. The lowest pressure occurs over the upper wing surface and the highest pressure under the wing. This pressure differential triggers the roll up of the airflow aft of the wing resulting in swirling air masses trailing downstream of the wing tips. After the roll up is completed, the wake consists of two counter-rotating cylindrical vortices. Most of the energy is within a few feet of the center of each vortex, but pilots should avoid a region within about 100 feet of the vortex core.

291

3-2. Vortex Strength.

a. The strength of the vortex is governed by the weight, speed, and shape of the wing of the generating aircraft. The vortex characteristics of any given aircraft can also be changed by extension of flaps or other wing configuring devices as well as by change in speed. However, as the basic factor is weight, the vortex strength increases proportionately. Peak vortex tangential speeds up to almost 300 feet per second have been recorded. The greatest vortex strength occurs when the generating aircraft is HEAVY, CLEAN, and SLOW.

b. Induced Roll -

1. In rare instances a wake encounter could cause in-flight structural damage of catastrophic proportions. However, the usual hazard is associated with induced rolling moments which can exceed the roll control authority of the encountering aircraft. In flight experiments, aircraft have been intentionally flown directly up trailing vortex cores of larger aircraft. It was shown that the capability of an aircraft to counteract the roll imposed by the wake vortex primarily depends on the wing span and counter-control responsiveness of the encountering aircraft.

2. Counter-control is usually effective and induced roll minimal in cases where the wingspan and ailerons of the encountering aircraft extend beyond the rotational flow field of the vortex. It is more difficult for aircraft with short wing span (relative to the generating aircraft) to counter the imposed roll induced by vortex flow. Pilots of short span aircraft, even of the high performance type, must be especially alert to vortex encounters.

3. The wake of larger aircraft requires the respect of all pilots.

3-3. Vortex Behavior.

a. Trailing vortices have certain behavioral characteristics which can help a pilot visualize the wake location and thereby take avoidance precautions.

1. Vortices are generated from the moment aircraft leave the ground, since trailing vortices are a by-product of wing lift. Prior to takeoff or touchdown pilots should note the rotation or touchdown point of the preceding aircraft.

2. The vortex circulation is outward, upward and around the wing tips when viewed from either ahead or behind the aircraft. Tests with large aircraft have shown that the vortices remain spaced a bit less than a wing span apart, drifting with the wind, at altitudes greater than a wing span from the ground. In view of this, if persistent vortex turbulence is encountered, a slight change of altitude and lateral position (preferably upwind) will provide a flight path clear of the turbulence.

3. Flight tests have shown that the vortices from larger (transport category) aircraft sink at a rate of several hundred feet per minute, slowing their descent and diminishing in strength with time and distance behind the generating aircraft. Atmospheric turbulence hastens breakup. Pilots should fly at or above the preceding aircraft's flight path, altering course as necessary to avoid the area behind and below generating aircraft. However vertical separation of 1,000 feet may be considered safe.

4. When the vortices of larger aircraft sink close to the ground (within 100 to 200 feet), they tend to move laterally over the ground at a speed of 2 or 3 knots.

b. A crosswind will decrease the lateral movement of the upwind vortex and increase the movement of the downwind vortex. Thus a light wind with a cross runway component of 1 to 5 knots could result in the upwind vortex remaining in the touchdown zone for a period of time and hasten the drift of the downwind vortex toward another runway. Similarly, a tailwind condition can move the vortices of the preceding aircraft forward into the touchdown zone. THE LIGHT QUARTERING TAILWIND REQUIRES MAXIMUM CAUTION. Pilots should be alert to large aircraft upwind from their approach and takeoff flight paths.

3-4. Operations Problem Areas.

a. A wake encounter can be catastrophic. In 1972 at Fort Worth a DC-9 got too close to a DC-10 (two miles back), rolled, caught a wingtip, and cartwheeled coming to rest in an inverted position on the runway. All aboard were killed. Serious and even fatal GA accidents induced by wake vortices are not uncommon. However, a wake encounter is not necessarily hazardous. It can be one or more jolts with varying severity depending upon the direction of the encounter, weight of the generating aircraft, size of the encountering aircraft, distance from the generating aircraft, and point of vortex encounter. The probability of induced roll increases when the encountering aircraft's heading is generally aligned with the flight path of the generating aircraft.

b. AVOID THE AREA BELOW AND BEHIND THE GENERATING AIRCRAFT, ESPECIALLY AT LOW ALTITUDE WHERE EVEN A MOMENTARY WAKE ENCOUNTER COULD BE HAZARDOUS.

c. Pilots should be particularly alert in calm wind conditions and situations where the vortices could:

1. Remain in the touchdown area.
2. Drift from aircraft operating on a nearby runway.
3. Sink into the takeoff or landing path from a crossing runway.

4. Sink into the traffic pattern from other airport operations.

5. Sink into the flight path of VFR aircraft operating on the hemispheric altitude 500 feet below.

d. Pilots of all aircraft should visualize the location of the vortex trail behind larger aircraft and use proper vortex avoidance procedures to achieve safe operation. It is equally important that pilots of larger aircraft plan or adjust their flight paths to minimize vortex exposure to other aircraft.

3-5. Vortex Avoidance Procedures.

a. Under certain conditions, airport traffic controllers apply procedures for separating IFR aircraft. The controllers will also provide to VFR aircraft, with whom they are in communication and which in the tower's opinion may be adversely affected by wake turbulence from a larger aircraft, the position, altitude and direction of flight of larger aircraft followed by the phrase "CAUTION - WAKE TURBULENCE." WHETHER OR NOT A WARNING HAS BEEN GIVEN, HOWEVER, THE PILOT IS EXPECTED TO ADJUST HIS OR HER OPERATIONS AND FLIGHT PATH AS NECESSARY TO PRECLUDE SERIOUS WAKE ENCOUNTERS.

b. The following vortex avoidance procedures are recommended for the various situations:

1. Landing behind a larger aircraft - same runway: Stay at or above the larger aircraft's final approach flight path - note its touchdown point - land beyond it.

2. Landing behind a larger aircraft - when parallel runway is closer than 2,500 feet: Consider possible drift to your runway - stay at or above the larger aircraft's final approach flight path - note its touchdown point.

3. Landing behind a larger aircraft - crossing runway: Cross above the larger aircraft's flight path.

4. Landing behind a departing larger aircraft - same runway: Note the larger aircraft's rotation point - land well prior to rotation point.

5. Landing behind a departing larger aircraft - crossing runway: Note the larger aircraft's rotation point - if past the intersection, continue the approach - land prior to the intersection. If larger aircraft rotates prior to the intersection, avoid flight below the larger aircraft's flight path. Abandon the approach unless a landing is ensured well before reaching the intersection.

6. Departing behind a larger aircraft: Note the larger aircraft's rotation point - rotate prior to larger aircraft's rotation point - continue climb above the larger aircraft's climb path until turning clear of his wake. Avoid subsequent headings

which will cross below and behind a larger aircraft. Be alert for any critical takeoff situation which could lead to a vortex encounter.

7. Intersection takeoffs - same runway: Be alert to adjacent larger aircraft operations, particularly upwind of your runway. If intersection takeoff clearance is received, avoid subsequent heading which will cross below a larger aircraft's path.

8. Departing or landing after a larger aircraft executing a low approach, missed approach or touch-and-go landing: Because vortices settle and move laterally near the ground, the vortex hazard may exist along the runway and in your flight path after a larger aircraft has executed a low approach, missed approach or a touch-and-go landing, particularly in light quartering wind conditions. You should ensure that an interval of at least 2 minutes has elapsed before your takeoff or landing.

9. En route VFR (1,000-foot altitude plus 500 feet): Avoid flight below and behind a large aircraft's path. If a larger aircraft is observed above on the same track (meeting or overtaking), adjust your position laterally, preferably upwind.

3-6. Pilot Responsibility.

a. Government and industry groups are making concerted efforts to minimize or eliminate the hazards of trailing vortices. However, the flight disciplines necessary to ensure vortex avoidance during VFR operations must be exercised by the pilot. Vortex visualization and avoidance procedures should be exercised by the pilot using the same degree of concern as in collision avoidance.

b. Wake turbulence may be encountered by aircraft in flight as well as when operating on the airport movement area.

c. Pilots are reminded that in operations conducted behind all aircraft, acceptance of instructions from ATC in the following situations is an acknowledgment that the pilot will ensure safe takeoff and landing intervals and accepts the responsibility of providing his own wake turbulence separation.

1. Traffic information,
2. Instructions to follow an aircraft, and
3. The acceptance of a visual approach clearance.

d. For operations conducted behind heavy aircraft, ATC will specify the word "heavy" when this information is known. Pilots of heavy aircraft should always use the word "heavy" in radio communications.

3-7. Air Traffic Wake Turbulence Separations.

a. Because of the possible effects of wake turbulence, controllers are required to apply no less than specified minimum separation for aircraft operating behind a heavy jet and, in certain instances, behind large nonheavy aircraft.

    1. Separation is applied to aircraft operating directly behind a heavy jet at the same altitude or less than 1,000 feet below:

        (a) Heavy jet behind heavy jet - 4 miles.

        (b) Small/large aircraft behind heavy jet - 5 miles.

    2. Also, separation, measured at the time the preceding aircraft is over the landing threshold is provided to small aircraft:

        (a) Small aircraft landing behind heavy jet - 6 miles.

        (b) Small aircraft landing behind large aircraft - 4 miles.

NOTE - See Aircraft Classes in Pilot/Controller Glossary.

    3. Additionally, appropriate time or distance intervals are provided to departing aircraft:

        (a) Two minutes or the appropriate 4 or 5 mile radar separation when takeoff behind a heavy jet will be:

            - from the same threshold

            - on a crossing runway and projected flight paths will cross

            - from the threshold of a parallel runway when staggered ahead of that of the adjacent runway by less than 500 feet and when the runways are separated by less than 2,500 feet.

NOTE - Pilots, after considering possible wake turbulence effects, may specifically request waiver of the 2-minute interval by stating, "request waiver of 2-minute interval" or a similar statement. Controllers may acknowledge this statement as pilot acceptance of responsibility for wake turbulence separation and, if traffic permits, issue takeoff clearance.

b. A 3-minute interval will be provided when a small aircraft will takeoff:

    1. From an intersection on the same runway (same or opposite direction) behind a departing large aircraft.

    2. In the opposite direction on the same runway behind a large aircraft takeoff or low/missed approach.

NOTE - This 3-minute interval may be waived upon specific pilot request.

c. A 3-minute interval will be provided for all aircraft taking off when the operations areas described in b(1) and (2) above, the preceding aircraft is a heavy jet, and the operations are on either the same runway or parallel runways separated by less than 2,500 feet. Controllers may not reduce or waive this interval.

d. Pilots may request additional separation e.g., 2 minutes instead of 4 or 5 miles for wake turbulence avoidance. This request should be made as soon as practical on ground control and at least before taxiing onto the runway.

NOTE - FAR 91.3(a) states: "The pilot in command of an aircraft is directly responsible for and is the final authority as to the operation of that aircraft."

SECTION 4. BIRD HAZARDS AND FLIGHT OVER NATIONAL REF - UGES, PARKS, AND FORESTS

4-1. Migratory Bird Activity.

a. Bird strike risk increases because of bird migration during the months of March through April, and August through November.

b. The altitudes of migrating birds vary with winds aloft, weather fronts, terrain elevations, cloud conditions, and other environmental variables. While over 90 percent of the reported bird strikes occur at or below 3,000 feet AGL, strikes at higher altitudes are common during migration. Ducks and geese are frequently observed up to 7,000 feet AGL and pilots are cautioned to minimize en route flying at lower altitudes during migration.

c. Considered the greatest potential hazard to aircraft because of their size, abundance, or habit of flying in dense flocks are gulls, waterfowl, vultures, hawks, owls, egrets, blackbirds, and starlings. Four major migratory flyways exist in the United States. The Atlantic flyway parallels the Atlantic Coast. The Mississippi Flyway stretches from Canada through the Great Lakes and follows the Mississippi River. The Central Flyway represents a broad area east of the Rockies, stretching from Canada through Central America. The Pacific Flyway follows the west coast and overflies major parts of Washington, Oregon, and California. There are also numerous smaller flyways which cross these major north-south migratory routes.

4-2. Reducing Bird Strike Risks.

a. The most serious strikes are those involving ingestion into an engine (turboprops and turbine jet engines) or windshield strikes. These strikes can result in emergency situations requiring prompt action by the pilot.

b. Engine ingestions may result in sudden loss of power or engine failure. Review engine out procedures, especially when operating from airports with known bird hazards or when operating near high bird concentrations.

c. Windshield strikes have resulted in pilots experiencing confusion, disorientation, loss of communications, and aircraft control problems. Pilots are encouraged to review their emergency procedures before flying in these areas.

d. When encountering birds en route, climb to avoid collision, because birds in flocks generally distribute themselves downward, with lead birds being at the highest altitude.

e. Avoid overflight of known areas of bird concentration and flying at low altitudes during bird migration. Charted wildlife refuges and other natural areas contain unusually high local concentration of birds which may create a hazard to aircraft.

4-3. Reporting Bird Strikes.

Pilots are urged to report strikes using FAA Form 52007, Bird Strike/Incident Report. This form is available at any FSS, General Aviation District Office, Air Carrier District Office, or at an FAA Regional Office. The data derived from these reports is used to develop standards to cope with this extensive hazard to aircraft and for documentation of necessary habitat control on airports.

4-4. Reporting Bird and Other Wildlife Activities.

If you observe birds or other animals on or near the runway, request airport management to disperse the wildlife before taking off. Also contact the nearest FAA ARTCC, FSS, or tower (including non-federal towers) regarding large flocks of birds and report the:
>   1. Geographic location
>   2. Bird type (geese, ducks, gulls, etc.)
>   3. Approximate numbers
>   4. Altitude
>   5. Direction of bird flight path

4-5. Pilot Advisories On Bird and Other Wildlife Hazards.

Many airports advise pilots of other wildlife hazards caused by large animals on the runway through the Airport/Facility Directory and the NOTAM system. Collisions of landing and departing aircraft and animals on the runway are increasing and are not limited to rural airports. These accidents have also occurred at several major airports. Pilots should exercise extreme caution when warned of the presence of wildlife on and in the vicinity of airports. If you observe deer or other large animals in close proximity to movement areas, advise the FSS, tower, or airport management.

4-6. Flights Over Charted U.S. Wildlife Refuges, Parks, and Forest Service Areas.

a. The landing of aircraft is prohibited on lands or waters administered by the National Park Service, U.S. Fish and Wildlife Service, or U.S. Forest Service without authorization from the respective agency. Exceptions include

    1. when forced to land due to an emergency beyond the control of the operator,

    2. at officially designated landing sites, or

    3. an approved official business of the federal government.

b. All aircraft are requested to maintain a minimum altitude of 2,000 feet above the surface of the following: National Parks, Monuments, Seashores, Lakeshores, Recreation Areas and Scenic Riverways administered by the National Park Service, National Wildlife Refuges, Big Game Refuges, Game Ranges and Wildlife Ranges administered by the U.S. Fish and Wildlife Service, and Wilderness and Primitive areas administered by the U.S. Forest Service.

NOTE - FAA Advisory Circular 91-36, Visual Flight Rules (VFR) Flight Near Noise-Sensitive Areas, defines the surface of a National Park Area (including Parks, Forests, Primitive Areas, Wilderness Areas, Recreational Areas, National Seashores, National Monuments, National Lakeshores, and National Wildlife Refuge and Range Areas) as: the highest terrain within 2,000 feet laterally of the route of flight, or the uppermost run of a canyon or valley.

c. Federal statutes prohibit certain types of flight activity and/or provide altitude restrictions over designated U.S. Wildlife Refuges, Parks, and Forest Service Areas. These designated areas, for example: Boundary Waters Canoe Wilderness Areas, Minnesota; Haleakala National Park, Hawaii; Yosemite National Park, California; are charted on Sectional Charts.

d. Federal regulations also prohibit air drops by parachute or other means of persons, cargo, or objects from aircraft on lands administered by the three agencies without authorization from the respective agency. Exceptions include

    1. emergencies involving the safety of human life, or

    2. threat of serious property loss.

SECTION 5. POTENTIAL FLIGHT HAZARDS

5-1. Accident Cause Factors.

a. The 10 most frequent cause factors for General Aviation Accidents that involve the pilot in command are:

1. Inadequate preflight preparation and/or planning.
2. Failure to obtain and/or maintain flying speed.
3. Failure to maintain direction control.
4. Improper level off.
5. Failure to see and avoid objects or obstructions.
6. Mismanagement of fuel.
7. Improper in-flight decisions or planning.
8. Misjudgment of distance and speed.
9. Selection of unsuitable terrain.
10. Improper operation of flight controls.

b. This list remains relatively stable and points out the need for continued refresher training to establish a higher level of flight proficiency for all pilots. A part of the FAA's continuing effort to promote increased aviation safety is the General Aviation Accident Prevention Program. For information on Accident Prevention activities contact your nearest General Aviation or Flight Standards District Office.

c. ALERTNESS - Be alert at all times, especially when the weather is good. Most pilots pay attention to business when they are operating in full IFR weather conditions, but strangely, air collisions almost invariably have occurred under ideal weather conditions. Unlimited visibility appears to encourage a sense of security which is not at all justified. Considerable information of value may be obtained by listening to advisories being issued in the terminal area, even though controller workload may prevent a pilot from obtaining individual service.

d. GIVING WAY - If you think another aircraft is too close to you, give way instead of waiting for the other pilot to respect the right-of-way to which you may be entitled. It is a lot safer to pursue the right-of-way angle after you have completed your flight.

5-2. VFR In Congested Areas.

A high percentage of near midair collisions occur below 8,000 feet AGL and within 30 miles of an airport. When operating VFR in these highly congested areas, whether you intend to land at an airport within the area or are just flying through, it is recommended that extra vigilance be maintained and that you monitor an appropriate control frequency. Normally the appropriate frequency is an approach control frequency. By such monitoring action you can "get the picture" of the traffic in your area. When the approach controller has radar, radar traffic advisories may be given to VFR pilots upon request. (Reference - Radar Traffic Information Service, Chapter 10).

5-3. Obstructions In Flight.

a. Antenna Towers - Extreme caution should be exercised when flying less than 2,100 feet above ground level (AGL) because of the numerous skeletal structures (radio and television antenna towers) exceeding 1,000 feet AGL with some extending higher than 2,000 feet AGL. Most skeletal structures are supported by guy wires. The wires are difficult to see in good weather and can be totally obscured during periods of dusk and reduced visibility. These wires can extend about 1,500 feet horizontally from a structure; therefore, all skeletal structures should be avoided by at least 2,000 feet.

b. Overhead Wires - Overhead transmission and utility lines often span approaches to runways and scenic flyways such as lakes, rivers, and canyons. The supporting structures of these lines may not always be readily visible and the wires may be virtually invisible under certain conditions. Most of these installations do not meet criteria which determine them to be obstructions to air navigation and therefore do not require marking and/or lighting. The supporting structures of some overhead transmission lines are equipped with flashing strobe lights. These lights indicate wires exist between the strobed structures.

5-4. Avoid Flight Beneath Unmanned Balloons.

a. The majority of unmanned free balloons currently being operated have, extending below them, either a suspension device to which the payload or instrument package is attached, or a trailing wire antenna, or both. In many instances these balloon subsystems may be invisible to the pilot until his aircraft is close to the balloon, thereby creating a potentially dangerous situation. Therefore, good judgment on the part of the pilot dictates that aircraft should remain well clear of all unmanned free balloons and flight below them should be avoided at all times.

b. Pilots are urged to report any unmanned free balloons sighted to the nearest FAA ground facility with which communication is established. Such information will assist FAA ATC facilities to identify and flight follow unmanned free balloons operating in the airspace.

5-5. Mountain Flying.

a. Your first experience of flying over mountainous terrain (particularly if most of your flight time has been over the flatlands of the Midwest) could be a never-to-be-forgotten nightmare if proper planning is not done and if you are not aware of the potential hazards awaiting. Those familiar section lines are not present in the mountains; those flat, level fields for forced landings are practically nonexistent; abrupt changes in wind direction and velocity occur, severe updrafts and downdrafts are common, particularly near or above abrupt changes of terrain such as cliffs or rugged areas; even the clouds look different and can build up with startling rapidity. Mountain flying need not be hazardous if you follow the recommendations below:

b. File a flight plan. Plan your route to avoid topography which would prevent a safe forced landing. The route should be over populated areas and well-known mountain passes. Sufficient altitude should be maintained to permit gliding to a safe landing in the event of engine failure.

c. Don't fly a light aircraft when the winds aloft, at your proposed altitude, exceed 35 miles per hour. Expect the winds to be of much greater velocity over mountain passes than reported a few miles from them. Approach mountain passes with as much altitude as possible. Downdrafts of from 1,500 to 2,000 feet per minute are not uncommon on the leeward side.

d. Don't fly near or above abrupt changes in terrain. Severe turbulence can be expected, especially in high wind conditions.

e. Some canyons run into a dead end. Don't fly so far up a canyon that you get trapped. ALWAYS BE ABLE TO MAKE A 180 DEGREE TURN!

f. Plan your trip for the early morning hours. As a rule, the air starts to get bad at about 10 a.m., and grows steadily worse until around 4 p.m., then gradually improves until dark. Mountain flying at night in a single engine light aircraft is asking for trouble.

g. When landing at a high altitude field, the same indicated airspeed should be used as at low elevation fields. Remember that due to the less dense air at altitude, this same indicated airspeed actually results in higher true airspeed, a faster landing speed, and more important, a longer landing distance. During gusty wind conditions which often prevail at high altitude fields, a power approach and power landing are recommended. Additionally, due to the faster groundspeed, your takeoff distance will increase considerably over that required at low altitudes.

h. Effects of Density Altitude. Performance figures in the aircraft owner's handbook for length of takeoff run, horsepower, rate of climb, etc., are generally based on standard atmosphere conditions (59 degrees Fahrenheit (15 degrees Celsius), pressure 29.92 inches of mercury) at sea level. However, inexperienced pilots, as well as experienced pilots, may run into trouble when they encounter an altogether different set of conditions. This is particularly true in hot weather and at higher elevations. Aircraft operations at altitudes above sea level and at higher than standard temperatures are commonplace in mountainous areas. Such operations quite often result in a drastic reduction of aircraft performance capabilities because of the changing air density. Density altitude is a measure of air density. It is not to be confused with pressure altitude, true altitude or absolute altitude. It is not to be used as a height reference, but as a determining criteria in the performance capability of an aircraft. Air density decreases with altitude. As air density decreases, density altitude increases. The further effects of high temperature and high humidity are cumulative, resulting in an increasing high density altitude condition. High density altitude reduces all aircraft performance parameters. To the pilot, this means that the normal horsepower output is reduced, propeller efficiency is reduced and a higher true airspeed is required to sustain the aircraft throughout its operating parameters. It means an increase in runway length requirements for takeoff and landings, and decreased rate of climb. An average small airplane, for example, requiring 1,000 feet for takeoff at sea level under standard atmospheric conditions will require a takeoff run of approximately 2,000 feet at an operational altitude of 5,000 feet.

NOTE - A turbo-charged aircraft engine provides some slight advantage in that it provides sea level horsepower up to a specified altitude above sea level.

1. Density Altitude Advisories - at airports with elevations of 2,000 feet and higher, control towers and FSSs will broadcast the advisory "Check Density Altitude" when the temperature reaches a predetermined level. These advisories will be broadcast on appropriate tower frequencies or, where available, ATIS. FSSs will broadcast these advisories as a part of Airport Advisory Service, and on TWEB.

2. These advisories are provided by air traffic facilities, as a reminder to pilots that high temperatures and high field elevations will cause significant changes in aircraft characteristics. The pilot retains the responsibility to compute density altitude, when appropriate, as a part of preflight duties.

NOTE - All FSSs will compute the current density altitude upon request.

i. Mountain Wave. Many pilots go all their lives without understanding what a mountain wave is. Quite a few have lost their lives because of this lack of understanding. One need not be a licensed meteorologist to understand the mountain wave phenomenon.

1. Mountain waves occur when air is being blown over a mountain range or even the ridge of a sharp bluff area. As the air hits the upwind side of the range, it starts to climb, thus creating what is generally a smooth updraft which turns into a turbulent downdraft as the air passes the crest of the ridge. From this point, for many miles downwind, there will be a series of downdrafts and updrafts. Satellite photos of the Rockies have shown mountain waves extending as far as 700 miles

downwind of the range. Along the east coast area, such photos of the Appalachian chain have picked up the mountain wave phenomenon over a hundred miles eastward. All it takes to form a mountain wave is wind blowing across the range at 15 knots or better at an intersection angle of not less than 30 degrees.

2. Pilots from flatland areas should understand a few things about mountain waves in order to stay out of trouble. When approaching a mountain range from the upwind side (generally the west), there will usually be a smooth updraft; therefore, it is not quite as dangerous an area as the lee of the range. From the leeward side, it is always a good idea to add an extra thousand feet or so of altitude because downdrafts can exceed the climb capability of the aircraft. Never expect an updraft when approaching a mountain chain from the leeward. Always be prepared to cope with a downdraft and turbulence.

3. When approaching a mountain ridge from the downwind side, it is recommended that the ridge be approached at approximately a 45 degree angle to the horizontal direction of the ridge. This permits a safer retreat from the ridge with less stress on the aircraft should severe turbulence and downdraft be experienced. If severe turbulence is encountered, simultaneously reduce power and adjust pitch until aircraft approaches maneuvering speed, then adjust power and trim to maintain maneuvering speed and fly away from the turbulent area.

5-6. Seaplane Safety.

a. Acquiring a seaplane class rating affords access to many areas not available to landplane pilots. Adding a seaplane class rating to your pilot certificate can be relatively uncomplicated and inexpensive. However, more effort is required to become a safe, efficient, competent "bush" pilot. The natural hazards of the backwoods have given way to modern man-made hazards. Except for the far north, the available bodies of water are no longer the exclusive domain of the airman. Seaplane pilots must be vigilant for hazards such as electric power lines, power, sail and rowboats, rafts, mooring lines, water skiers, swimmers, etc.

b. Seaplane pilots must have a thorough understanding of the right-of-way rules as they apply to aircraft versus boats. Once a seaplane has landed on the water, it is considered a vessel, and nautical rules as well as FAR apply. Seaplane pilots are expected to know and adhere to both Inland Navigation Rules and FAR 91.115 Right of Way Rules; Water Operations which states, in part, that aircraft on the water "...shall, insofar as possible, keep clear of all vessels and avoid impeding their navigation...." In general, while on the surface with engine running, an aircraft must give way to all non-powered vessels. Additionally, good operating procedures apply. Since a seaplane in the water is not as maneuverable as one in the air, the aircraft on the water has right-of-way over one in the air, and one taking off has right-of-way over one landing. Also, as is the case with all vessels, you may be held accountable for any damage caused by your wake while taxiing.

c. Unless they are under federal jurisdiction, navigable bodies of water are under the jurisdiction of the state, or in a few cases, privately owned. Unless they are specifically restricted, aircraft have as much right to operate on these bodies of water as other vessels. To avoid problems, check with federal or local officials in advance of operating on unfamiliar waters. The nearest Flight Standards District Office can usually offer some practical suggestions as well as regulatory information. If you land on a restricted body of water because of an in-flight emergency, or in ignorance of the restrictions you have violated, report as quickly as practical to the nearest local official having jurisdiction and explain your situation.

d. When operating over or into remote areas, appropriate attention should be given to survival gear. Minimum kits are recommended for summer and winter, and are required by law for flight into sparsely settled areas of Canada and Alaska. Alaska State Department of Transportation and Canadian Ministry of Transport officials can provide specific information on survival gear requirements. The kit should be assembled in one container and be easily reachable and preferably floatable.

e. United States Coast Guard (USCG) regulations require approved personal flotation devices (PFD) on all vessels including seaplanes operating on navigable waters of the United States. All PFDs must be in good and serviceable condition and of an appropriate size for the persons who intend to wear them. Wearable PFDs must be readily accessible and throwable devices must be immediately available for use. Seaplanes must have one USCG Type I, II, III, IV or V PFD on board for each occupant. One additional Type IV (approved device designed to be thrown to a person in the water) is also required. It is imperative that passengers be briefed on the location and proper use of available PFDs prior to leaving the dock. For additional information on approved PFDs contact your local State Boating Office or the USCG Director of Auxiliary for your district.

5-7. Flight Operations In Volcanic Dust.

a. Major volcanic eruptions have caused high altitude dust clouds from large amounts of discharged volcanic ash. Volcanic dust clouds create an extreme hazard to aircraft operating near the active volcanoes. Incidents have occurred while flying through volcanic dust clouds at night which resulted in either significant engine thrust loss and/or multiple engine shut downs along with the wing leading edges and windshields were abraded.

b. Pilots should be aware of the following information and be instructed to take the appropriate action to preclude flying into volcanic dust clouds. Flight into an area of known volcanic activity that is producing volcanic dust clouds must be avoided. This is particularly important during the hours of darkness or in daytime instrument meteorological conditions when the volcanic dust cloud may not be detected by the flight crew. If volcanic activity is reported, the planned flight should remain well clear of the area and, if possible, stay on the upwind side of the volcano. Airborne weather radar systems are not designed to detect volcanic dust clouds.

c. The following, however, has been reported by flight crews who have experienced encounters with volcanic dust clouds:

1. Smoke or dust appearing in the cockpit;

2. An acrid odor similar to electrical smoke;

3. Multiple engine malfunctions, such as stalls, increasing (egt), torching from tailpipe, and flameouts;

4. At night, St. Elmo's fire or other static discharges accompanied by a bright orange glow in the engine inlets;

5. A fire warning in the forward cargo area.

d. Volcanic dust clouds may extend for several hundred miles. Volcanic dust can cause rapid erosion and damage to the internal components of engines with loss of thrust within 50 seconds. If volcanic dust is encountered, several major engine manufacturers recommend the following procedures:

1. Disengage autothrottle (if engaged). This will prevent the autothrottle from increasing engine thrust.

2. Reduce thrust to idle, altitude permitting. This will provide an additional engine stall margin and lower engine turbine temperatures.

3. Turn on continuous ignition.

4. Turn on all accessory airbleeds including all air conditioning packs, nacelles and wing anti-ice. This will provide an additional engine stall margin by reducing engine pressure.

5. Exit the cloud by the shortest route possible.

e. It may become necessary to shut down and then restart engines to prevent exceeding (egt) limits. Volcanic dust may block the pitot system and result in unreliable airspeed indications. Pilots who operate into areas of volcanic activity should be aware of this information.

SECTION 6. SAFETY, ACCIDENT, AND HAZARD REPORTS

6-1. Aviation Safety Reporting Program.

a. The FAA has established a voluntary Aviation Safety Reporting Program designed to stimulate the free and unrestricted flow of information concerning deficiencies and discrepancies in the aviation system. This is a positive program intended to ensure the safest possible system by identifying and correcting unsafe conditions before they lead to accidents. The primary objective of the program is to obtain information to evaluate and enhance the safety and efficiency of the present system.

b. This program applies primarily to that part of the system involving the safety of aircraft operations, including departure, en route, approach and landing operations and procedures, ATC procedures, pilot-controller communications, the aircraft movement area of the airport, and near midair collisions. Pilots, air traffic controllers, and all other members of the aviation community and the general public are asked to file written reports of any discrepancy or deficiency noted in these areas.

c. The report should give the date, time, location, persons and aircraft involved (if applicable), nature of the event, and all pertinent details.

d. To ensure receipt of this information, the program provides for the waiver of certain disciplinary actions against persons, including pilots and air traffic controllers, who file timely written reports concerning potentially unsafe incidents. To be considered timely, reports must be delivered or postmarked within 10 days of the incident unless that period is extended for good cause. Reporting forms are available at FAA facilities.

e. The FAA utilizes the National Aeronautics and Space Administration (NASA) to act as an independent third party to receive and analyze reports submitted under the program. This program is described in ADVISORY CIRCULAR-0046.

6-2. Aircraft Accident and Incident Reporting.

a. Occurrences Requiring Notification - The operator of an aircraft shall immediately, and by the most expeditious means available, notify the nearest National Transportation Safety Board (NTSB) Field Office when:

   1. An aircraft accident or any of the following listed incidents occur:

(a) Flight control system malfunction or failure.

(b) Inability of any required flight crew member to perform his normal flight duties as a result of injury or illness.

(c) Failure of structural components of a turbine engine excluding compressor and turbine blades and vanes.

(d) In flight fire.

(e) Aircraft collide in flight.

(f) Damage to property, other than the aircraft, estimated to exceed $25,000 for repair (including materials and labor) or fair market value in the event of total loss, whichever is less.

(g) For large multi-engine aircraft (more than 12,500 pounds maximum certificated takeoff weight):

(1) In flight failure of electrical systems which requires the sustained use of an emergency bus powered by a back-up source such as a battery, auxiliary power unit, or air-driven generator to retain flight control or essential instruments;

(2) In-flight failure of hydraulic systems that results in sustained reliance on the sole remaining hydraulic or mechanical system for movement off light control surfaces;

(3) Sustained loss of the power or thrust produced by two or more engines; and

(4) An evacuation of aircraft in which an emergency egress system is utilized.

2. An aircraft is overdue and is believed to have been involved in an accident.

b. Manner of Notification -

1. The most expeditious method of notification to the NTSB by the operator will be determined by the circumstances existing at that time. The NTSB has advised that any of the following would be considered examples of the type of notification that would be acceptable:

(a) Direct telephone notification.

(b) Telegraphic notification.

(c) Notification to the FAA who would in turn notify the NTSB by direct communication; i.e., dispatch or telephone.

c. Items To Be Notified - The notification required above shall contain the following information, if available:

1. Type, nationality, and registration marks of the aircraft;

2. Name of owner and operator of the aircraft;

3. Name of the pilot-in-command;

4. Date and time of the accident, or incident;

5. Last point of departure, and point of intended landing of the aircraft;

6. Position of the aircraft with reference to some easily defined geographical point;

7. Number of persons aboard, number killed, and number seriously injured;

8. Nature of the accident, or incident, the weather, and the extent of damage to the aircraft so far as is known; and

9. A description of any explosives, radioactive materials, or other dangerous articles carried.

d. Followup Reports -

1. The operator shall file a report on NTSB Form 6120.1 or 6120.2, available from NTSB Field Offices or from the NTSB, Washington, DC, 20594.

(a) Within 10 days after an accident;

(b) When, after 7 days, an overdue aircraft is still missing;

(c) A report on an incident for which notification is required as described in subparagraph a(1) shall be filed only as requested by an authorized representative of the NTSB.

2. Each crew member, if physically able at the time the report is submitted, shall attach a statement setting forth the facts, conditions and circumstances relating to the accident or incident as they appear to him. If the crew member is incapacitated, he shall submit the statement as soon as he is physically able.

e. Where To File the Reports -

1. The operator of an aircraft shall file with the NTSB Field Office nearest the accident or incident any report required by this section.

2. The NTSB Field Offices are listed under U.S. Government in the telephone directories in the following cities: Anchorage, AK; Atlanta, GA; Chicago, IL; Denver, CO; Forth Worth, TX; Kansas City, MO; Los Angeles, CA; Miami, FL; New York, NY; Seattle, WA.

6-3. Near Midair Collision Reporting.

a. Purpose and Data Uses - The primary purpose of the Near Midair Collision (NMAC) Reporting Program is to provide information for use in enhancing the safety and efficiency of the National Airspace System. Data obtained from NMAC reports are used by the FAA to improve the quality of FAA services to users and to develop programs, policies, and procedures aimed at the reduction of NMAC occurrences. All NMAC reports are thoroughly investigated by Flight Standards Facilities in coordination with Air Traffic Facilities. Data from these investigations are transmitted to FAA Headquarters in Washington, DC, where they are compiled and analyzed, and where safety programs and recommendations are developed.

b. Definition - A near midair collision is defined as an incident associated with the operation of an aircraft in which a possibility of collision occurs as a result of proximity of less than 500 feet to another aircraft, or a report is received from a pilot or a flight crew member stating that a collision hazard existed between two or more aircraft.

c. Reporting Responsibility - It is the responsibility of the pilot and/or flight crew to determine whether a near midair collision did actually occur and, if so, to initiate an NMAC report. Be specific, as ATC will not interpret a casual remark to mean that an NMAC is being reported. The pilot should state "I wish to report a near midair collision."

d. Where To File Reports - Pilots and/or flight crew members involved in NMAC occurrences are urged to report each incident immediately:

    1. By radio or telephone to the nearest FAA ATC facility or FSS.

    2. In writing, in lieu of the above, to the nearest Air Carrier District Office (ACDO), General Aviation District Office (GADO), or Flight Standards District Office (FSDO).

e. Items To Be Reported -

    1. Date and Time (UTC) of incident.

    2. Location of incident and altitude.

    3. Identification and type of reporting aircraft, air crew destination, name and home base of pilot.

    4. Identification and type of other aircraft, air crew destination, name and home base of pilot.

    5. Type of flight plans; station altimeter setting used.

    6. Detailed weather conditions at altitude or flight level.

    7. Approximate courses of both aircraft: indicate if one or both aircraft were climbing or descending.

    8. Reported separation in distance at first sighting, proximity at closest point horizontally and vertically, and length of time in sight prior to evasive action.

    9. Degree of evasive action taken, if any (from both aircraft, if possible).

    10. Injuries, if any.

f. Investigation - The district office responsible for the investigation and reporting of NMACs will be:

1. The Air Carrier or Flight Standards District Office in whose area the incident occurred when an air carrier aircraft is involved.

2. The General Aviation or Flight Standards District Office in whose area the incident occurred in all other cases.

g. Existing radar, communication, and weather data will be examined in the conduct of the investigation. When possible, all cockpit crew members will be interviewed regarding factors involving the NMAC incident. Air traffic controllers will be interviewed in cases where one or more of the involved aircraft was provided ATC service. Both flight and ATC procedures will be evaluated. When the investigation reveals a violation of an FAA regulation, enforcement action will be pursued.

TEST QUESTIONS

1. Which of the following will NOT be automatically included in a standard briefing?

A. ATC delays.
B. Information on military training routes.
C. Current conditions.

2. Which of the following would be included in a SIGMET?

A. Moderate icing.
B. Severe icing.
C. Severe turbulence.

3. Ceilings less than 500 feet and/or visibility less than 1 mile would be classified as

A. LIFR.
B. IFR.
C. MVFR.

4. Which of the following designations constitutes a "ceiling"?

A. Scattered.
B. Thin broken.
C. Overcast.

5. Structural icing that forms a rough milky appearance is known as

A. clear.
B. rime.
C. mixed.

6. Small-scale intense downdrafts which spread out upon reaching the surface are known as

A. microburst.
B. CAT.
C. wind thrust.

7. Any thunderstorm identified as severe should be avoided by at least

A. 5 miles.
B. 10 miles.
C. 20 miles.

8. When flying at or above 18,000 feet MSL the altimeter should be set to

A. the local setting.
B. 31.00" hg.
C. 29.92" hg.

9. A 1 inch error on the altimeter equals

A. 1,000 feet of altitude.
B. 100 feet of altitude.
C. 10 feet of altitude.

10. In order to avoid the wake turbulence when departing behind a large aircraft you should note the point at which the larger aircraft rotated and

A. lift off before that point.
B. lift off at that point.
C. lift off after that point.

11. All aircraft are requested to maintain at least what altitude above a National Park?

A. 2,000 feet MSL.
B. 2,000 feet AGL.
C. 1,000 feet AGL.

12. Which of the following occurrences require NTSB notification?

A. Radio failure.
B. Flat tire.
C. In-flight fire.

ANSWERS

1. B 2. A 3. A 4. C 5. B 6. A 7. C 8. C 9. A 10. A 11. B 12. C

14

MEDICAL FACTS FOR PILOTS

SECTION 1. FITNESS FOR FLIGHT

1-1. Fitness For Flight.

a. Medical Certification -

1. All pilots except those flying gliders and free air balloons must possess valid medical certificates in order to exercise the privileges of their airman certificates. The periodic medical examinations required for medical certification are conducted by designated Aviation Medical Examiners, who are physicians with a special interest in aviation safety and training in aviation medicine.

Duration of Medical Certificates		
Pilot Certificate	Medical Class	Duration
Private	1st Class 2nd Class 3rd Class	24 Calender Months 24 Calender Months 24 Calender Months
Commercial	1st Class 2nd Class 3rd Class	12 Calender Months 12 Calender Months Not Applicable
ATP	1st Class 2nd Class 3rd Class	6 Calender Months Not Applicable Not Applicable

2. The standards for medical certification are contained in FAR 67. Pilots who have a history of certain medical conditions described in these standards are mandatorily disqualified from flying. These medical conditions include a personality disorder manifested by overt acts, a psychosis, alcoholism, drug dependence, epilepsy, an unexplained disturbance of consciousness, myocardial infarction, angina pectoris and diabetes requiring medication for its control. Other medical

conditions may be temporarily disqualifying, such as acute infections, anemia, and peptic ulcer. Pilots who do not meet medical standards may still be qualified under special issuance provisions or the exemption process. This may require that either additional medical information be provided or practical flight tests be conducted.

3. An actual medical certificate is not required to begin flight training, but student pilots should visit an Aviation Medical Examiner as soon as possible in their flight training in order to avoid unnecessary training expenses should they not meet the medical standards. For the same reason, the student pilot who plans to enter commercial aviation should apply for the highest class of medical certificate that might be necessary in the pilot's career.

Caution: The FARs prohibit a pilot who possesses a current medical certificate from performing crew member duties while the pilot has a known medical condition or increase of a known medical condition that would make the pilot unable to meet the standards for the medical certificate.

b. Illness -

1. Even a minor illness suffered in day-to-day living can seriously degrade performance of many piloting tasks vital to safe flight. Illness can produce fever and distracting symptoms that can impair judgment, memory, alertness, and the ability to make calculations. Although symptoms from an illness may be under adequate control with a medication, the medication itself may decrease pilot performance.

2. The safest rule is not to fly while suffering from any illness. If this rule is considered too stringent for a particular illness, the pilot should contact an Aviation Medical Examiner for advice.

c. Medication -

1. Pilot performance can be seriously degraded by both prescribed and over-the-counter medications, as well as by the medical conditions for which they are taken. Many medications, such as tranquilizers, sedatives, strong pain relievers, and cough suppressant preparations, have primary effects that may impair judgment, memory, alertness, coordination, vision, and the ability to make calculations. Others, such as antihistamines, blood pressure drugs, muscle relaxants, and agents to control diarrhea and motion sickness, have side effects that may impair the same critical functions. Any medication that depresses the nervous system, such as a sedative, tranquilizer or antihistamine, can make a pilot much more susceptible to hypoxia.

2. The FARs prohibit pilots from performing crew member duties while using any medication that affects the faculties in any way contrary to safety. The safest rule is not to fly as a crew member while taking any medication, unless approved to do so by the FAA.

d. Alcohol -

1. Extensive research has provided a number of facts about the hazards of alcohol consumption and flying. **As little as ONE OUNCE OF LIQUOR, ONE BOTTLE OF BEER, OR FOUR OUNCES OF WINE can impair flying skills, with the alcohol consumed in these drinks being detectable in the breath and blood for at least 3 hours.** Even after the body completely destroys a moderate amount of alcohol, a pilot can still be severely impaired for many hours by hangover. There is simply no way of increasing the destruction of alcohol or alleviating a hangover. Alcohol also renders a pilot much more susceptible to disorientation and hypoxia.

2. A consistently high alcohol-related fatal aircraft accident rate serves to emphasize that alcohol and flying are a potentially lethal combination. The FARs prohibit pilots from performing crewmember duties within 8 hours after drinking any alcoholic beverage or while under the influence of alcohol. However, due to the slow destruction of alcohol, a pilot may still be under influence 8 hours after drinking a moderate amount of alcohol. **Therefore, an excellent rule is to allow at least 12 TO 24 HOURS BETWEEN "BOTTLE AND THROTTLE," depending on the amount of alcoholic beverage consumed.**

e. Fatigue -

1. Fatigue continues to be one of the most treacherous hazards to flight safety, as it may not be apparent to a pilot until serious errors are made. Fatigue is best described as either acute (short-term) or chronic (long-term).

2. A normal occurrence of everyday living, acute fatigue is the tiredness felt after long periods of physical and mental strain, including strenuous muscular effort, immobility, heavy mental workload, strong emotional pressure, monotony, and lack of sleep. Consequently, coordination and alertness, so vital to safe pilot performance, can be reduced. Acute fatigue is prevented by adequate rest and sleep, as well as by regular exercise and proper nutrition.

3. Chronic fatigue occurs when there is not enough time for full recovery between episodes of acute fatigue. Performance continues to fall off, and judgment becomes impaired so that unwarranted risks may be taken. Recovery from chronic fatigue requires a prolonged period of rest.

f. Stress -

1. Stress from the pressures of everyday living can impair pilot performance, often in very subtle ways. Difficulties, particularly at work, can occupy thought processes enough to markedly decrease alertness. Distraction can so interfere with judgment that unwarranted risks are taken, such as flying into deteriorating weather conditions to keep on schedule. Stress and fatigue can be an

extremely hazardous combination.

2. Most pilots do not leave stress "on the ground." Therefore, when more than usual difficulties are being experienced, a pilot should consider delaying flight until these difficulties are satisfactorily resolved.

g. Emotion - Certain emotionally upsetting events, including a serious argument, death of a family member, separation or divorce, loss of job, and financial catastrophe, can render a pilot unable to fly an aircraft safely. The emotions of anger, depression, and anxiety from such events not only decrease alertness but also may lead to taking risks that border on self-destruction. Any pilot who experiences an emotionally upsetting event should not fly until satisfactorily recovered from it.

h. Personal Checklist -Aircraft accident statistics show that pilots should be conducting preflight checklists on themselves as well as their aircraft, for pilot impairment contributes to many more accidents than failures of aircraft systems. A personal checklist, which includes all of the categories of pilot impairment as discussed in this section, that can be easily committed to memory is being distributed by the FAA in the form of a wallet-sized card.

PERSONAL CHECKLIST (I.M.S.A.F.E.)
  I'm physically and mentally safe to fly - not being impaired by:
    Illness,
    Medication,
    Stress,
    Alcohol,
    Fatigue,
    Emotion.

1-2. Effects of Altitude.

General - Hypoxia is a state of oxygen deficiency in the body sufficient to impair functions of the brain and other organs. Hypoxia from exposure to altitude is due only to the reduced barometric pressures encountered at altitude, for the concentration of oxygen in the atmosphere remains about 21 percent from the ground out to space.

a. Hypoxic Hypoxia (Altitude Hypoxia) -
1. Hypoxic Hypoxia is a result of an atmospheric oxygen deficiency. In other words, the problem is not the result of a physical disability. Altitude being the main culprit, it is commonly referred to as Altitude Hypoxia. It is considered to be

one of the most lethal of all physiological causes of accidents.

2. Although a deterioration in night vision occurs at a cabin pressure altitude as low as 5,000 feet, other significant effects of altitude hypoxia usually do not occur in the normal healthy pilot below 12,000 feet. From 12,000 to 15,000 feet of altitude, judgment, memory, alertness, coordination, and ability to make calculations are impaired. Symptoms include:

(a) Headache
(b) Drowsiness
(c) Increased Breathing Rate
(d) Euphoria
(e) Blue Fingernails and Lips
(f) Impaired Decision Making
(g) Reduced Field of Vision

The effects appear following increasingly shorter periods of exposure to increasing altitude. In fact, a pilot's reactive consciousness can seriously deteriorate within minutes at altitudes as low as 15,000 feet. Reactive consciousness refers to a state of awareness that still allows for rational decision making.
EXAMPLE:

Altitude	Reactive Consciousness
18,000 FT.	20 - 30 Minutes
20,000 FT.	5 - 12 Minutes
25,000 FT.	2 - 3 Minutes

b. Anemic Hypoxia -

1. Anemic Hypoxia is a result of the body's inability to adequately process oxygen. Although there may be a sufficient amount of oxygen available, a biological problem is limiting the respiratory system's effectiveness. Carbon monoxide inhaled in smoking or from exhaust fumes, lowered hemoglobin (anemia), and certain medications can reduce the oxygen-carrying capacity of the blood to the degree that the amount of oxygen provided to body tissues will already be equivalent to the oxygen provided to the tissues when exposed to a cabin pressure altitude of several thousand feet. Small amounts of alcohol and low doses of certain drugs, such as antihistamines, tranquilizers, sedatives and analgesics can, through their depressant action, render the brain much more susceptible to hypoxia. Extreme heat and cold, fever, and anxiety increase the body's demand for oxygen, and

hence its susceptibility to hypoxia.

2. The effects of hypoxia are usually quite difficult to recognize, especially when they occur gradually. Since symptoms of hypoxia do not vary in an individual, the ability to recognize hypoxia can be greatly improved by experiencing and witnessing the effects of hypoxia during an altitude chamber "flight." The FAA provides this opportunity through aviation physiology training, which is conducted at the FAA Civil Aeromedical Institute and at many military facilities across the United States. To attend the Physiological Training Program at the Civil Aeromedical Institute, Mike Monroney Aeronautical Center, Oklahoma City, OK, contact by telephone (405) 680-4837, or by writing Airmen Education Branch, AAM-420, CAMI, Mike Monroney Aeronautical Center, P.O. Box 25082, Oklahoma City, OK 73125.

NOTE - To attend the Physiological Training Program at one of the military installations having the training capability, an application form and a fee must be submitted. Full particulars about location, fees, scheduling procedures, course content, individual requirements, etc. are contained in the Physiological Training Application, form number AC-3150-7, which is obtained by contacting the Accident Prevention Specialist or the Office Forms Manager in the nearest FAA office.

3. Hypoxia is prevented by heeding factors that reduce tolerance to altitude, by enriching the inspired air with oxygen from an appropriate oxygen system, and by maintaining a comfortable, safe cabin pressure altitude. For optimum protection, pilots are encouraged to use supplemental oxygen above 10,000 feet during the day, and above 5,000 feet at night. The FARs require that at the minimum, flight crew be provided with and use supplemental oxygen after 30 minutes of exposure to cabin pressure altitudes between 12,500 and 14,000 feet and immediately on exposure to cabin pressure altitudes above 14,000 feet. Every occupant of the aircraft must be provided with supplemental oxygen at cabin pressure altitudes above 15,000 feet.

c. Ear Block -

1. As the aircraft cabin pressure decreases during ascent, the expanding air in the middle ear pushes the eustachian tube open, and by escaping down it to the nasal passages, equalizes in pressure with the cabin pressure. But during descent, the pilot must periodically open the eustachian tube to equalize pressure. This can be accomplished by swallowing, yawning, tensing muscles in the throat, or if these do not work, by a combination of closing the mouth, pinching the nose closed, and attempting to blow through the nostrils (Valsalva maneuver).

2. Either an upper respiratory infection, such as a cold or sore throat, or a nasal allergic condition can produce enough congestion around the eustachian tube to make equalization difficult. Consequently, the difference in pressure between the middle ear and aircraft cabin can build up to a level that will hold the eustachian tube

closed, making equalization difficult if not impossible. The problem is commonly referred to as an "ear block."

3. An ear block produces severe ear pain and loss of hearing that can last from several hours to several days. Rupture of the ear drum can occur in flight or after landing. Fluid can accumulate in the middle ear and become infected.

4. An ear block is prevented by not flying with an upper respiratory infection or nasal allergic condition. Adequate protection is usually not provided by decongestant sprays or drops to reduce congestion around the eustachian tubes. Oral decongestants have side effects that can significantly impair pilot performance.

5. If an ear block does not clear shortly after landing, a physician should be consulted.

d. Sinus Block -

1. During ascent and descent, air pressure in the sinuses equalizes with the aircraft cabin pressure through small openings that connect the sinuses to the nasal passages. Either an upper respiratory infection, such as a cold or sinusitis, or a nasal allergic condition can produce enough congestion around an opening to slow equalization, and as the difference in pressure between the sinus and cabin mounts, eventually plug the opening. This "sinus block" occurs most frequently during descent.

2. A sinus block can occur in the frontal sinuses, located above each eyebrow, or in the maxillary sinuses, located in each upper cheek. It will usually produce excruciating pain over the sinus area. A maxillary sinus block can also make the upper teeth ache. Bloody mucus may discharge from the nasal passages.

3. A sinus block is prevented by not flying with an upper respiratory infection or nasal allergic condition. Adequate protection is usually not provided by decongestant sprays or drops to reduce congestion around the sinus openings. Oral decongestants have side effects that can impair pilot performance.

4. If a sinus block does not clear shortly after landing, a physician should be consulted.

e. Decompression Sickness After Scuba Diving -

1. A pilot or passenger who intends to fly after scuba diving should allow the body sufficient time to rid itself of excess nitrogen absorbed during diving. If not, decompression sickness due to evolved gas can occur during exposure to low altitude and create a serious in-flight emergency.

2. The recommended waiting time before flight to cabin pressure altitudes of 8,000 feet or less is at least 4 hours after diving which has not required controlled ascent (nondecompression diving), and at least 24 hours after diving which has required controlled ascent (decompression diving). The waiting time before flight

to cabin pressure altitudes above 8,000 feet should be at least 24 hours after any scuba diving.

1-3. Hyperventilation In Flight.

a. Hyperventilation or an abnormal increase in the volume of air breathed in and out of the lungs (too rapid or deep), can occur subconsciously when a stressful situation is encountered in flight. Hyperventilation causes a disruption in the balance of oxygen and carbon dioxide within the body. Symptoms include:

1. Dizziness
2. Suffocation
3. Drowsiness
4. Tingling in the Extremities
5. Muscle Spasms
6. Increased Heart Rate
7. Unconsciousness

b. The symptoms of hyperventilation subside within a few minutes after the rate and depth of breathing are consciously brought back under control. The buildup of carbon dioxide in the body can be hastened by controlled breathing in and out of a paper bag held over the nose and mouth.

c. Early symptoms of hyperventilation and hypoxia are similar. Moreover, hyperventilation and hypoxia can occur at the same time. Therefore, if a pilot is using an oxygen system when symptoms are experienced, the oxygen regulator should immediately be set to deliver 100 percent oxygen, and then the system checked to assure that it has been functioning effectively before giving attention to rate and depth of breathing.

1-4. Carbon Monoxide Poisoning In Flight.

a. Carbon monoxide is a colorless, odorless, and tasteless gas contained in exhaust fumes. When breathed even in minute quantities over a period of time, it can significantly reduce the ability of the blood to carry oxygen. Carbon monoxide has a much greater affinity for hemoglobin of the blood than oxygen. In other words, it is much easier for the blood to absorb carbon monoxide as compared to oxygen. If there is enough carbon monoxide present, it will totally block the oxygen from entering the bloodstream. In addition, the effects of carbon monoxide poisoning may last from 24 to 48 hours. Symptoms are very similar to those of hypoxia. They include:

1. Dizziness
2. Uneasiness
3. Confusion
4. Headache
5. Loss of Muscular Control
6. Unconsciousness

b. Most heaters in light aircraft work by air flowing over the exhaust manifold. Use of these heaters while exhaust fumes are escaping through manifold cracks and seals is responsible every year for several nonfatal and fatal aircraft accidents from carbon monoxide poisoning.

c. A pilot who detects the odor of exhaust or experiences symptoms of headache, drowsiness, or dizziness while using the heater should suspect carbon monoxide poisoning, and immediately shut off the heater and open air vents. If symptoms are severe or continue after landing, medical treatment should be sought.

1-5. Illusions In Flight.

a. Introduction - Many different illusions can be experienced in flight. Some can lead to spatial disorientation. Others can lead to landing errors. Illusions rank among the most common factors cited as contributing to fatal aircraft accidents.

b. Illusions Leading to Spatial Disorientation -

1. Various complex motions and forces and certain visual scenes encountered in flight can create illusions of motion and position. Spatial disorientation from these illusions can be prevented only by visual reference to reliable, fixed points on the ground or to flight instruments.

2. The leans - An abrupt correction of a banked attitude, which has been entered too slowly to stimulate the motion sensing system in the inner ear, can create the illusion of banking in the opposite direction. The disoriented pilot will roll the aircraft back into its original dangerous attitude, or if level flight is maintained, will feel compelled to lean in the perceived vertical plane until this illusion subsides.

(a) Coriolis illusion - An abrupt head movement in a prolonged constant-rate turn that has ceased stimulating the motion sensing system can create the illusion of rotation or movement in an entirely different axis. The disoriented pilot will maneuver the aircraft into a dangerous attitude in an attempt to stop rotation.

323

This most overwhelming of all illusions in flight may be prevented by not making sudden, extreme head movements, particularly while making prolonged constant-rate turns under IFR conditions.

(b) Graveyard spin - A proper recovery from a spin that has ceased stimulating the motion sensing system can create the illusion of spinning in the opposite direction. The disoriented pilot will return the aircraft to its original spin.

(c) Graveyard spiral - An observed loss of altitude during a coordinated constant-rate turn that has ceased stimulating the motion sensing system can create the illusion of being in a descent with the wings level. The disoriented pilot will pull back on the controls, tightening the spiral and increasing the loss of altitude.

(d) Somatogravic illusion - A rapid acceleration during takeoff can create the illusion of being in a nose up attitude. The disoriented pilot will push the aircraft into a nose low, or dive attitude. A rapid deceleration by a quick reduction of the throttles can have the opposite effect, with the disoriented pilot pulling the aircraft into a nose up, or stall attitude.

(e) Inversion illusion - An abrupt change from climb to straight and level flight can create the illusion of tumbling backwards. The disoriented pilot will push the aircraft abruptly into a nose low attitude, possibly intensifying this illusion.

(f) Elevator illusion - An abrupt upward vertical acceleration, usually by an updraft, can create the illusion of being in a climb. The disoriented pilot will push the aircraft into a nose low attitude. An abrupt downward vertical acceleration, usually by a downdraft, has the opposite effect, with the disoriented pilot pulling the aircraft into a nose up attitude.

(g) False horizon - Sloping cloud formations, an obscured horizon, a dark scene spread with ground lights and stars, and certain geometric patterns of ground light can create illusions of not being aligned correctly with the actual horizon. The disoriented pilot will place the aircraft in a dangerous attitude.

(h) Autokinesis - In the dark, a static light will appear to move about when stared at for many seconds. The disoriented pilot will lose control of the aircraft in attempting to align it with the light.

3. Illusions Leading to Landing Errors -

(a) Various surface features and atmospheric conditions encountered in landing can create illusions of incorrect height above and distance from the runway threshold. Landing errors from these illusions can be prevented by anticipating them during approaches, aerial visual inspection of unfamiliar airports before landing, using electronic glide slope or VASI systems when available, and maintaining optimum proficiency in landing procedures.

(b) Runway width illusion -

(1) A narrower-than-usual runway can create the illusion that the aircraft is at a higher altitude than it actually is. The pilot who does not recognize this illusion will fly a lower approach, with the risk of striking objects along the approach path or landing short.

(2) A wider-than-usual runway can have the opposite effect, with the risk of leveling out high and landing hard or overshooting the runway.

(c) Runway and terrain slopes illusion -

(1) Upsloping runways - An upsloping runway, upsloping terrain, or both, can create the illusion that the aircraft is at a higher altitude than it actually is. The pilot who does not recognize this illusion will fly a lower approach.

(2) Downsloping runway - A downsloping runway, downsloping approach terrain, or both, can have the opposite effect.

(d) Featureless terrain illusion - An absence of ground features, as when landing over water, darkened areas, and terrain made featureless by snow, can create the illusion that the aircraft is at a higher altitude than it actually is. The pilot who does not recognize this illusion will fly a lower approach.

(e) Atmospheric illusions - Rain on the windscreen can create the illusion of greater height, and atmospheric haze can create the illusion of being at a greater distance from the runway. The pilot who does not recognize these illusions will fly a lower approach. Penetration of fog can create the illusion of pitching up. The pilot who does not recognize this illusion will steepen the approach, often quite abruptly.

(f) Ground lighting illusions - Lights along a straight path, such as a road, and even lights on moving trains can be mistaken for runway and approach lights. Bright runway and approach lighting systems, especially where few lights illuminate the surrounding terrain, may create the illusion of less distance to the runway. The pilot who does not recognize this illusion will fly a higher approach. Conversely, the pilot overflying terrain which has few lights to provide height cues may make a lower than normal approach.

1-6. Vision In Flight.

a. Introduction -
Of the body senses, vision is the most important for safe flight. Major factors that determine how effectively vision can be used are the level of illumination and the technique of scanning the sky for other aircraft.

b. Vision Under Dim and Bright Illumination -
1. Under conditions of dim illumination, small print and colors on aeronau-

tical charts and aircraft instruments become unreadable unless adequate cockpit lighting is available. Moreover, another aircraft must be much closer to be seen unless its navigation lights are on.

2. In darkness, vision becomes more sensitive to light, a process called dark adaptation. Although exposure to total darkness for at least 30 minutes is required for complete dark adaptation, a pilot can achieve a moderate degree of dark adaptation within 20 minutes under dim red cockpit lighting. Since red light severely distorts colors, especially on aeronautical charts, and can cause serious difficulty in focusing the eyes on objects inside the aircraft, its use is advisable only where optimum outside night vision capability is necessary. Even so, white cockpit lighting must be available when needed for map and instrument reading, especially under IFR conditions. Dark adaptation is impaired by exposure to cabin pressure altitudes above 5,000 feet, carbon monoxide inhaled in smoking and from exhaust fumes, deficiency of Vitamin A in the diet, and by prolonged exposure to bright sunlight. Since any degree of dark adaptation is lost within a few seconds of viewing a bright light, a pilot should close one eye when using a light to preserve some degree of night vision.

3. Excessive illumination, especially from light reflected off the canopy, surfaces inside the aircraft, clouds, water, snow, and desert terrain, can produce glare, with uncomfortable squinting, watering of the eyes, and even temporary blindness. Sunglasses for protection from glare should absorb at least 85 percent of visible light (15 percent transmittance) and all colors equally (neutral transmittance), with negligible image distortion from refractive and prismatic errors.

c. Scanning for Other Aircraft -

1. Scanning the sky for other aircraft is a key factor in collision avoidance. It should be used continuously by the pilot and copilot (or right-seat passenger) to cover all areas of the sky visible from the cockpit. Although pilots must meet specific visual acuity requirements, the ability to read an eye chart does not ensure that one will be able to efficiently spot other aircraft. Pilots must develop an effective scanning technique which maximizes one's visual capabilities. The probability of spotting a potential collision threat obviously increases with the time spent looking outside the cockpit. Thus, one must use time sharing techniques to efficiently scan the surrounding airspace while monitoring instruments as well.

2. While the eyes can observe an approximate 200 degree arc of the horizon at one glance, only a very small center area called the fovea, in the rear of the eye, has the ability to send clear, sharply focused messages to the brain. All other visual information that is not processed directly through the fovea will be of less detail. An aircraft at a distance of 7 miles which appears in sharp focus within the foveal

326

center of vision would have to be as close as 7/10 of a mile in order to be recognized if it were outside of foveal vision. Because the eyes can focus only on this narrow viewing area, effective scanning is accomplished with a series of short, regularly spaced eye movements that bring successive areas of the sky into the central visual field. Each movement should not exceed 10 degrees, and each area should be observed for at least 1 second to enable detection. Although horizontal back-and-forth eye movements seem preferred by most pilots, each pilot should develop a scanning pattern that is most comfortable and then adhere to it to assure optimum scanning.

3. Studies show that the time a pilot spends on visual tasks inside the cabin should represent no more that 1/4 to 1/3 of the scan time outside, or no more than 4 to 5 seconds on the instrument panel for every 16 seconds outside. Since the brain is already trained to process sight information that is presented from left to right, one may find it easier to start scanning over the left shoulder and proceed across the windshield to the right.

4. Pilots should realize that their eyes may require several seconds to refocus when switching views between items in the cockpit and distant objects. The eyes will also tire more quickly when forced to adjust to distances immediately after close-up focus, as required for scanning the instrument panel. Eye fatigue can be reduced by looking from the instrument panel to the left wing past the wing tip to the center of the first scan quadrant when beginning the exterior scan. After having scanned from left to right, allow the eyes to return to the cabin along the right wing from it's tip inward. Once back inside, one should automatically commence the panel scan.

5. Effective scanning also helps avoid "empty-field myopia." This condition usually occurs when flying above the clouds or in a haze layer that provides nothing specific to focus on outside the aircraft. This causes the eyes to relax and seek a comfortable focal distance which may range from 10 to 30 feet. For the pilot, this means looking without seeing, which is dangerous.

1-7. Aerobatic Flight.

a. Airmen planning to engage in aerobatics should be aware of the physiological stresses associated with accelerative forces during aerobatic maneuvers. Many prospective aerobatic trainees enthusiastically enter aerobatic instruction but find their first experiences with G forces to be unanticipated and very uncomfortable. To minimize or avoid potential adverse effects, the aerobatic instructor and trainee must have a basic understanding of the physiology of G force adaptation.

b. Forces experienced with a rapid push-over maneuver result in the blood and body organs being displaced toward the head. Depending on forces involved and individual tolerance, the airman may experience discomfort, headache, "red-out," and even unconsciousness.

c. Forces experienced with a rapid pull-up maneuver result in the blood and body organ displacement toward the lower part of the body away from the head. Since the brain requires continuous blood circulation for an adequate oxygen supply, there is physiologic limit to the time the pilot can tolerate higher forces before losing consciousness. As the blood circulation to the brain decreases as a result of forces involved, the airman will experience "narrowing" of visual fields, "gray-out," "black-out," and unconsciousness. Even a brief loss of consciousness in a maneuver can lead to improper control movement causing structural failure of the aircraft or collision with another object or terrain.

d. In steep turns, the centrifugal forces tend to push the pilot into the seat, thereby resulting in blood and body organ displacement toward the lower part of the body as in the case of rapid pull-up maneuvers and with the same physiologic effects and symptoms.

e. Physiologically, humans progressively adapt to imposed strains and stress, and with practice, any maneuver will have decreasing effect. Tolerance to G forces is dependent on human physiology and the individual pilot. These factors include the skeletal anatomy, the cardiovascular architecture, the nervous system, the quality of the blood, the general physical state, and experience and recency of exposure. The airman should consult an Aviation Medical Examiner prior to aerobatic training and be aware that poor physical condition can reduce tolerance to accelerative forces.

f. The above information provides the airman a brief summary of the physiologic effects of G forces. It does not address methods of "counteracting" these effects. There are numerous references on the subject of G forces during aerobatics available to the airman. Among these are "G Effects on the Pilot During Aerobatics," FAA-AM-72-28, and "G Incapacitation in Aerobatic Pilots: A Flight Hazard" FAA-AM-82-13. These are available from the National Technical Information Service, Springfield, Virginia 22161. (Reference - FAA Advisory Circular 91-61, "A Hazard in Aerobatics: Effects of G Forces on Pilots.")

1-8. Judgment Aspects of Collision Avoidance.

a. Introduction - The most important aspects of vision and the techniques to scan for other aircraft are described in Vision in Flight. Pilots should also be familiar

328

with the following information to reduce the possibility of midair collisions.

b. Determining Relative Altitude - Use the horizon as a reference point. If the other aircraft is above the horizon, it is probably on a higher flight path. If the aircraft appears to be below the horizon, it is probably flying at a lower altitude.

c. Taking Appropriate Action - Pilots should be familiar with rules on right-of-way, so if an aircraft is on an obvious collision course, one can take immediately evasive action, preferably in compliance with applicable Federal Aviation Regulations.

d. Consider Multiple Threats - The decision to climb, descend, or turn is a matter of personal judgment, but one should anticipate that the other pilot may also be making a quick maneuver. Watch the other aircraft during the maneuver and begin your scanning again immediately since there may be other aircraft in the area.

e. Collision Course Targets - Any aircraft that appears to have no relative motion and stays in one scan quadrant is likely to be on a collision course. Also, if a target shows no lateral or vertical motion, but increases in size, take evasive action.

f. Recognize High Hazard Areas -

      1. Airways and especially VORs and airport traffic areas are places where aircraft tend to cluster.

      2. Remember, most collisions occur during days when the weather is good. Being in a "radar environment" still requires vigilance to avoid collisions.

g. Cockpit Management - Studying maps, checklists, and manuals before flight, with other proper preflight planning; e.g., noting necessary radio frequencies and organizing cockpit materials, can reduce the amount of time required to look at these items during flight, permitting more scan time.

h. Windshield Conditions - Dirty or bug-smeared windshields can greatly reduce the ability of pilots to see other aircraft. Keep a clean windshield.

i. Visibility Conditions - Smoke, haze, dust, rain, and flying towards the sun can also greatly reduce the ability to detect targets.

j. Visual Obstructions in the Cockpit -

      1. Pilots need to move their heads to see around blind spots caused by fixed aircraft structures, such as door posts, wings, etc. It will be necessary at times to maneuver the aircraft; e.g., lift a wing, to facilitate seeing.

      2. Pilots must ensure curtains and other cockpit objects; e.g., maps on glare shield, are removed and stowed during flight.

k. Lights On -

      1. Day or night, use of exterior lights can greatly increase the conspicuity of any aircraft.

      2. Keep interior lights low at night.

l. ATC support - ATC facilities often provide radar traffic advisories on a workload-permitting basis. Flight through Airport Radar Service Areas (ARSAs) requires communication with ATC. Use this support whenever possible or when required.

TEST QUESTIONS

1. Large accumulations of carbon monoxide in the human body result in

A. tightness across the forehead.
B. loss of muscular power.
C. an increased sense of well-being.

2. The most effective method for scanning for other aircraft for collision avoidance during daylight hours is to use

A. regularly spaced concentration on the 3-, 9-, and 12-o'clock positions.
B. a series of short, regularly spaced eye movements to search each 10 degree sector.
C. peripheral vision by scanning small sectors and utilizing offcenter viewing.

3. How can you determine if another aircraft is on a collision course with your aircraft?

A. The other aircraft will always appear to get larger and closer at a rapid rate.
B. The nose of each aircraft is pointed at the same point in space.
C. There will be no apparent relative motion between your aircraft and the other aircraft.

4. Which statement best defines hypoxia?

A. A state of oxygen deficiency in the body.
B. An abnormal increase in the volume of air breathed.
C. A condition of gas bubble formation around the joints of muscles.

5. Which would most likely result in hyperventilation?

A. Emotional tension, anxiety, or, fear.
B. The excessive consumption of alcohol.
C. An extremely slow rate of breathing and insufficient oxygen.

6. Susceptibility to carbon monoxide poisoning increases as

A. altitude increases.
B. altitude decreases.
C. air pressure increases.

7. What preparation should a pilot make to adapt the eyes for night flying?

A. Wear sunglasses after sunset until ready for flight.
B. Avoid red lights at least 30 minutes before the flight.
C. Avoid bright white lights at least 30 minutes before the flight.

8. A state of temporary confusion resulting from misleading information being sent to the brain by various sensory organs is defined as

A. spatial disorientation.
B. hyperventilation.
C. hypoxia.

ANSWERS

1. B 2. B 3. C 4. A 5. A 6. A 7. C 8. A

15

AERONAUTICAL CHARTS AND RELATED PUBLICATIONS

SECTION 1. TYPES OF CHARTS AVAILABLE

1-1. General.

Aeronautical charts for the U.S., its territories, and possessions are produced by the National Ocean Service (NOS), a part of the Department of Commerce, from information furnished by the FAA.

1-2. Obtaining Civil Aeronautical Charts.

En route Aeronautical Charts, En route Supplements, Approach Procedure Charts, Regional Airport/Facility Directories, and other publications described in this chapter are available upon subscription from the:

> National Ocean Service
> NOAA Distribution Branch (N/CG33)
> Riverdale, Maryland
> 20737 Telephone: (301)-436-6990

Most charts are also available at your local FBO.

1-3. Types of VFR Charts Available.

1. Sectional Charts
2. VFR Terminal Area Charts
3. World Aeronautical Charts (U.S.)
4. Planning Charts

1-4. General Description of Each VFR Chart Series.

 a. SECTIONAL CHARTS -
     1. Sectional charts are the most commonly used charts for VFR flight. They cover the 48 contiguous states and Alaska, Hawaii, Puerto Rico, and the Virgin

Islands. Sectional charts are produced to the following scale: 1:500,000 (1 in = 6.86 NM). They are designed for visual navigation of slow and medium speed aircraft.

2. Topographic information features the portrayal of relief (terrain features) and a judicious selection of visual checkpoints including cities, highways, rivers, railroads, etc. Aeronautical information includes visual and radio aids to navigation, airports, controlled airspace, restricted areas, obstructions, and related data. These charts also depict the airspace designated as "Terminal Control Area" (TCA), which provides for the control or segregation of all aircraft within the terminal control area. Charts are revised semiannually, except for several Alaskan Sectionals and the Puerto Rico-Virgin Islands Terminal Area which are revised annually. The projected date of obsolescence is recorded on the front of each chart.

3. The front panel of the sectional shows how the U.S. is divided into separate charts. Each is named for the primary city within its coverage. Color gradations are used to depict variance in elevation. Colors range from green (sea level) to brown (above 12,000 feet). Maximum elevations are portrayed by bold numbers located within each quadrangle.

4. A legend on the back of each chart details all information contained on the sectional. This legend is subdivided into specific subject areas in order to simplify the material.

b. VFR TERMINAL AREA CHARTS -

1. VFR Terminal Area Charts should be used when flying in or around a Terminal Control Area (TCA). Availability of specific VFR Terminal Area Charts are depicted on sectional charts by a wide, blue line which encloses the terminal area.

2. These charts enlarge the terminal area to twice that depicted on the sectional. The scale is 1:250,000 (1 in = 3.43 NM).

3. Terminal charts give a more detailed topographical depiction when compared to the sectional charts. In addition they show the lateral limits of the various sections of the (TCA). Floors and ceilings are shown in hundreds of feet above mean sea level (MSL).

c. WORLD AERONAUTICAL CHARTS -

1. World Aeronautical Charts are very similar to sectional charts. These charts are designed to provide a standard series of aeronautical charts, covering land areas of the world, at a size and scale convenient for navigation by moderate speed aircraft. They are produced at a scale of 1:1,000,000 (1 in = 13.7 NM).

2. Topographic information includes cities and towns, principal roads, railroads, distinctive landmarks, drainage, and relief. The latter is shown by spot elevations, contours, and gradient tints. Aeronautical information includes visual

334

and radio aids to navigation, airports, airways, restricted areas, obstructions, and other pertinent data. These charts are revised annually except several Alaskan charts and the Mexican/Caribbean charts which are revised every 2 years.

d. CHARTED VFR FLYWAY PLANNING CHARTS -

1. These charts are designed to identify flight paths clear of the major controlled traffic flows. The program is intended to provide charts showing multiple VFR routings through high-density traffic areas which may be used as an alternative to flight within TCAs. Ground references are provided as guides for improved visual navigation but most terrain and geographic information have been omitted. These charts are intended to aid in PLANNING not navigation.

2. These charts are not intended to discourage VFR operations within the TCAs, but are designed for information and planning purposes. They are produced at a scale of 1:250,000 (1 in = 3.43 NM). These charts are revised semiannually and are published on the back of the existing VFR Terminal Area Charts.

e. PLANNING CHARTS -

1. VFR/IFR Planning Chart - These charts are designed to fulfill the requirements of preflight planning for flights under VFR/IFR. They are produced at a scale of 1:2,333,232 (1 in = 32 NM). The chart is printed in two parts in such a manner that, when assembled, it forms a composite VFR Planning Chart on one side and IFR Planning Chart on the other. Information on the IFR chart depicts low altitude airways and mileages, navigational facilities, special use airspace areas, time zones, airports, isogonic lines, and related data. Information on the VFR chart includes selected populated places, large bodies of water, major drainage, shaded relief, navigational facilities, airports, special use airspace areas, military training routes, and related data.

2. Flight Case Planning Chart - This chart is designed for preflight and en route flight planning for VFR flights. It is produced at a scale of 1:4,374,803 (1 in = 60 NM). This chart contains basically the same information as the VFR Planning Chart with the addition of selected FSSs and Weather Service Offices (WFOs) located at airport sites, parachute jumping areas, a tabulation of special use airspace areas, a mileage table listing distances between 174 major airports, and a city/aerodrome location index.

3. Gulf of Mexico and Caribbean Planning Chart - This chart is designated for preflight planning for VFR flights. It is produced at a scale of 1:6,270,551 (1 in = 86 NM). This chart is on the reverse of the Puerto Rico-Virgin Islands Terminal Area Chart. Information includes mileage between Airports of Entry, a selection of special use airspace areas, and a Directory of Airports with their available facilities and servicing.

4. North Atlantic Route Chart - This five-color chart is designed for use by air traffic controllers in monitoring transatlantic flights and by FAA planners. Oceanic control areas, coastal navigation aids, major coastal airports, and oceanic reporting points are depicted. Geographic coordinates for NAVAIDs and reporting points are included. The chart may be used for pre- and in-flight planning. This chart is revised each 24 weeks. The chart is available in two sizes, full size (58 by 41 inches) scale: 1 :5,500,000; half size (29 by 20 1/2 inches) scale: 1:1 11,000,000.

5. North Pacific Oceanic Route Chart - This chart series, like the North Atlantic Route Chart series, is designed for FAA air traffic controllers' use in monitoring transoceanic air traffic. Charts are available in two scales: one 1:12,000,000 composite small scale planning chart, which covers the entire North Pacific, and four 1:7,000,000 Area Charts. They are revised every 24 weeks. The charts are available unfolded (flat only) and contain established intercontinental air routes including all reporting points with geographic positions.

1-5. Related Publications.

 a. THE AIRPORT/FACILITY DIRECTORY (A/FD) -

1. The Airport/Facility Directory provides one of the most complete sources of flight information concerning public aerodromes in the United States. It contains a detailed listing of all airports, heliports, and seaplane bases. This directory is issued in seven volumes with each volume covering a specific geographic area of the conterminous U.S., including Puerto Rico and the U.S. Virgin Islands.

2. The Airport/Facility Directory lists airports alphabetically by state, and then by the city associated with each. There is a legend in the front of each publication to enable the user to decipher the abundance of information presented. Airport information contained within the directory includes: runway data, lighting, services available, communications, and navigation aids.

3. Although the majority of information in the A/FD pertains to airports, there are several additional sections that contain additional flight information. These include special notices, FAA and NWS telephone numbers, VOR receiver checkpoints, parachute jumping areas, and the aeronautical chart bulletin.

 b. ALASKA SUPPLEMENT -

This supplement is a joint Civil and Military Flight Information Publication (FLIP), published and distributed every 56 days by the NOS. It is designed for use with the Flight Information Publication En route Charts, Alaska Terminal, WAC and Sectional Aeronautical Charts. This Supplement contains an Airport/Facility Directory of all airports shown on En route Charts, and those requested by appropriate agencies, communications data, navigational facilities, special notices and procedures applicable to the area of chart coverage.

c. PACIFIC SUPPLEMENT - This Chart Supplement is a Civil Flight Information Publication, published and distributed every 56 days by the NOS. It is designed for use with the Flight Information En route Publication Charts and the Sectional Aeronautical Chart covering the State of Hawaii and that area of the Pacific served by U.S. facilities. An Amendment Notice is published 4 weeks after each issue of the Supplement. This chart Supplement contains an Airport/Facility Directory of all airports open to the public, and those requested by appropriate agencies, communications data, navigational facilities, special notices and procedures applicable to the Pacific area.

d. DIGITAL AERONAUTICAL CHART SUPPLEMENT (DACS) - DACS is a subset of the data NOAA provides to FAA controllers every 56 days. The DACS is designed to assist with flight planning and should not be considered a substitute for a chart. The supplement is divided into nine individual sections. They are:

        Section 1 - High Altitude Airways, Conterminous U.S.

        Section 2 - Low Altitude Airways, Conterminous U.S.

        Section 3 - Selected Instrument Approach Procedure NAVAID and FIX Data.

        Section 4 - Military Training Routes.

        Section 5 - Alaska, Hawaii, Puerto Rico, Bahamas and Selected Oceanic Routes.

        Section 6 - STARs, Standard Terminal Arrivals and Profile Descent Procedures.

        Section 7 - SIDs, Standard Instrument Departures.

        Section 8 - Preferred IFR Routes (Low and High Altitudes).

        Section 9 - Air Route and Airport Surveillance Radar Facilities (updated yearly).

NOTE - Section 3 has a Change Notice that will be issued at the mid-28 day point and contains changes that occurred after the 56 day publication. Sections 8 and 9 are not digital products, but contain pertinent air route data associated with the other sections.

e. NOAA AERONAUTICAL CHART USER'S GUIDE - This guide is designed to be used as a teaching aid, reference document, and an introduction to the wealth of information provided on NOAA's aeronautical charts and publications. The guide includes the complete contents of the VFR Chart User's Guide, and a new discussion of IFR chart terms and symbols. This guide also includes a comprehensive index of symbols used on NOAA's VFR, IFR, and Planning charts.

f. DEFENSE MAPPING AGENCY AEROSPACE CENTER (DMAAC) - Defense Mapping Agency Aeronautical Charts and Products are available prepaid from:

DIRECTOR
DMA Combat Support Center
Attention: PMSR
Washington, DC 20315-0010
Phone: CONUS Toll-free telephone number
1-800-862-0342

1. Pilotage Charts (PC/TPC) - Scale 1:500,000 used for detail preflight planning and mission analysis. Emphasis in design is on ground features significant in visual and radar, low-level high-speed navigation.

2. Jet Navigation Charts (JNC-A) - Scale 1:3,000,000. Designed to provide greater coverage than the 1:2,000,000 scale Jet Navigation Charts described below. Uses include preflight planning and en route navigation by long-range jet aircraft with dead reckoning, radar, celestial and grid navigation capabilities.

3. LORAN Navigation & Consol LORAN Navigation Charts (LJC/CJC) - Scale 1:2,000,000. Used for preflight planning and in-flight navigation on long-range flights in the Polar areas and adjacent regions utilizing LORAN and CONSOL navigation aids.

4. Continental Entry Chart (CEC) - Scale 1:2,000,000. Used for CONSOLAN and LORAN navigation for entry into the U.S. when a high degree of accuracy is required to comply with Air Defense identification and reporting procedures. Also suitable as a basic dead reckoning sheet and for celestial navigation.

5. Aerospace Planning Chart (ASC) - Scale 1:9,000,000 and 1:18,000,000. Six charts at each scale and with various projections, cover the world. Charts are useful for general planning, briefings, and studies.

6. Air Distance/Geography Chart (GH-2, 2a) - Scales 1:25,000,000 and 1:50,000,000. This chart shows great circle distances between major airports. It also shows major cities, international boundaries, shaded relief and gradient tints.

7. LORAN C Navigation Chart (LCC) - Scale 1:3,000,000. Primarily designed for preflight and in-flight long-range navigation where LORAN-C is used as the basic navigation aid.

8. DOD Weather Plotting Chart (WPC) - Various scales. Designed as non-navigational outline charts which depict locations and identifications of meteorological observing stations. Primarily used to forecast and monitor weather and

atmospheric conditions throughout the world.

9. Flight Information Publications (FLIP) - These include En route Low Altitude and High Altitude Charts, En route Supplements, Terminal (Instrument Approach Charts), and other informational publications for various areas of the world.

NOTE: FLIP. Terminal publications do not necessarily include all instrument approach procedures for all airports. They include only those required for military operations.

10. World Aeronautical (WAC) and Operational Navigation Charts (ONC)- The Operational Navigation Charts (ONC) have the same purpose and contain essentially the same information as the WAC series except the terrain is portrayed by shaded relief as well as contours. The ONC series is replacing the WAC series and the WACs will be available only where the ONCs have not been issued. ONCs are 42 by 57 1/2 inches, WACs are 22 by 30 inches. These charts are revised on a regular schedule.

11. Jet Navigation Charts - These charts are designed to fulfill the requirements for long-range high-altitude, high-speed navigation. They are produced at a scale of 1:2,000,000 (1 in = 27.4 NM). Topographic features include large cities, roads, railroads, drainage and relief. The latter is indicated by contours, spot elevations and gradient tints. All aeronautical information necessary to conform to the purpose of the chart is shown. This includes restricted areas, L/MF and VOR ranges, radio beacons and a selection of standard broadcasting stations and airports. The runway patterns of the airports are shown to exaggerated scale in order that they may be readily identified as visual landmarks. Universal Jet Navigation Charts are used as plotting charts in the training and practice of celestial and dead reckoning navigation. They may also be used for grid navigational training.

12. Global Navigational Charts - These charts are designed to fulfill the requirements for aeronautical planning, operations over long distances, and en route navigation in long-range, high-altitude, high-speed aircraft. They are produced at a scale of 1:5,000,000 (1 in = 68.58 NM). Global Navigation Charts (GNC) are 42 by 57 1/2 inches. They show principal cities, towns and drainage, primary roads and railroads, prominent culture and shadient relief augmented with tints and spot elevations. Aeronautical data includes radio aids to navigation, aerodrome and restricted areas. Charts 1 and 26 have a polar navigation grid and charts 2 and 6 have sub-polar navigation grids. Global LORAN Navigation Charts (GLCs) are the same size and scale and cover the same area as the GNC charts. They contain major cities only, coast lines, major lakes and rivers, and land tint. No relief or vegetation. Aeronautical data includes radio aids to navigation and LORAN lines of position.

1-6. Auxiliary Charts.

a. AIRPORT OBSTRUCTION CHARTS (OC) - The Airport Obstruction Chart is a 1:12,000 scale graphic depicting Federal Aviation Regulations Part 77 (FAR 77) surfaces, a representation of objects that penetrate these surfaces, aircraft movement and apron areas, navigational aids, prominent airport buildings, and a selection of roads and other planimetric detail in the airport vicinity. Also included are tabulations of runway and other operational data.

b. MILITARY TRAINING ROUTES -

1. Charts and Booklet: The Defense Mapping Agency Aerospace Center (DMAAC) publishes a narrative description in booklet form and charts depicting the IFR and VFR Training Routes.

2. The charts and booklet are published every 56 days. Both the charts and narrative route description booklet are available to the general public as a brochure by single copy or annual subscription

3. Subscription and single-copy requests should be for the "DOD Area Planning AP/lB, Military Training Routes."

NOTE: The DOD provides these booklets and charts to each FSS for use in preflight pilot briefings.

Pilots should review this information to acquaint themselves with those routes that are located along their route of flight and in the vicinity of the airports from which they operate.

TEST QUESTIONS

1. The date at which a sectional chart is projected to become obsolete for the purpose of navigation can be found

A. Only by contacting NOAA.
B. On the chart itself.
C. Only by contacting the FAA.

2. Which of the following is NOT depicted on a sectional chart?

A. Radio aids to navigation.
B. Distances between major cities.
C. Railroads.

3. Which one of the following charts would be most helpful when flying VFR in or around terminal control areas?

A. Terminal area chart.
B. World aeronautical chart.
C. VFR planning chart.

4. Which publication provides detailed airport information including radio frequencies, runway length and width, hours of operation, etc.?

A. Sectional chart.
B. FAR/AIM.
C. Airport/Facility directory.

5. Which of the following charts is designed for navigation by high-performance aircraft traveling at moderate airspeeds and higher altitudes?

A. World aeronautical charts.
B. Sectional charts.
C. VFR flyway planning charts.

6. The main function of a VFR Flyway Planning Chart is

A. For avoiding major controlled traffic flows.
B. For operation within a (TCA).
C. Navigation for high speed aircraft.

ANSWERS

1. B 2. B 3. A 4. C 5. A 6. A

PRIVATE PILOT
PRACTICAL TEST STANDARDS for
AIRPLANE SINGLE-ENGINE LAND

INTRODUCTION

PRACTICAL TEST STANDARD CONCEPT

FARs (Federal Aviation Regulations) specify the areas in which knowledge and skill must be demonstrated by the applicant before the issuance of a pilot certificate or rating. The FARs provide the flexibility to permit the FAA to publish practical test standards containing specific TASKS (procedures and maneuvers) in which pilot competency must be demonstrated. The FAA will add, delete, or revise TASKS whenever it is determined that changes are needed in the interest of safety. Adherence to provisions of the regulations and the practical test standards is mandatory for the evaluation of pilot applicants.

FLIGHT INSTRUCTOR RESPONSIBILITY

An appropriately rated flight instructor is responsible for training the student to the acceptable standards as outlined in the objective of each TASK within the appropriate practical test standard. The flight instructor must certify that the applicant is able to perform safely as a private pilot and is competent to pass the required practical test for the certificate or rating sought.

EXAMINER[1] RESPONSIBILITY

The examiner who conducts the practical test is responsible for determining that the applicant meets standards outlined in the objective of each TASK within the appropriate test standard. The examiner shall meet this responsibility by accomplishing an ACTION that is appropriate for each TASK. For each TASK that involves "knowledge only" elements, the examiner will orally quiz the applicant on those elements. For each TASK that involves both "knowledge and skill" elements, the examiner will orally quiz the applicant regarding knowledge elements and ask the applicant to perform the skill elements. The examiner will determine that the applicant's knowledge and skill meet the objective in all required TASKS. Oral questioning may be used at any time during the practical test.

[1] The word "examiner" is used to denote either the FAA inspector or FAA designated pilot examiner who conducts an official flight test.

PRACTICAL TEST STANDARD DESCRIPTION

The AREAS OF OPERATION are phases of flight arranged in a logical sequence within each standard. They begin with the preparation of the flight and end with the conclusion of the flight. The examiner, however, may conduct the practical test in any sequence that results in a complete and efficient test.

The TASKS are procedures and maneuvers appropriate to an AREA OF OPERATION. The number after the pilot operation relates that TASK to the regulatory requirement.

The REFERENCE identifies the publication(s) that describe(s) the TASK. Descriptions of TASKS are not included in the standards because this information can be found in the listed references. Publications other than those listed may be used for references if their content conveys substantially the same meaning as the referenced publications.

References upon which this practical test book is based include:

FAR Part 61	Certification: Pilots and Flight Instructors
FAR Part 91	General Operating and Flight Rules
AC 00-6	Aviation Weather
AC 00-45	Aviation Weather Services
AC 61-21	Flight Training Handbook
AC 61-23	Pilot's Handbook of Aeronautical Knowledge
AC 61-27	Instrument Flying Handbook
AC 61-84	Role of Preflight Preparation
AC 67-2	Medical Handbook for Pilots
AC 91-13	Cold Weather Operation of Aircraft
AC 91-55	Reduction of Electrical Systems Failure Following Engine Starting
AIM	Airman's Information Manual

NOTE: The latest revision of the reference should be used.

The OBJECTIVE lists, in sequence, the important elements that must be satisfactorily performed to demonstrate competency in a TASK. The OBJECTIVE includes:

(1) specifically what the applicant should be able to do,
(2) the conditions under which the TASK is to be performed, and
(3) the minimum acceptable standards of performance.

344

USE OF THE PRACTICAL TEST BOOK

The FAA requires that each practical test be conducted in strict compliance with the appropriate practical test standards for issuance of a pilot certificate or rating. When using the practical test book, the examiner must evaluate the applicant's knowledge and skill in sufficient depth to determine that the standards of performance listed for all TASKS are met.

When the examiner determines, during the performance of one TASK, that the knowledge and skill objective of another TASK is met, it may not be necessary to require the performance of the other TASK.

The examiner may, for any valid reason, elect to evaluate certain TASKS orally. Such TASKS include those that do not conform to the manufacturer's recommendations or operating limitations or those that are impracticable, such as night flying, operations over congested areas, or unsuitable terrain, etc.

The examiner is not required to follow the precise order in which the AREAS OF OPERATION and TASKS appear in each section. The examiner may change the sequence or combine TASKS with similar objectives to conserve time. Examiners will develop a plan of action that includes the order and combination of TASKS to be demonstrated by the applicant in a manner that will result in an efficient and valid test. The examiner shall accurately evaluate the applicant's ability to perform safely as a pilot throughout the practical test.

Suggested examples of combining TASKS are:

(1) descending turns may be combined with high altitude emergencies;
(2) rectangular course may be combined with airport traffic pattern; and
(3) navigation during flight by reference to instruments may be combined with visual navigation.

Other TASKS with similar OBJECTIVES may be combined to conserve time. However, the OBJECTIVES of all TASKS must be demonstrated and evaluated at some time during the practical test.

Examiners will place special emphasis upon areas of aircraft operation which are most critical to flight safety. Among these areas are correct aircraft control and sound judgment in decision making. Although these areas may not be shown under each TASK, they are essential to flight safety and will receive careful evaluation throughout the practical test. If these areas are shown in the OBJECTIVE, additional emphasis will be placed on them. THE EXAMINER WILL ALSO EMPHASIZE STALL/SPIN AWARE-NESS, SPATIAL DISORIENTATION, COLLISION AVOIDANCE,

WAKE TURBULENCE AVOIDANCE, LOW-LEVEL WIND SHEAR, USE OF THE CHECKLIST, AND OTHER AREAS AS DIRECTED BY FUTURE REVISIONS OF THIS STANDARD.

USE OF DISTRACTIONS DURING PRACTICAL TESTS

Numerous studies indicate that many accidents have occurred when the pilot's attention has been distracted during various phases of flight. Many accidents have resulted from engine failure during takeoffs and landings where safe flight was possible if the pilot had used correct control technique and divided attention properly.

Distractions that have been found to cause problems are:

(1) preoccupation with situations inside or outside the cockpit;
(2) maneuvering to avoid other traffic; or
(3) maneuvering to clear obstacles during takeoffs, climbs, approaches, or landings.

To strengthen this area of pilot training and evaluation, the examiner will provide realistic distractions throughout the practical test. Many distractions may be used to evaluate the applicant's ability to divide attention while maintaining safe flight. Some examples of distractions are:

(1) simulating engine failure;
(2) simulating radio tuning and communications;
(3) identifying a field suitable for emergency landings;
(4) identifying features or objects on the ground;
(5) reading the outside air temperature gauge;
(6) removing objects from the glove compartment or map case; and
(7) questioning by the examiner.

PRACTICAL TEST PREREQUISITES

An applicant for a private pilot practical test is required by FARs to:

(1) pass the appropriate pilot written test since the beginning of the 24th month before the month in which the flight test is taken;
(2) obtain the applicable instruction and aeronautical experience prescribed for the pilot certificate sought;
(3) possess a current medical certificate appropriate to the certificate or rating sought;
(4) meet the age requirement for the issuance of the certificate or rating sought; and
(5) obtain a written statement from an appropriately rated flight instructor certifying that the applicant has been given flight instruction in

346

preparation for the practical test within 60 days preceding the date of application. The statement shall also state that the instructor finds the applicant competent to pass the practical test, and that the applicant has satisfactory knowledge of the subject area(s) in which a deficiency was indicated by the airman written test report.

NOTE: AC 61-65, Certification: Pilots and Flight Instructors, states that the instructor may sign the instructor's recommendation on the reverse side of FAA Form 8710-1, Airman Certificate and/or Rating Application, in lieu of the previous statement provided all appropriate FAR Part 61 requirements are substantiated by reliable records.

AIRCRAFT AND EQUIPMENT REQUIREMENTS FOR THE PRACTICAL TEST

The applicant is required to provide an appropriate and airworthy aircraft for the practical test. The aircraft must be equipped for, and its operating limitations must not prohibit the pilot operations required on the test.

SATISFACTORY PERFORMANCE

The ability of an applicant to perform the required TASKS is based on:

(1) executing TASKS within the aircraft's performance capabilities and limitations, including use of the aircraft's systems;
(2) executing emergency procedures and maneuvers appropriate to the aircraft;
(3) piloting the aircraft with smoothness and accuracy;
(4) exercising good judgment;
(5) applying aeronautical knowledge; and
(6) showing mastery of the aircraft within the standards outlined in this book, with the successful outcome of a TASK never seriously in doubt.

UNSATISFACTORY PERFORMANCE

If, in the judgment of the examiner, the applicant does not meet the standards of performance of any TASK performed, the associated PILOT OPERATION is failed and therefore, the practical test is failed.

The examiner or applicant may discontinue the test at any time after the failure of a PILOT OPERATION makes the applicant ineligible for the certificate or rating sought. The test will be continued ONLY with the consent of the applicant. If the test is discontinued, the applicant is entitled to credit for only those TASKS satisfactorily performed. However, during the retest and at the discretion of the examiner, any TASK may be reevaluated, including those previously passed.

The tolerances stated in the OBJECTIVE represent the minimum performance expected in good flying conditions.

Consistently exceeding tolerances or failure to take prompt corrective action when tolerances are exceeded, is unsatisfactory performance.

Any action, or lack thereof, by the applicant which requires corrective intervention by the examiner to maintain safe flight will be disqualifying. The applicant shall use proper and effective scanning techniques to clear the area before performing maneuvers. Ineffective performance in these areas will be disqualifying.

RECORDING UNSATISFACTORY PERFORMANCE

The term PILOT OPERATION is used in regulations to denote areas (procedures and maneuvers) in which the applicant must demonstrate competency prior to being issued a pilot certificate. This practical test book uses terms AREA OF OPERATION and TASK to denote areas in which competency must be demonstrated. When a disapproval notice is issued, the examiner will record the applicant's unsatisfactory performance in terms of PILOT OPERATIONS appropriate to the practical test conducted.

I. AREA OF OPERATION:
PREFLIGHT PREPARATION

A. TASK: CERTIFICATES AND DOCUMENTS

PILOT OPERATION - 1

REFERENCES: FAR Parts 61 and 91; AC 61-21, AC 61-23; Pilot's Handbook and Flight Manual.

Objective. To determine that the applicant:

1. Exhibits knowledge by explaining the appropriate -

   (a) pilot certificate, privileges and limitations.
   (b) medical certificate, class and duration.
   (c) personal pilot logbook or flight record.
   (d) FCC station license and operator's permit, as required.

2. Exhibits knowledge by locating and explaining the significance and importance of the -

   (a) airworthiness and registration certificates.
   (b) operating limitations, handbooks, or manuals.
   (c) equipment list.
   (d) weight and balance data.
   (e) maintenance requirements and appropriate records.

B. TASK: OBTAINING WEATHER INFORMATION

NOTE: This TASK is NOT required for the addition of a single-engine land class rating.

PILOT OPERATION - 1

REFERENCES: AC 00-6, AC 00-45, AC 61-21, AC 61-23, AC 61-84.

Objective. To determine that the applicant:

1. Exhibits knowledge of aviation weather information by obtaining, reading, and analyzing -

   (a) weather reports and forecasts.
   (b) weather charts.
   (c) pilot weather reports.

(d) SIGMETs and AIRMETs.
(e) Notices to Airmen.
(f) wind-shear reports.

2. Makes a competent go/no-go decision based on the available weather information.

C. TASK: DETERMINING PERFORMANCE AND LIMITATIONS

PILOT OPERATION - 1

REFERENCES: AC 61-21, AC 61-23, AC 61-84; Airplane Handbook and Flight Manual.

Objective. To determine that the applicant:

1. Exhibits knowledge by explaining airplane weight and balance, performance, and limitations, including adverse aerodynamic effects of exceeding the limits.
2. Uses available and appropriate performance charts, tables, and data.
3. Computes weight and balance, and determines that weight and center of gravity will be within limits during all phases of flight.
4. Calculates airplane performance, considering density altitude, wind, terrain, and other pertinent conditions.
5. Describes the effects of atmospheric conditions on airplane performance.
6. Makes a competent decision on whether the required performance is within the operating limitations of the airplane.

D. TASK: CROSS-COUNTRY FLIGHT PLANNING

NOTE: This TASK is NOT required for the addition of a single-engine land class rating.

PILOT OPERATION - 7

REFERENCES: AC 61-21, AC 61-23, AC 61-84.

Objective. To determine that the applicant:

1. Exhibits knowledge by planning, within 30 minutes, a VFR cross-country flight of a duration near the range of the airplane, considering fuel and loading.

350

2. Selects and uses current and appropriate aeronautical charts.
3. Plots a course for the intended route of flight with fuel stops, if necessary.
4. Selects prominent en route check points.
5. Computes the flight time, headings, and fuel requirements.
6. Selects appropriate radio navigation aids and communication facilities.
7. Identifies airspace, obstructions, and alternate airports.
8. Extracts pertinent information from the Airport/Facility Directory and other flight publications, including NOTAMs.
9. Completes a navigation log.
10. Completes and files a VFR flight plan.

E. TASK: AIRPLANE SYSTEMS

PILOT OPERATION - 1

REFERENCES: AC 61-21; Airplane Handbook and Flight Manual.

Objective. To determine that the applicant exhibits knowledge by explaining the airplane systems and operation including, as appropriate:

1. Primary flight controls and trim.
2. Wing flaps, leading edge devices, and spoilers.
3. Flight instruments.
4. Landing gear.
5. Engine.
6. Propeller.
7. Fuel system.
8. Hydraulic system.
9. Electrical system.
10. Environmental system.
11. Oil system.
12. Deice and anti-ice systems.
13. Avionics.
14. Vacuum system.

F. TASK: AEROMEDICAL FACTORS

PILOT OPERATION - 1

REFERENCES: AC 61-21, AC 67-2; AIM.

Objective.   To determine that the applicant:

1. Exhibits knowledge of the elements related to aeromedical factors, including the symptoms, effects, and corrective action of -

   (a) hypoxia.
   (b) hyperventilation.
   (c) middle ear and sinus problems.
   (d) spatial disorientation.
   (e) motion sickness.
   (f) carbon monoxide poisoning.

2. Exhibits knowledge of the effects of alcohol and drugs, and the relationship to flight safety.

3. Exhibits knowledge of nitrogen excesses during scuba dives, and how this effects a pilot or passenger during flight.

II. AREA OF OPERATION:
GROUND OPERATIONS

A. TASK: VISUAL INSPECTION

PILOT OPERATION - 1

REFERENCES: AC 61-21; Airplane Handbook and Flight Manual.

Objective. To determine that the applicant:

1. Exhibits knowledge of airplane visual inspection by explaining the reasons for checking all items.
2. Inspects the airplane by following a checklist.
3. Determines that the airplane is in condition for safe flight emphasizing -

   (a) fuel quantity, grade, and type.
   (b) fuel contamination safeguards.
   (c) fuel venting.
   (d) oil quantity, grade, and type.
   (e) fuel, oil, and hydraulic leaks.
   (f) flight controls.
   (g) structural damage.
   (h) exhaust system.
   (i) tiedown, control lock, and wheel chock removal.
   (j) ice and frost removal.
   (k) security of baggage, cargo, and equipment.

B. TASK: COCKPIT MANAGEMENT

PILOT OPERATION - 1

REFERENCE: AC 61-21.

Objective. To determine that the applicant:

1. Exhibits knowledge of cockpit management by explaining related safety and efficiency factors.
2. Organizes and arranges the material and equipment in an efficient manner.
3. Ensures that the safety belts and shoulder harnesses are fastened.

4. Adjusts and locks the rudder pedals and pilot's seat to a safe position and ensures full control movement.
5. Briefs occupants on the use of safety belts and emergency procedures.
6. Exhibits adequate crew coordination.

C. TASK: STARTING ENGINE

PILOT OPERATION - 1

REFERENCES: AC 61-21, AC 61-23, AC 91-13, AC 91-55; Airplane Handbook and Flight Manual.

Objective. To determine that the applicant:

1. Exhibits knowledge by explaining engine starting procedures, including starting under various atmospheric conditions.
2. Performs all the items on the checklist.
3. Accomplishes correct starting procedures with emphasis on -

   (a) positioning the airplane to avoid creating hazards.
   (b) determining that the area is clear.
   (c) adjusting the engine controls.
   (d) setting the brakes.
   (e) preventing airplane movement after engine start.
   (f) avoiding excessive engine RPM and temperature.
   (g) checking the engine instruments after engine start.

D. TASK: TAXIING

PILOT OPERATION - 2

REFERENCE: AC 61-21.

Objective. To determine that the applicant:

1. Exhibits knowledge by explaining safe taxi procedures.
2. Adheres to signals and clearances, and follows the proper taxi route.
3. Performs a brake check immediately after the airplane begins moving.
4. Controls taxi speed without excessive use of brakes.
5. Recognizes and avoids hazards.
6. Positions the controls for the existing wind conditions.
7. Avoids careless and reckless operations.

E. TASK: PRETAKEOFF CHECK

PILOT OPERATION - 1

REFERENCES: AC 61-21; Airplane Handbook and Flight Manual.

Objective. To determine that the applicant:

1. Exhibits knowledge of the pretakeoff check by explaining the reasons for checking all items.
2. Positions the airplane to avoid creating hazards.
3. Divides attention inside and outside of the cockpit.
4. Accomplishes the checklist items.
5. Ensures that the airplane is in safe operating condition.
6. Reviews the critical takeoff performance airspeeds and distances.
7. Describes takeoff emergency procedures.
8. Obtains and interprets takeoff and departure clearances.

F. TASK: POSTFLIGHT PROCEDURES

PILOT OPERATION - 3

REFERENCES: AC 61-21; Airplane Handbook and Flight Manual.

Objective. To determine that the applicant:

1. Exhibits knowledge by explaining the postflight procedures, including taxiing, parking, shutdown, securing, and postflight inspection.
2. Selects and taxies to the designated or suitable parking area, considering wind conditions and obstructions.
3. Parks the airplane properly.
4. Follows the recommended procedure for engine shutdown, cockpit securing, and deplaning passengers.
5. Secures the airplane properly.
6. Performs a satisfactory postflight inspection.

III. AREA OF OPERATION:
AIRPORT AND TRAFFIC PATTERN OPERATIONS

NOTE: This AREA OF OPERATION is NOT required for the addition of a single-engine land class rating.

A. TASK: RADIO COMMUNICATIONS AND ATC LIGHT SIGNALS

PILOT OPERATION - 2

REFERENCES: AC 61-21, AC 61-23; AIM.

Objective. To determine that the applicant:

1. Exhibits knowledge by explaining radio communication, ATC light signals, procedures at controlled and uncontrolled airports, and prescribed procedures for radio failure.
2. Selects the appropriate frequencies for the facilities to be used.
3. Transmits requests and reports using the recommended standard phraseology.
4. Receives, acknowledges, and complies with radio communications.

B. TASK: TRAFFIC PATTERN OPERATIONS

PILOT OPERATION - 2

REFERENCES: AC 61-21, AC 61-23; AIM.

Objective. To determine that the applicant:

1. Exhibits knowledge by explaining traffic pattern procedures at controlled and uncontrolled airports, including collision, wind shear, and wake turbulence avoidance.
2. Follows the established traffic pattern procedures according to instructions or rules.
3. Corrects for wind drift to follow the appropriate ground track.
4. Maintains proper spacing from other traffic.
5. Maintains the traffic pattern altitude, $\pm$ 100 feet.
6. Maintains the desired airspeed, $\pm$ 10 knots.
7. Completes the prelanding cockpit checklist.
8. Maintains orientation with the runway in use.

C. TASK: AIRPORT AND RUNWAY MARKING AND LIGHTING

PILOT OPERATION - 2

REFERENCES: AC 61-21; AIM.

Objective. To determine that the applicant:

1. Exhibits knowledge by explaining airport and runway markings and lighting aids.
2. Identifies and interprets airport, runway, taxiway marking, and lighting aids.

IV. AREA OF OPERATION:
TAKEOFFS AND CLIMBS

A. TASK: NORMAL AND CROSSWIND TAKEOFFS AND CLIMBS

PILOT OPERATION - 5

REFERENCES: AC 61-21; Airplane Handbook and Flight Manual.

Objective. To determine that the applicant:

1. Exhibits knowledge by explaining the elements of normal and crosswind takeoffs and climbs, including airspeeds, configurations, and emergency procedures.
2. Selects the recommended wing flap setting.
3. Aligns the airplane on the runway centerline.
4. Applies aileron deflection properly.
5. Advances the throttle smoothly to maximum allowable power.
6. Checks engine instruments.
7. Maintains directional control on runway centerline.
8. Adjusts aileron deflection during acceleration.
9. Rotates at the recommended[1] airspeed and accelerates to V_y and establishes wind-drift correction.
10. Establishes the pitch attitude for V_y and maintains V_y, $\pm$ 5 knots.
11. Retracts the wing flaps, as recommended, or at a safe altitude.
12. Retracts the landing gear, if retractable, after a positive rate of climb has been established and a safe landing can no longer be accomplished on the remaining runway.
13. Maintains takeoff power to a safe maneuvering altitude.
14. Maintains a straight track over the extended runway centerline until a turn is required.
15. Completes after-takeoff checklist.

NOTE: If a crosswind condition does not exist, the applicant's knowledge of the TASK will be evaluated through oral testing.

---

[1] The term "recommended" refers to the manufacturer's recommendation. If the manufacturer's recommendation is not available, the description in AC 61-21 will be used.

B. TASK: SHORT-FIELD TAKEOFF AND CLIMB

PILOT OPERATION - 8

REFERENCES: AC 61-21; Airplane Handbook and Flight Manual.

Objective. To determine that the applicant:

1. Exhibits knowledge by explaining the elements of a short-field takeoff and climb, including the significance of appropriate airspeeds and configurations, emergency procedures, and expected performance for existing operating conditions.
2. Selects the recommended wing flap setting.
3. Positions the airplane at the beginning of the takeoff runway aligned on the runway centerline.
4. Advances the throttle smoothly to maximum allowable power.
5. Maintains directional control on the runway centerline.
6. Rotates at the recommended airspeed and accelerates to V_x.
7. Climbs at V_x or recommended airspeed, +5, -0 knots until obstacle is cleared, or until at least 50 feet above the surface, then accelerates to V_y and maintains V_y, $\pm$ 5 knots.
8. Retracts the wing flaps, as recommended, or at a safe altitude.
9. Retracts the landing gear, if retractable, after a positive rate of climb has been established and a safe landing can no longer be accomplished on the remaining runway.
10. Maintains takeoff power to a safe maneuvering altitude.
11. Maintains a straight track over the extended runway centerline until a turn is required.
12. Completes after-takeoff checklist.

C. TASK: SOFT-FIELD TAKEOFF AND CLIMB

PILOT OPERATION - 8

REFERENCES: AC 61-21; Airplane Handbook and Flight Manual.

Objective. To determine that the applicant:

1. Exhibits knowledge by explaining the elements of a soft-field takeoff and climb, including the significance of appropriate airspeeds and configurations, emergency procedures, and hazards associated with climbing at an airspeed less than V_x.
2. Selects the recommended wing flap setting.

359

3. Taxis onto the takeoff surface at a speed consistent with safety.
4. Aligns the airplane on takeoff path, without stopping, and advances the throttle smoothly to maximum allowable power.
5. Maintains directional control on the center of the takeoff path.
6. Lifts off at the lowest possible airspeed and remains in ground effect while accelerating.
7. Accelerates to and maintains V_x, +5, -0 knots, if obstructions must be cleared, otherwise to V_y, $\pm$ 5 knots.
8. Retracts the wing flaps, as recommended, or at a safe altitude.
9. Retracts the landing gear, if retractable, after a positive rate of climb has been established and a safe landing can no longer be accomplished on the remaining runway.
10. Maintains takeoff power to a safe maneuvering altitude.
11. Maintains a straight track over the extended runway centerline until a turn is required.
12. Completes after-takeoff checklist.

V. AREA OF OPERATION:
CROSS-COUNTRY FLYING

NOTE: This AREA OF OPERATION is NOT required for the addition of a single-engine land class rating.

A. TASK: PILOTAGE AND DEAD RECKONING

PILOT OPERATION - 7

REFERENCES: AC 61-21, AC 61-23.

Objective. To determine that the applicant:

1. Exhibits knowledge by explaining pilotage and dead reckoning techniques and procedures.
2. Follows the preplanned course solely by visual reference to landmarks.
3. Identifies landmarks by relating the surface features to chart symbols.
4. Navigates by means of precomputed headings, groundspeed, and elapsed time.
5. Combines pilotage and dead reckoning.
6. Verifies the airplane position within 3 nautical miles of the flight planned route at all times.
7. Arrives at the en route checkpoints and destination $\pm$ 5 minutes of the initial or revised ETA.
8. Corrects for, and records, the differences between preflight fuel, groundspeed, and heading calculations and those determined en route.
9. Maintains the selected altitudes, within $\pm$ 200 feet.
10. Maintains the desired heading, $\pm$ 10°.
11. Follows the climb, cruise, and descent checklists.

B. TASK: RADIO NAVIGATION

PILOT OPERATION - 7

REFERENCES: AC 61-21, AC 61-23.

Objective. To determine that the applicant:

1. Exhibits knowledge by explaining radio navigation, equipment, procedures, and limitations.
2. Selects and identifies the desired radio facility.

3. Locates position relative to the radio navigation facility.
4. Intercepts and tracks a given radial or bearing.
5. Locates position using cross radials or bearings.
6. Recognizes or describes the indication of station passage.
7. Recognizes signal loss and takes appropriate action.
8. Maintains the appropriate altitude, $\pm$ 200 feet.

C. TASK: DIVERSION

PILOT OPERATION - 7

REFERENCES: AC 61-21, AC 61-23.

Objective. To determine that the applicant:

1. Exhibits knowledge by explaining the procedures for diverting, including the recognition of adverse weather conditions.
2. Selects an appropriate alternate airport and route.
3. Diverts toward the alternate airport promptly.
4. Makes a reasonable estimate of heading, groundspeed, arrival time, and fuel consumption to the alternate airport.
5. Maintains the appropriate altitude, $\pm$ 200 feet.

D. TASK: LOST PROCEDURES

PILOT OPERATION - 7

REFERENCES: AC 61-21, AC 61-23.

Objective. To determine that the applicant:

1. Exhibits knowledge by explaining lost procedures, including the reasons for-

   (a) maintaining the original or an appropriate heading, identifying landmarks, and climbing, if necessary.
   (b) proceeding to and identifying the nearest concentration of prominent landmarks.
   (c) using available radio navigation aids or contacting an appropriate facility for assistance.
   (d) planning a precautionary landing if deteriorating visibility and/or fuel exhaustion is imminent.

2. Selects the best course of action when given a lost situation.

VI. AREA OF OPERATION:
FLIGHT BY REFERENCE TO INSTRUMENTS

NOTE: This AREA OF OPERATION is NOT required for the addition of a single-engine land class rating.

A. TASK: STRAIGHT-AND-LEVEL FLIGHT

PILOT OPERATION - 6

REFERENCES: AC 61-21, AC 61-23, AC 61-27.

Objective. To determine that the applicant:

1. Exhibits knowledge by explaining flight solely by reference to instruments as related to straight-and-level flight.
2. Makes smooth and coordinated control applications.
3. Maintains straight-and-level flight for at least 3 minutes.
4. Maintains the desired heading, $\pm 10°$.
5. Maintains the desired altitude, ± 100 feet.
6. Maintains the desired airspeed, ± 10 knots.

B. TASK: STRAIGHT, CONSTANT AIRSPEED CLIMBS

PILOT OPERATION - 6

REFERENCES: AC 61-21, AC 61-23, AC 61-27.

Objective. To determine that the applicant:

1. Exhibits knowledge by explaining flight solely by reference to instruments as related to straight, constant airspeed climbs.
2. Establishes the climb pitch attitude and power setting on an assigned heading.
3. Makes smooth and coordinated control applications.
4. Maintains the desired heading, $\pm 10°$.
5. Maintains the desired airspeed, ± 10 knots.
6. Levels off at the desired altitude, ± 100 feet.

C. TASK: STRAIGHT, CONSTANT AIRSPEED DESCENTS

PILOT OPERATION - 6

REFERENCES: AC 61-21, AC 61-23, AC 61-27.

Objective. To determine that the applicant:

1. Exhibits knowledge by explaining flight solely by reference to instruments as related to straight, constant airspeed descents.
2. Determines the minimum safe altitude at which the descent should be terminated.
3. Establishes the descent configuration, pitch, and power setting on the assigned heading.
4. Makes smooth and coordinated control applications.
5. Maintains the desired heading, $\pm$ 10°.
6. Maintains the desired airspeed, $\pm$ 10 knots.
7. Levels off at the desired altitude, $\pm$ 100 feet.

D. TASK: TURNS TO HEADINGS

PILOT OPERATION - 6

REFERENCES: AC 61-21, AC 61-23, AC 61-27.

Objective. To determine that the applicant:

1. Exhibits knowledge by explaining flight solely by reference to instruments as related to turns to headings.
2. Enters and maintains approximately a standard-rate turn with smooth and coordinated control applications.
3. Maintains the desired heading, $\pm$ 10°.
4. Maintains the desired airspeed, $\pm$ 10 knots.
5. Maintains the desired bank angle.
6. Rolls out at the desired heading, $\pm$ 10°.

E. TASK: UNUSUAL FLIGHT ATTITUDES

PILOT OPERATION - 6

REFERENCES: AC 61-21, AC 61-23, AC 61-27.

NOTE: Unusual flight attitudes, such as a start of a power-on spiral or an approach to a climbing stall, shall not exceed 45° bank or 10° pitch from level flight.

Objective. To determine that the applicant:

1. Exhibits knowledge by explaining flight solely by reference to instruments as related to unusual flight attitudes.
2. Recognizes unusual flight attitudes promptly.
3. Properly interprets the instruments.
4. Recovers to a stabilized level flight attitude by prompt, smooth, coordinated control, applied in the proper sequence.
5. Avoids excessive load factor, airspeed, and stall.

F. TASK: RADIO AIDS AND RADAR SERVICES

PILOT OPERATION - 6

REFERENCES: AC 61-21, AC 61-23, AC 61-27.

Objective. To determine that the applicant:

1. Exhibits knowledge by explaining radio aids and radar services available for use during flight solely by reference to instruments.
2. Selects, tunes, and identifies the appropriate facility.
3. Follows verbal instructions or radio navigation aids for guidance.
4. Determines the minimum safe altitude.
5. Maintains the desired altitude, ± 100 feet.
6. Maintains the desired heading, ± 10°.

VII. AREA OF OPERATION:
FLIGHT AT CRITICALLY SLOW AIRSPEEDS

A. TASK: FULL STALLS - POWER OFF

PILOT OPERATION - 4

REFERENCE: AC 61-21.

Objective. To determine that the applicant:

1. Exhibits knowledge by explaining the aerodynamic factors and flight situations that may result in full stalls - power off, including proper recovery procedures, and hazards of stalling during uncoordinated flight.
2. Selects an entry altitude that will allow the recoveries to be completed no lower than 1,500 feet AGL.
3. Establishes the normal approach or landing configuration and airspeed with the throttle closed or at a reduced power setting.
4. Establishes a straight glide or a gliding turn with a bank angle of 30°, $\pm$ 10° in coordinated flight.
5. Establishes and maintains a landing pitch attitude that will induce a full stall.
6. Recognizes the indications of a full stall and promptly recovers by decreasing the angle of attack, leveling the wings, and adjusting the power, as necessary, to regain normal flight attitude.
7. Retracts the wing flaps and landing gear (if retractable) and establishes straight-and-level flight or climb.
8. Avoids secondary stalls, excessive airspeed, excessive altitude loss, spins, and flight below 1,500 feet AGL.

B. TASK: FULL STALLS - POWER ON

PILOT OPERATION - 4

REFERENCE: AC 61-21.

Objective. To determine that the applicant:

1. Exhibits knowledge by explaining the aerodynamic factors and flight situations that may result in full stalls - power on, including proper recovery procedures, and hazards of stalling during uncoordinated flight.

366

2. Selects an entry altitude that will allow the recoveries to be completed no lower than 1,500 feet AGL.
3. Establishes takeoff or normal climb configuration.
4. Establishes takeoff or climb airspeed before applying takeoff or climb power. (Reduced power may be used to avoid excessive pitch-up during entry only.)
5. Establishes and maintains a pitch attitude straight ahead or in a turn with a bank angle of 20°, ± 10°, that will induce a full stall.
6. Applies proper control to maintain coordinated flight.
7. Recognizes the indications of a full stall and promptly recovers by decreasing the angle of attack, leveling the wings, and adjusting the power, as necessary, to regain normal flight attitude.
8. Retracts the wing flaps and landing gear (if retractable) and establishes straight-and-level flight or climb.
9. Avoids secondary stalls, excessive airspeed, excessive altitude loss, spins, and flight below 1,500 feet AGL.

C. TASK: IMMINENT STALLS - POWER ON AND POWER OFF

PILOT OPERATION - 4

REFERENCE: AC 61-21.

Objective. To determine that the applicant:

1. Exhibits knowledge by explaining the aerodynamic factors associated with imminent stalls (power on and power off), an awareness of speed loss in different configurations, and the procedure for resuming normal flight attitude.
2. Selects an entry altitude that will allow the recoveries to be completed no lower than 1,500 feet AGL.
3. Establishes a takeoff, a climb, or an approach config-uration with the appropriate power setting.
4. Establishes a pitch attitude on a constant heading, ± 10°, or 20° bank turns, ± 10°, that will induce an imminent stall.
5. Applies proper control to maintain coordinated flight.
6. Recognizes and recovers from imminent stalls at the first indication of buffeting or decay of control effectiveness by reducing angle of attack and adjusting power, as necessary, to regain normal flight attitude.
7. Avoids full stall, secondary stall, excessive airspeed, excessive altitude loss, spins, and flight below 1,500 feet AGL.

D. TASK: MANEUVERING AT CRITICALLY SLOW AIRSPEED

PILOT OPERATION - 4

REFERENCE: AC 61-21.

Objective. To determine that the applicant:

1. Exhibits knowledge by explaining the flight characteristics and controllability associated with maneuvering at critically slow airspeeds.
2. Selects an entry altitude that will allow the maneuver to be performed no lower than 1,500 feet AGL.
3. Establishes and maintains a critically slow airspeed while -

   (a) in coordinated straight and turning flight in various configurations and bank angles, and
   (b) in coordinated departure climbs and landing approach descents in various configurations.

4. Maintains the desired altitude, $\pm$ 100 feet, when a constant altitude is specified, and levels off from climbs and descents, $\pm$ 100 feet.
5. Maintains the desired heading during straight flight, $\pm$ 10°.
6. Maintains the specified bank angle, $\pm$ 10°, in coordinated flight.
7. Maintains a critically slow airspeed, +5, -0 knots.

E. TASK: CONSTANT ALTITUDE TURNS

PILOT OPERATION - 10

REFERENCE: AC 61-21.

Objective. To determine that the applicant:

1. Exhibits knowledge by explaining the performance factors associated with constant altitude turns, including increased load factors, power required, and overbanking tendency.
2. Selects an entry altitude that will allow the maneuver to be performed no lower than 1,500 feet AGL.
3. Establishes an airspeed which does not exceed the airplane design maneuvering speed.
4. Enters a 360° turn maintaining a bank angle of 40° to 50° in coordinated flight.

X. AREA OF OPERATION:
EMERGENCY OPERATIONS

A. TASK: EMERGENCY APPROACH AND LANDING (SIMULATED)

PILOT OPERATION - 10

REFERENCES: AC 61-21; Airplane Handbook and Flight Manual.

Objective. To determine that the applicant:

1. Exhibits knowledge by explaining approach and landing procedures to be used in various emergencies.
2. Establishes and maintains the recommended best-glide airspeed and configuration during simulated emergencies.
3. Selects a suitable landing area within gliding distance.
4. Plans and follows a flight pattern to the selected landing area, considering altitude, wind, terrain, obstructions, and other factors.
5. Follows an appropriate emergency checklist.
6. Attempts to determine the reason for the simulated malfunction.
7. Maintains positive control of the airplane.

NOTE: Examiner should terminate the emergency approach at or above minimum safe altitude.

B. TASK: SYSTEM AND EQUIPMENT MALFUNCTIONS

PILOT OPERATION - 10

REFERENCES: AC 61-21; Airplane Handbook and Flight Manual.

Objective. To determine that the applicant:

1. Exhibits knowledge by explaining causes of, indications of, and pilot actions for, malfunction of various systems and equipment.
2. Analyzes the situation and takes appropriate action for simulated emergencies such as -

(a) partial power loss.
(b) rough running engine or overheat.

(c) carburetor or induction icing.
(d) loss of oil pressure.
(e) fuel starvation.
(f) engine compartment fire.
(g) electrical system malfunction.
(h) gear or flap malfunction.
(i) door opening in flight.
(j) trim inoperative.
(k) loss of pressurization.
(l) other malfunctions.

XI. AREA OF OPERATION:
APPROACHES AND LANDINGS

A. TASK: NORMAL AND CROSSWIND APPROACHES AND LANDINGS

PILOT OPERATION - 5

REFERENCES: AC 61-21; Airplane Handbook and Flight Manual.

Objective. To determine that the applicant:

1. Exhibits knowledge by explaining the elements of normal and crosswind approaches and landings, including airspeeds, configurations, crosswind limitations, and related safety factors.
2. Maintains the proper ground track on final approach.
3. Establishes the approach and landing configuration and power required.
4. Maintains the recommended approach airspeed $\pm$ 5 knots.
5. Makes smooth, timely, and correct control application during the final approach and transition from approach to landing roundout.
6. Touches down smoothly at approximate stalling speed, at or within 500 feet beyond a specified point, with no appreciable drift, and the airplane longitudinal axis aligned with the runway centerline.
7. Maintains directional control, increasing aileron deflection into the wind, as necessary, during the after-landing roll.

NOTE: If a crosswind condition does not exist, the applicant's knowledge of the TASK will be evaluated through oral testing.

B. TASK: FORWARD SLIPS TO LANDING

PILOT OPERATION - 5

REFERENCE: AC 61-21.

Objective. To determine that the applicant:

1. Exhibits knowledge by explaining the elements of a forward slip to a landing, including the purpose, technique, limitation, and the effect on airspeed indications.

2. Establishes a forward slip at a point from which a landing can be made in a desired area using the recommended airspeed and configuration.
3. Maintains a ground track aligned with the runway centerline.
4. Maintains an airspeed which results in minimum floating during the landing roundout.
5. Recovers smoothly from the slip.
6. Touches down smoothly at approximate stalling speed at and within 500 feet beyond a specified point, with no appreciable drift, and the airplane longitudinal axis aligned with the runway centerline.
7. Maintains directional control during the after-landing roll.

C. TASK: GO-AROUND

PILOT OPERATION - 5

REFERENCES: AC 61-21; Airplane Handbook and Flight Manual.

Objective. To determine that the applicant:

1. Exhibits knowledge by explaining the element of the go-around procedure, including proper decision, recommended airspeeds, drag effect of wing flaps and landing gear, and coping with undesirable pitch and yaw.
2. Makes a proper decision to go around.
3. Applies takeoff power and establishes the proper pitch attitude to attain the recommended airspeed.
4. Retracts the wing flaps, as recommended, and at a safe altitude.
5. Retracts the landing gear, if retractable, after a positive rate of climb has been established.
6. Trims the airplane and climbs at V_y, $\pm$ 5 knots, and tracks the appropriate traffic pattern.

D. TASK: SHORT-FIELD APPROACH AND LANDING

PILOT OPERATION - 8

REFERENCES: AC 61-21; Airplane Handbook and Flight Manual.

Objective. To determine that the applicant:

1. Exhibits knowledge by explaining the elements of a short-field approach and landing, including airspeed, configuration, and related safety factors.
2. Considers obstructions, landing surface, and wind conditions.
3. Selects a suitable touchdown point.
4. Establishes the short-field approach and landing configuration, airspeed, and descent angle.
5. Maintains control of the descent rate and the recommended airspeed, $\pm$ 5 knots, along the extended runway centerline.
6. Touches down at or within 200 feet beyond a specified point, with minimum float, no appreciable drift, and the airplane longitudinal axis aligned with the runway centerline.
7. Maintains directional control during the after-landing roll.
8. Applies braking and controls, as necessary, to stop in the shortest distance consistent with safety.

E. TASK: SOFT-FIELD APPROACH AND LANDING

PILOT OPERATION - 8

REFERENCES: AC 61-21; Airplane Handbook and Flight Manual.

Objective. To determine that the applicant:

1. Exhibits knowledge by explaining the elements of a soft-field approach and landing procedure, including airspeed, configurations, operations on various surfaces, and related safety factors.
2. Evaluates obstructions, landing surface, and wind conditions.
3. Establishes the recommended soft-field approach and landing configuration and airspeed.
4. Maintains recommended airspeed, $\pm$ 5 knots, along the extended runway centerline.

5. Touches down smoothly at minimum descent rate and groundspeed, with no appreciable drift, and the airplane longitudinal axis aligned with the runway centerline.
6. Maintains directional control during the after-landing roll.
7. Maintains proper position of flight controls and sufficient speed to taxi on soft surface.